THE abc OF
BRITISH RAILWAYS
LOCOMOTIVES

PART I—Nos. 1-9999
and
70000—99999
ALSO G.W. DIESEL RAILCARS

SUMMER
1957
EDITION

LONDON:

Ian Allan Ltd

NOTES ON THE USE OF THIS BOOK

1. This booklet lists British Railways locomotives numbered between 1 and 9999, 70000 and 99999 and G.W. Diesel Railcars in service at January 26th, 1957. This range of numbers covers all Western Region (ex-G.W.R.) engines, with the exception of diesel and gas turbine locomotives, which are dealt with in the ABC OF BRITISH RAILWAYS DIESEL LOCOMOTIVES AND TRAINS.

2. This book is divided into three parts :—

(a) A list of ex-G.W. classes, with dimensions and sub-divisions, and summary of locomotives in the class.

(b) A numerical list of ex-G.W. locomotives showing the class of each, and the name, if any.

(c) A list of B.R. standard and Class " WD " locomotives.

3. The following notes are a guide to the system of reference marks and other details given in the lists of dimensions shown for each class in the list of classes.

(a) In the lists of dimensions " Su " indicates a superheated class, and " SS " indicates that some locomotives of the class are superheated.

(b) Locomotives are fitted with two inside cylinders, slide valves and Stephenson link motion, except where otherwise shown, e.g. (O) indicates outside cylinders and " P.V." piston valves.

(c) The date on which a design of locomotive first appeared or was modified is indicated by " Introduced."

(d) The code given in smaller bold type at the head of each class, e.g., " 4MT " denotes its British Railways power classification.

4. All locomotives between 1 and 9999 are of G.W.R. origin, except where otherwise shown.

5. The following is a list of abbreviations used to indicate the pre-grouping owners of certain Western Region locomotives :

BPGV	Burry Port & Gwendraeth Valley Railway.	SHT	Swansea Harbour Trust.
Car.R.	Cardiff Railway.	TV	Taff Vale Railway.
P & M	Powlesland & Mason (Contractor).	V of R	Cambrian Railways (Vale of Rheidol).
RR	Rhymney Railway.	W & L	Cambrian Railways (Welshpool and Llanfair).

BRITISH RAILWAYS LOCOMOTIVE
SHEDS AND SHED CODES

THIS LIST INCLUDES ONLY THOSE DEPOTS WHICH HAVE ENGINES
ALLOCATED TO THEM. IT DOES NOT INCLUDE OVERNIGHT
STABLING OR SIGNING-ON POINTS.

ALL B.R. LOCOMOTIVES CARRY THE CODE OF THEIR HOME DEPOT
ON A SMALL PLATE AFFIXED TO THE SMOKEBOX DOOR.

LONDON MIDLAND REGION

1A	**Willesden**	9A	**Longsight**
1B	Camden	9B	Stockport (Edgeley)
1C	Watford	9C	Macclesfield
1D	Devons Road (Bow)	9D	Buxton
1E	Bletchley	9G	Northwich
	Leighton Buzzard		
		10A	**Springs Branch (Wigan)**
2A	**Rugby**	10B	Preston
	Seaton	10C	Patricroft
2B	Nuneaton	10D	Sutton Oak
2C	Warwick		
2D	Coventry	11A	**Carnforth**
2E	Northampton	11B	Barrow
2F	Market Harborough		Coniston
		11C	Oxenholme
3A	**Bescot**	11D	Tebay
3B	Bushbury	11E	Lancaster
3C	Walsall		
3D	Aston	12A	**Carlisle (Upperby)**
3E	Monument Lane	12B	Penrith
		12C	Workington
5A	**Crewe North**		
	Whitchurch	14A	**Cricklewood**
5B	Crewe South	14B	Kentish Town
5C	Stafford	14C	St. Albans
5D	Stoke		
5E	Alsager	15A	**Wellingborough**
5F	Uttoxeter	15B	Kettering
		15C	Leicester
6A	**Chester**	15D	Bedford
6B	Mold Junction		
6C	Birkenhead	16A	**Nottingham**
6D	Chester (Northgate)	16B	Kirkby
6E	Wrexham	16C	Mansfield
6F	Bidston		
6G	Llandudno Junction	17A	**Derby**
6H	Bangor	17B	Burton
6J	Holyhead		Horninglow
6K	Rhyl		Overseal
		17C	Coalville
8A	**Edge Hill**		
8B	Warrington		
	Warrington (Arpley)		
8C	Speke Junction		
8E	Brunswick (Liverpool)		

17D	Rowsley		22A	**Bristol**
	Cromford		22B	Gloucester
	Middleton			Dursley
	Sheep Pasture			Tewkesbury
17E	Heaton Mersey			
17F	Trafford Park		24A	**Accrington**
			24B	Rose Grove
			24C	Lostock Hall
18A	**Toton**		24D	Lower Darwen
18B	Westhouses		24E	Blackpool
18C	Hasland			Blackpool North
18D	Staveley		24F	Fleetwood
	Sheepbridge			
			26A	**Newton Heath**
19A	**Sheffield**		26B	Agecroft
19B	Millhouses		26C	Bolton
19C	Canklow		26D	Bury
			26E	Lees
20F	Skipton			
20G	Hellifield		27A	**Bank Hall**
			27B	Aintree
21A	**Saltley**		27C	Southport
21B	Bournville		27D	Wigan (L. & Y.)
21C	Bromsgrove		27E	Walton

EASTERN REGION

30A	**Stratford**		32B	Ipswich
	Brentwood			Felixstowe Town
	Chelmsford			Stowmarket
	Enfield Town			
	Epping		32C	Lowestoft
	Ilford		32D	Yarmouth (South Town)
	Wood St. (Walthamstow)		32E	Yarmouth (Vauxhall)
30B	Hertford East		32F	Yarmouth Beach
	Buntingford		32G	Melton Constable
	Ware			Norwich City
30C	Bishops Stortford			
30E	Colchester		33A	**Plaistow**
	Braintree		33B	Tilbury
	Clacton		33C	Shoeburyness
	Maldon			
	Walton-on-Naze		34A	**Kings Cross**
30F	Parkeston		34B	Hornsey
			34C	Hatfield
31A	**Cambridge**		34D	Hitchin
	Ely		34E	Neasden
	Huntingdon East			Aylesbury
	Saffron Walden			Chesham
31B	March			
	Wisbech		35A	**New England**
31C	Kings Lynn			Spalding
	Hunstanton			Stamford
31D	South Lynn		35B	Grantham
31E	Bury St. Edmunds		35C	Peterborough (Spital)
	Sudbury (Suffolk)			
			36A	**Doncaster**
32A	**Norwich**		36B	Mexborough
	Cromer Beach			Wath
	Dereham		36C	Frodingham
	Swaffham		36D	Barnsley
	Wymondham		36E	Retford
				Newark

38A	**Colwick**		40B	Immingham
38B	Annesley			Grimsby
38C	Leicester (G.C.)			New Holland
38D	Staveley		40C	Louth
38E	Woodford Halse		40D	Tuxford
39A	**Gorton**		40E	Langwith Junction
	Dinting		40F	Boston
	Hayfield			Sleaford
40A	**Lincoln**			
	Lincoln (St. Marks)		41A	**Sheffield (Darnall)**

NORTH EASTERN REGION

50A	**York**		52F	North Blyth
50B	Leeds (Neville Hill)			South Blyth
50C	Selby			
50D	Starbeck		53A	**Hull (Dairycoates)**
50E	Scarborough		53B	Hull (Botanic Gardens)
50F	Malton		53C	Hull (Springhead)
	Pickering			Alexandra Dock
50G	Whitby		53D	Bridlington
			53E	Goole
51A	**Darlington**		54A	**Sunderland**
	Middleton-In-Teesdale			Durham
51B	Newport (Yorks)		54B	Tyne Dock
51C	West Hartlepool		54C	Borough Gardens
51D	Middlesbrough		54D	Consett
51E	Stockton			
51F	West Auckland		55A	**Leeds (Holbeck)**
51G	Haverton Hill		55B	Stourton
51H	Kirkby Stephen		55C	Farnley Junction
51J	Northallerton		55D	Royston
51K	Saltburn		55E	Normanton
			55F	Manningham
52A	**Gateshead**		55G	Huddersfield
	Bowes Bridge			
52B	Heaton		56A	**Wakefield**
52C	Blaydon		56B	Ardsley
	Alston		56C	Copley Hill
	Hexham		56D	Mirfield
52D	Tweedmouth		56E	Sowerby Bridge
	Alnmouth		56F	Low Moor
52E	Percy Main		56G	Bradford

SCOTTISH REGION

60A	**Inverness**		61B	Aberdeen (Ferryhill)
	Dingwall		61C	Keith
	Kyle of Lochalsh			Banff
60B	Aviemore			Elgin
	Boat of Garten		62A	**Thornton**
60C	Helmsdale			Anstruther
	Dornoch			Burntisland
	Tain			Ladybank
60D	Wick			Methil
	Thurso		62B	Dundee (Tay Bridge)
60E	Forres			Arbroath
61A	**Kittybrewster**			Dundee West
	Ballater			Montrose
	Fraserburgh			St. Andrews
	Inverurie		62C	Dunfermline
	Peterhead			Alloa

63A	**Perth South**		65D	Dawsholm
	Aberfeldy			Dumbarton
	Crieff		65E	Kipps
63B	Stirling South		65F	Grangemouth
	Killin		65G	Yoker
	Stirling (Shore Road)		65H	Helensburgh
63C	Forfar		65I	Balloch
63D	Oban		65J	Fort William
	Ballachulish			Mallaig
64A	**St. Margarets**		66A	**Polmadie (Glasgow)**
	(Edinburgh)		66B	Motherwell
	Dunbar		66C	Hamilton
	Galashiels		66D	Greenock (Ladyburn)
	Longniddry			Greenock (Princes Pier)
	North Berwick			
64B	Haymarket		67A	**Corkerhill (Glasgow)**
64C	Dalry Road		67B	Hurlford
64D	Carstairs			Beith
64E	Polmont			Muirkirk
64F	Bathgate		67C	Ayr
64G	Hawick		67D	Ardrossan
	Riccarton			
	St. Boswells		68A	**Carlisle (Kingmoor)**
			68B	Dumfries
65A	**Eastfield (Glasgow)**		68C	Stranraer
	Arrochar			Newton Stewart
65B	St. Rollox		68D	Beattock
65C	Parkhead		68E	Carlisle Canal

SOUTHERN REGION

70A	**Nine Elms**		72B	Salisbury
70B	Feltham		72C	Yeovil
70C	Guildford		72D	Plymouth
70D	Basingstoke			Callington
70E	Reading		72E	Barnstaple Junction
70F	Fratton			Ilfracombe
70G	Newport (I.O.W.)			Torrington
70H	Ryde (I.O.W.)		72F	Wadebridge
71A	**Eastleigh**		73A	**Stewarts Lane**
	Andover Junction		73B	Bricklayers Arms
	Lymington		73C	Hither Green
	Winchester		73D	Gillingham (Kent)
71B	Bournemouth		73E	Faversham
	Branksome			
71G	Bath (S. & D.)		74A	**Ashford (Kent)**
	Radstock		74B	Ramsgate
71H	Templecombe		74C	Dover
71I	Southampton Docks			Folkestone
71J	Highbridge		74D	Tonbridge
			74E	St. Leonards
72A	**Exmouth Junction**		75A	**Brighton**
	Bude		75B	Redhill
	Exmouth		75C	Norwood Junction
	Lyme Regis		75D	Horsham
	Okehampton		75E	Three Bridges
	Seaton		75F	Tunbridge Wells West

WESTERN REGION

81A	**Old Oak Common**		81D	Reading
81B	Slough			Henley-on-Thames
	Marlow		81E	Didcot
	Watlington		81F	Oxford
81C	Southall			Fairford

82A	**Bristol (Bath Road)**	85C	Hereford
	Bath		Ledbury
	Wells		Leominster
	Weston-super-Mare		Ross
	Yatton	85D	Kidderminster
82B	St. Philip's Marsh		
82C	Swindon	86A	**Newport**
	Chippenham		**(Ebbw Junction)**
82D	Westbury	86B	Newport (Pill)
	Frome	86C	Cardiff (Canton)
82E	Yeovil	86D	Llantrisant
82F	Weymouth	86E	Severn Tunnel Junction
	Bridport	86F	Tondu
		86G	Pontypool Road
			Abergavenny
83A	**Newton Abbot**	86H	Aberbeeg
	Ashburton	86J	Aberdare
	Kingsbridge	86K	Tredegar
83B	Taunton		
	Bridgwater	87A	**Neath**
83C	Exeter		Glyn Neath
	Tiverton Junction		Neath (N. & B.)
83D	Laira (Plymouth)	87B	Duffryn Yard
	Launceston	87C	Danygraig
83E	St. Blazey	87D	Swansea East Dock
	Bodmin	87E	Landore
	Moorswater	87F	Llanelly
83F	Truro		Burry Port
83G	Penzance		Pantyfynnon
	Helston	87G	Carmarthen
	St. Ives	87H	Neyland
			Cardigan
			Milford Haven
84A	**Wolverhampton**		Pembroke Dock
	(Stafford Road)		Whitland
84B	Oxley	87J	Goodwick
84C	Banbury	87K	Swansea (Victoria)
84D	Leamington Spa		Gurnos
84E	Tyseley		Llandovery
	Stratford-on-Avon		Upper Bank
84F	Stourbridge Junction		
84G	Shrewsbury	88A	**Cardiff (Cathays)**
	Builth Road		Radyr
	Clee Hill	88B	Cardiff East Dock
	Craven Arms	88C	Barry
	Knighton	88D	Merthyr
84H	Wellington (Salop)		Cae Harris
84J	Croes Newydd		Dowlais Central
	Bala		Rhymney
	Penmaenpool	88E	Abercynon
	Trawsfynydd	88F	Treherbert
84K	Chester		Ferndale
		89A	**Oswestry**
85A	**Worcester**		Llanidloes
	Evesham		Moat Lane
	Kingham	89B	Brecon
85B	Gloucester		Builth Wells
	Brimscombe	89C	Machynlleth
	Cheltenham		Aberayron
	Cirencester		Aberystwyth
	Lydney		Aberystwyth (V. of R.)
	Tetbury		Portmadoc
			Pwllheli

4-6-0　6MT　1000 Class

" County "

Introduced 1945: Hawksworth design.
*Fitted with double chimney.
Weight: Loco.　76 tons 17 cwt.
　　　　Tender 49 tons 0 cwt.
Pressure: 280 lb. Su.
Cyls.: (O) $18\frac{1}{2}'' \times 30''$.
Driving Wheels: 6' 3".
T.E.: 32,580 lb.
P.V.

1001–8/10–13/5–21/3–6/8/9
*1000/9/14/22/7　　　Total 30

4-6-0　5P　4000 Class

" Star "

Introduced 1907: Churchward design.
　Developed from No. 4000 (originally
　No. 40, introduced 1906 as a 4-4-2),
　earlier locomotives subsequently
　fitted with new boilers and super-
　heaters, remainder built as such.
Weight: Loco.　75 tons 12 cwt.
　　　　Tender 46 tons 14 cwt.
Pressure: 225 lb. Su.
Cyls.: (4) $15'' \times 26''$.
Driving Wheels: 6' 8½".
T.E.: 27,800 lb.
Inside Walschaerts valve gear and
　rocking shafts.　P.V.

4056/61　　　　　　Total 2

4-6-0　7P　4073 Class

" Castle "

*Introduced 1923: Collett design, de-
　veloped from " Star " (4000/37,
　5083–92 converted from " Star ").
†Introduced 1946: fitted with 3-row
　superheater.
‡Introduced 1947: fitted with 4-row
　superheater.
¶Introduced 1956: fitted with double
　chimney.

Weight: Loco.　79 tons 17 cwt.
　　　　Tender 46 tons 14 cwt.
Pressure: 225 lb. Su.
Cyls.: (4) $16'' \times 26''$.
Driving Wheels: 6' 8½".
T.E.: 31,625 lb.
Inside Walschaerts valve gear and
　rocking shafts.　P.V.

*4000/37/73–86/8/9/91–6/8/9,
　5000–25/7–32/4/5/7–42/4–8/51
　–6/8–60/2/6–70/3/6/8/80/3–92
†5065/72/4/5/7/9/81/2/93/6–9,
　7000–3/5–17/20/1/3/5–8/31–3/
　5–7
‡4087/97, 5026/33/6/43/9/50/7/61/
　3/4/71/94/5, 7004/19/22/4/9/
　30/4
*¶4090
†¶7018　　　　　　Total 167

4-6-0　5MT　4900 Class

" Hall "

*Introduced 1924: Collett rebuild with
　6' 0" driving wheels of " Saint "
　(built 1907).
†Introduced 1928: Modified design for
　new construction, with higher-
　pitched boiler, modified footplate
　and detail differences.
Weight: Loco. $\begin{cases} 72 \text{ tons } 10 \text{ cwt.*} \\ 75 \text{ tons } 0 \text{ cwt.†} \end{cases}$
　　　　Tender 46 tons 14 cwt.
Pressure: 225 lb. Su.
Cyls. (O) $18\frac{1}{2}'' \times 30''$.
Driving Wheels: 6' 0".
T.E.: 27,275 lb.
P.V.
*4900
†4901–10/2–99, 5900–99, 6900–58
　　　　　　　　　Total 258

4-6-0 8P 6000 Class
" King "

*Introduced 1927: Collett design.
†Introduced 1947. Fitted with 4-row superheater.
‡Introduced 1955. Fitted with double chimney.
Weight: Loco.   89 tons 0 cwt.
        Tender 46 tons 14 cwt.
Pressure: 250 lb. Su.
Cyls.: (4) $16\frac{1}{4}" \times 28"$.
Driving Wheels: 6' 6".
T.E.: 40,285 lb.
Inside Walschaerts valve gear and rocking shafts. P.V.

*6014/26
†6008/12/6/8/9/23/9
‡†6000–7/9–11/3/5/7/20–2/4/5/
   7/8

Total 30

4-6-0 5MT 6800 Class
" Grange "

Introduced 1936: Collett design, variation of " Hall " with smaller wheels, incorporating certain parts of withdrawn 4300 2-6-0 locos.
Weight: Loco.   74 tons 0 cwt.
        Tender 40 tons 0 cwt.
Pressure: 225 lb. Su.
Cyls.: (O) $18\frac{1}{2}" \times 30"$.
Driving Wheels: 5' 8".
T.E.: 28,875 lb.
P.V.

6800–79   Total 80

4-6-0 5MT 6959 Class
" Modified Hall "

Introduced 1944: Hawksworth development of " Hall," with larger superheater, " one-piece " main frames and plate framed bogie.
Weight: Loco.   75 tons 16 cwt.
        Tender 46 tons 14 cwt.
Pressure: 225 lb. Su.
Cyls.: (O) $18\frac{1}{2}" \times 30"$.
Driving Wheels: 6' 0".
T.E.: 27,275 lb.
P.V.

6959–99, 7900–29

Total 71

4-6-0 5MT 7800 Class
" Manor "

Introduced 1938: Collett design for secondary lines, incorporating certain parts of withdrawn 4300 2-6-0 locos.
Weight: Loco.   68 tons 18 cwt.
        Tender 40 tons 0 cwt.
Pressure: 225 lb. Su.
Cyls.: (O) $18" \times 30"$.
Driving Wheels: 5' 8".
T.E.: 27,340 lb.
P.V.

7800–29

Total 30

4-4-0 " City " Class

Introduced 1903: Dean design.
Weight: Loco.   55 tons 6 cwt.
        Tender 36 tons 15 cwt.
Pressure: 200 lb. Su.
Cyls.: $18" \times 26"$.
Driving Wheels: 6' $8\frac{1}{2}"$.
T.E.: 17,790 lb.

3440   Total 1

Withdrawn 1931 and preserved in York Museum. Returned to service 1957 for hauling enthusiasts' specials.

4-4-0 2P 9000 Class

Introduced 1936: Collett rebuild, incorporating " Duke " type boiler and " Bulldog " frames for light lines.
Weight: Loco.   49 tons 0 cwt.
     Tender $\begin{cases} 40 \text{ tons 0 cwt.} \\ 36 \text{ tons 15 cwt.} \end{cases}$
Pressure: 180 lb. SS.
Cyls.: $18" \times 26"$.
Driving Wheels: 5' 8".
T.E.: 18,955 lb.

9004/5/8–18/20–8   Total 22

2-8-0 8F 2800 Class

*Introduced 1903: Churchward design, earlier locos. subsequently fitted with new boiler and superheater.
†Introduced 1938: Collett locos., with side window cab and detail alterations.

Weight: Loco. $\begin{cases} 75 \text{ tons } 10 \text{ cwt.*} \\ 76 \text{ tons } 5 \text{ cwt.†} \end{cases}$
          Tender 40 tons 0 cwt.
Pressure: 225 lb. Su.
Cyls.: (O) 18½″ × 30″.
Driving Wheels: 4′ 7½″.
T.E.: 35,380 lb.
P.V.

*2800–2883

†2884–99, 3800–66

Total 167

2-8-0   7F   R.O.D. Class

Introduced 1911: Robinson G. C. design
   (L.N.E.R. O4), built from 1917 for
   Railway Operating Division, R.E.,
   taken into G.W. stock from 1919 and
   subsequently fitted with G.W boiler
   mountings and details
Weight: Loco.   73 tons 11 cwt.
          Tender 47 tons 6 cwt.
Pressure: 185 lb. Su.
Cyls.:(O) 21″ × 26″.
Driving Wheels: 4′ 8″.
T.E.: 32,200 lb.
P.V.

3011/5/24/36/41

Total 5

2-8-0   7F   4700 Class

Introduced 1919: Churchward mixed
   traffic design (4700 built with smaller
   boiler and later rebuilt).
Weight: Loco.   82 tons 0 cwt.
          Tender 46 tons 14 cwt.
Pressure: 225 lb. Su.
Cyls.: (O) 19″ × 30″.
Driving Wheels: 5′ 8″.
T.E.: 30,460 lb.
P.V

4700–8   **Total 9**

2-6-0   4MT   4300 Class

*Introduced 1911. Churchward design
†Introduced 1925: Locos. with detail
   alterations affecting weight.
‡Introduced 1932: Locos. with side
   window cab and detail alterations
Weight: Loco. $\begin{cases} 62 \text{ tons } 0 \text{ cwt.*} \\ 64 \text{ tons } 0 \text{ cwt.†} \\ 65 \text{ tons } 6 \text{ cwt.‡} \end{cases}$
          Tender 40 tons 0 cwt.
Pressure: 200 lb. Su.
Cyls.: (O) 18½″ × 30″.
Driving Wheels: 5′ 8″.
T.E.: 25,670 lb.
P.V.

*4326/58/75/7, 5306/10–5/8/9/
  21–6/8/30–9/41/4/5/7/50/1/
  3/5–8/60–2/7–72/5–82/4–6/8/
  90–4/6–9, 6300–14/6–20/2–82/
  4–99, 7305–21

†7300–4

‡7323/9/39, 9300/2–6/8–16/8/9

                          Total 210

0-6-0   3MT   2251 Class

Introduced 1930: Collett design.
Weight:
   Loco.   43 tons 8 cwt.
   Tender $\begin{cases} 36 \text{ tons } 15 \text{ cwt.} \\ 47 \text{ tons } 6 \text{ cwt. (ex-R.O.D.} \\ \text{tender from } 3000 \text{ Class} \\ 2\text{-}8\text{-}0). \end{cases}$
Pressure: 200 lb. Su.
Cyls.: 17½″ × 24″.
Driving Wheels: 5′ 2″.
T.E.: 20,155 lb.

2200–99, 3200–19   **Total 120**

0-6-0   2MT   2301 Class

Introduced 1883: Dean design, later
   fitted with superheater.
Weight: Loco.   36 tons 16 cwt.
          Tender 34 tons 5 cwt.
Pressure: 180 lb. Su.
Cyls.: 17½″ × 24″.
Driving Wheels: 5′ 2″.
T.E.: 18,140 lb.

2538

                          Total 1

2-8-2T   8F   7200 Class

Introduced 1934: Collett rebuild with
   extended bunker and trailing wheels
   of Churchward 4200 class 2-8-0T.
Weight: 92 tons 2 cwt.
Pressure: 200 lb. Su.
Cyls.: (O) 19″ × 30″.
Driving Wheels: 4′ 7½″.
T.E.: 33,170 lb.
P.V

7200–53

                          Total 54

2-8-0T {7F* / 8F†}   4200 Class

*Introduced 1910: Churchward design.

†**5205 class.** Introduced 1923: with enlarged cyls. and detail alterations.

Weight: { 81 tons 12 cwt.*
{ 82 tons 2 cwt.†

Pressure: 200 lb. Su.

Cyls.: { (O) 18½″ × 30″.*
{ (O) 19″ × 30″.†

Driving Wheels: 4′ 7½″.

T.E. { 31,450 lb.*
{ 33,170 lb.†

P.V.

*4200/1/3/6–8/11–5/7/8/21–33/5–8/41–3/6–8/50–99, 5200–4

†5205–64   **Total 151**

2-6-2T   4MT   3100 Class

Introduced 1938: Collett rebuild with higher pressure and smaller wheels of Churchward 3150 class (introduced 1906).

Weight: 81 tons 9 cwt.

Pressure: 225 lb. Su.

Cyls.: (O) 18½″ × 30″.

Driving Wheels: 5′ 3″.

T.E. 31,170 lb.

P.V.

3100–4   **Total 5**

2-6-2T   4MT   3150 Class

Introduced 1906: Churchward design, developed from his original 3100 class of 1903 but with larger boiler, subsequently fitted with superheater.

Weight: 81 tons 12 cwt.

Pressure: 200 lb. Su.

Cyls.: (O) 18½″ × 30″.

Driving Wheels: 5′ 8″.

T.E.: 25,670 lb.

P.V.

3150/63/70–2/4/6/7/80/3/6/7/90   **Total 13**

2-6-2T   4MT   4500 Class

*Introduced 1906: Churchward design for light branches, developed from 4400 class with larger wheels, earlier locos. subsequently fitted with superheater.

†**4575 class.** Introduced 1927: with detail alterations and increased weight.

‡Introduced 1953. Push-and-pull fitted.

Weight: { 57 tons 0 cwt.*
{ 61 tons 0 cwt.†

Pressure: 200 lb. Su.

Cyls.: (O) 17″ × 24″.

Driving Wheels: 4′ 7½″.

T.E.: 21,250 lb.

P.V.

*4505/7/8/19/24/6/36/8/40/5–74

†4575–7/9/80/2–5/7/3/90–7/9, 5500–10/3–23/5–8/30–3/6–44/6–54/6–8/61–7/9–71/3

‡4578/81/9, 5511/24/9/34/5/45/55/9/60/8/72/4   **Total 136**

2-6-2T   4MT   5100 & 6100 Classes

*5100 class.** Introduced 1928: Collett rebuild with detail alterations and increased weight of Churchward 3100 class (introduced 1903 and subsequently fitted with superheater).

†**5101 class.** Introduced 1929. Modified design for new construction.

‡**6100 class.** Introduced 1931: Locos. for London suburban area with increased boiler pressure.

Weight: { 75 tons 10 cwt.*
{ 78 tons 9 cwt.†‡

Pressure: { 200 lb. Su.*†
{ 225 lb. Su.‡

Cyls.: (O) 18″ × 30″.

Driving Wheels: 5′ 8″.

T.E. { 24,300 lb.*†
{ 27,340 lb.‡

P.V.

*5148

†4100–79, 5101–10/50–8/60–99

‡6100–69   **Total 210**

For full details of
DIESEL & GAS TURBINE
LOCOMOTIVES

running on the Western Region,

see the
ABC OF B.R. LOCOMOTIVES
PT. 2. Nos. 10000-39999

2-6-2T 4MT 8100 Class

Introduced 1938: Collett rebuild with higher pressure and smaller wheels of Churchward locos. in 5100 class.
Weight: 76 tons 11 cwt.
Pressure: 225 lb. Su.
Cyls.: (O) 18″ × 30″.
Driving Wheels: 5′ 6″.
T.E.: 28,165 lb.
P.V.

8100-9   Total 10

2-6-2T unclass. V of R

*Introduced 1902: Davies and Metcalfe design for V. of R. 1′ 11½″ gauge.
†Introduced 1923: G.W. development of V. of R. design.
Weight: 25 tons 0 cwt.
Gauge: 1′ 11½″.
Pressure: 165 lb.
Cyls. (O) $\begin{cases} 11″ × 17″.* \\ 11½″ × 17″.† \end{cases}$
Driving Wheels: 2′ 6″.
T.E. $\begin{cases} 9,615 lb.* \\ 10,510 lb.† \end{cases}$
Walschaerts valve gear.
*9
†7/8   Total 3

0-6-2T 5MT 5600 Class

*Introduced 1924: Collett design for service in Welsh valleys.
†Introduced 1927: Locos. with detail alterations.
Weight: $\begin{cases} 68 tons 12 cwt.* \\ 69 tons 7 cwt.† \end{cases}$
Pressure: 200 lb. Su.
Cyls.: 18″ × 26″.
Driving Wheels: 4′ 7½″.
T.E.: 25,800 lb.
P.V.
*5600-99
†6600-99   Total 200

0-6-2T 4F Rhymney Rly.

Introduced 1921: Hurry Riches Rhymney "R1" class, development of "R" (introduced 1907).
Weight: 66 tons 0 cwt.
Pressure: 175 lb.
Cyls.: 18½″ × 26″.
Driving Wheels: 4′ 6″.
T.E. 24,520 lb.

36/8, 42
                                   Total 3

0-6-2T 4P TV

Introduced 1924: G.W. rebuild with superheated taper boiler of Cameron T.V. "A" class (introduced 1914).
Weight: 65 tons 14 cwt.
Pressure: 200 lb. Su.
Cyls.: 17½″ × 26″.
Driving Wheels: 5′ 3″.
T.E. 21,480 lb.
304/5/49/64/5/70/3/81/3/5/90/3/7/8
                                   Total 14

0-6-0PT 2F 850 Class

Introduced 1910: Dean saddletanks, subsequently rebuilt with pannier tanks.
Weight: 36 tons 3 cwt.
Pressure: 165 lb.
Cyls.: 16″ × 24″.
Driving Wheels: 4′ 1½″.
T.E.: 17,410 lb.
2008/12
                                   Total 2

0-6-0ST 0F 1361 Class

Introduced 1910: Churchward design for dock shunting.
Weight: 35 tons 4 cwt.
Pressure: 150 lb.
Cyls.: (O) 16″ × 20″.
Driving Wheels: 3′ 8″.
T.E.: 14,835 lb.

1361–5   **Total 5**

0-6-0PT 1F 1366 Class

Introduced 1934: Collett development of 1361 class, with pannier tanks.
Weight: 35 tons 15 cwt.
Pressure: 165 lb.
Cyls.: (O) 16″ × 20″.
Driving Wheels: 3′ 8″.
T.E.: 16,320 lb.

1366–71   **Total 6**

0-6-0PT 4F 1500 Class

Introduced 1949: Hawksworth short-wheelbase heavy shunting design
Weight: 58 tons 4 cwt.
Pressure: 200 lb.
Cyls.: (O) 17½″ × 24″.
Driving Wheels: 4′ 7½″.
T.E.: 22,515 lb.
Walschaerts valve gear. P.V.

1500–9   **Total 10**

0-6-0PT 2F 1600 Class

Introduced 1949: Hawksworth light branch line and shunting design.
Weight: 41 tons 12 cwt.
Pressure: 165 lb.
Cyls.: 16½″ × 24″.
Driving Wheels: 4′ 1½″.
T.E.: 18,515 lb.

1600–69   **Total 70**

0-6-0PT 2F 2021 Class

2021 class. Introduced 1897: Dean saddletank, subsequently rebuilt with pannier tanks. Nos. 2101 onwards built with domeless boiler and Belpaire firebox, interchanged later throughout the class.
Weight: 39 tons 15 cwt.
Pressure: 165 lb.
Cyls.: 16½″ × 24″.
Driving Wheels: 4′ 1½″.
T.E.: 18,515 lb.

2069, 2134/60

         Total 3

0-6-0PT 1P 5400 Class

Introduced 1931: Collett design for light passenger work, push-and-pull fitted.
Weight: 46 tons 12 cwt.
Pressure: 165 lb.
Cyls.: 16½″ × 24″.
Driving Wheels: 5′ 2″.
T.E.: 14,780 lb.

5400/2–7/9–24

         Total 23

0-6-0PT 3F 5700 Class

*Introduced 1929: Collett design for shunting and light goods work developed from 2021 class.
†Introduced 1930: Locos. with steam brake and no A.T.C. fittings, for shunting only.
§Introduced 1933: Locos. with detail alterations, modified cab (except 8700) and increased weight.
‡Introduced 1933: Locos. with condensing gear for working over L.T. Metropolitan line.
¶ Introduced 1948: Steam brake locos. with increased weight.

Weight: { 47 tons 10 cwt.*†
        50 tons 15 cwt.‡
        49 tons 0 cwt.§ ¶
Pressure: 200 lb.
Cyls.: 17½″ × 24″.
Driving Wheels: 4′ 7½″
T.E.: 22,515 lb.

13

*5701–45/7–51/3–61/3–91/3–9,
  7700–10/2–99, 8701–49
†6700–49
§3600–3799, 4600–99, 8700/50–99
  9600–82, 9711–99
‡9700–10
¶6750–79

Total 857

0-6-0PT   2P*   2F†
6400 & 7400 Classes

*6400 class.** Introduced 1932: Collett
  design for light passenger work,
  variation of 5400 class with smaller
  wheels, push-and-pull fitted.
†7400 class.** Introduced 1936 : Non-
  push-and-pull fitted locos.
Weight: { 45 tons 12 cwt.*
         { 45 tons 9 cwt.†
Pressure: 180 lb.
Cyls.: 16½″ × 24″.
Driving Wheels: 4′ 7½″.
T.E.: 18,010 lb.
*6400–39
†7400–49

Total : 6400 Class 40
7400 Class 50

0-6-0PT   4F   9400 Class

*Introduced 1947: Hawksworth taper
  boiler design for heavy shunting.
†Introduced 1949: Locos. with non-
  superheated boiler.
Weight: 55 tons 7 cwt.
Pressure: 200 lb. SS.
Cyls.: 17½″ × 24″
Driving Wheels: 4′ 7½″.
T.E.: 22,515 lb.
*9400–9
†3400–9, 8400–99, 9410–99

Total 210

0-6-0T   1F   BPGV

Introduced 1910 : Hudswell Clarke
  design for B.P.G.V., rebuilt by
  G.W.R

Weight: 37 tons 15 cwt.
Pressure: 165 lb.
Cyls.: (O) 15″ × 22″.
Driving Wheels: 3′ 9″.
T.E.: 15,430 lb.

2198   **Total 1**

0-6-0T   Unclass.   W & L
(Line closed: locos. stored.)

Introduced 1902: Beyer Peacock design
  for 2′ 6″ gauge W. & L. Section,
  Cambrian Railways.
Weight: 19 tons 18 cwt.
Gauge: 2′ 6″.
Pressure: 150 lb.
Cyls.: (O) 11½″ × 16″.
Driving Wheels: 2′ 9″.
T.E.: 8,175 lb.
Walschaerts valve gear.

822/3   **Total 2**

0-4-2T   1P
1400 & 5800 Classes

*1400 class introduced 1932: Collett
  design for light branch work (originally designated 4800 class). Push-
  and-pull fitted.
†5800 class introduced 1933:   Non
  push-and-pull fitted locos.
Weight: 41 tons 6 cwt.
Pressure: 165 lb.
Cyls.: 16″ × 24″.
Driving Wheels: 5′ 2″
T.E.: 13,900 lb.
*1400/1/3/5–10/2/4/7–24/6–59/
  61–74
†5800–7/9–19   **Total 86**

0-4-0T   3F   1101 Class

Introduced 1926: Avonside Engine Co.
  design to G.W. requirements for
  dock shunting.
Weight: 38 tons 4 cwt.
Pressure: 170 lb.
Cyls.: (O) 16″ × 24″.
Driving Wheels: 3′ 9½″.
T.E.: 19,510 lb.
Walschaerts valve gear.

1101–6   **Total 6**

0-4-0ST of Cardiff Rly.

Introduced 1893: Kitson design for Cardiff Railway.

Weight: 25 tons 10 cwt.

Pressure: 160 lb.

Cyls.: (O) 14″ × 21″.

Driving Wheels: 3′ 2½″.

T.E.: 14,540 lb.

Hawthorn Kitson valve gear.

1338   **Total 1**

0-4-0ST of P & M

Introduced 1907: Peckett design for P. & M.

Weight: 33 tons 10 cwt.

Pressure: 150 lb.

Cyls.: (O) 15″ × 21″.

Driving Wheels: 3′ 7″.

T.E.: 14,010 lb.

1151/2   **Total 2**

0-4-0ST of SHT

Introduced 1905: Barclay design for S.H.T.

Weight: 28 tons 0 cwt.

Pressure: 160 lb.

Cyls.: (O) 14″ × 22″.

Driving Wheels: 3′ 5″.

T.E.: 14,305 lb.

1140   **Total 1**

Introduced 1906: Peckett design for S.H.T. (similar to 1151/2).

Weight: 33 tons 10 cwt.

Pressure: 150 lb.

Cyls.: (O) 15″ × 21″.

Driving Wheels: 3′ 7″.

T.E.: 14,010 lb.

1143/5   **Total 2**

Introduced 1909: Hawthorn Leslie design for S.H.T.

Weight: 26 tons 17 cwt.

Pressure: 150 lb.

Cyls.: (O) 14″ × 22″.

Driving Wheels: 3′ 6″.

T.E.: 13,090 lb.

1144   **Total 1**

Introduced 1911: Hudswell Clarke design for S.H.T.

Weight: 28 tons 15 cwt.

Pressure: 160 lb.

Cyls.: (O) 15″ × 22″.

Driving Wheels: 3′ 4″.

T.E.: 16,830 lb.

1142   **Total 1**

LOCOMOTIVE SUPERINTENDENTS AND CHIEF
MECHANICAL ENGINEERS OF THE G.W.R. & W.R.

Sir Daniel Gooch	...	1837—1864
Joseph Armstrong	...$\left\{\begin{array}{l}\text{1854—1864*}\\\text{1864—1877}\end{array}\right.$	
George Armstrong ... ... (*Bro. of J. Armstrong*)	...$\left\{\begin{array}{l}\text{1864—}\\\text{1877—1892*}\end{array}\right.$	
William Dean	...$\left\{\begin{array}{l}\text{—1877*}\\\text{1877—1902}\end{array}\right.$	
G. J. Churchward	...	1902—1921
Charles B. Collett	...	1922—1941
F. W. Hawksworth	...	1941—1949

* In charge of standard gauge locomotives at Stafford Road Works, Wolverhampton, with wide powers in design and construction. The exact dates of Geo. Armstrong's and Dean's terms of service there cannot be definitely ascertained from existing records.

G.W.R. DIESEL RAILCARS

Car No.	Date	Engines	Total b.h.p.	Seats	Car No.	Date	Engines	Total b.h.p.	Seats
4*	1934	2	242	44	17‡	1936	2	242	—
5-7	1935	2	242	70	18§	1937	2	242	70
8	1936	2	242	70	19-32	1940	2	210	48
11/12†	1936	2	242	63	33, 38‖	1942	4	420	92
13-16	1936	2	242	70	34‡	1941	2	210	—

* Buffet and lavatory facilities.
† Lavatory facilities.
‡ Parcels cars.
§ Experimentally geared to haul trailer car, became prototype of subsequent designs.

‖ Twin-coach unit with buffet and lavatory facilities. Adjoining statistics apply per 2-car unit. This unit can work as a 3-car set by the addition of an ordinary corridor coach.

4	8	14	18	21	24	27	30	33
5	11	15	19	22	25	28	31	34
6	12	16	20	23	26	29	32	38
7	13	17						

Ex-S.H.T. 0-4-0ST No. 1142

[E. J. Dew

Ex-P.M. 0-4-0ST No. 1152

[A. R. Carpenter

Ex-Cardiff Rly. 0-4-0ST No. 1338

[R. Russell

Top: 1101 Class 0-4-0T
No. 1102 [P. J. Sharpe

Centre: 1400 Class
0-4-2T No. 1426
[A. R. Carpenter

Left: 1366 Class 0-6-0PT
No. 1368
[C. H. S. Owen

Top: Ex-R.R. R1 Class
0-6-2T No. 38
[T. K. Widd

Centre: Ex-T.V. A Class
0-6-2T No. 361 (since
withdrawn)
[T. K. Widd

Right: 5600 Class 0-6-2T
No. 6647 [R. J. Buckley

1600 Class 0-6-0PT No. 1601   [A. R. Carpenter

5400 Class 0-6-0PT No. 5413   [A. R. Carpenter

5700 Class 0-6-0PT No. 7722   [R. J. Buckley

7400 Class 0-6-0PT No. 7401 [G. Wheeler

9400 Class 0-6-0PT No. 3408 [R. K. Evans

1500 Class 0-6-0PT No. 1505 [Brian E. Morrison

2800 Class 2-8-0 No. 2813   [A. E. Brown

2800 Class 2-8-0 No. 2899 (with side-window cab)   [A. R. Carpenter

4700 Class 2-8-0 No. 4701   [R. Russell

R.O.D. Class 2-8-0 No. 3028 (since withdrawn)   [A. R. Carpenter

4300 Class 2-6-0 No. 7300   [G. Wheeler

4300 Class 2-6-0 No. 9310 (with side-window cab)   [T. K. Widd

6000 Class 4-6-0 No. 6013 *King Henry VIII* [G. Wheeler

4073 Class 4-6-0 No. 5004 *Llanstephen Castle* [P. Ransome-Wallis

4000 Class 4-6-0 No. 4056 *Princess Margaret* [D. S. Fish

NUMERICAL LIST OF WESTERN REGION
STEAM LOCOMOTIVES

Locomotives are of G.W. origin except where
indicated by other initials

2-6-2T   V of R

7 Owain Glyndŵr
8 Llywelyn
9 Prince of Wales

0-6-2T   RR

36   38   42

0-6-2T   TV

304	365	383	393
305	370	385	397
349	373	390	398
364	381		

0-6-0T   W & L

822   823

(Line closed: locos. stored.)

4-6-0   1000 Class
" County "

1000 County of Middlesex
1001 County of Bucks
1002 County of Berks

1003 County of Wilts
1004 County of Somerset
1005 County of Devon
1006 County of Cornwall
1007 County of Brecknock
1008 County of Cardigan
1009 County of Carmarthen
1010 County of Caernarvon
1011 County of Chester
1012 County of Denbigh
1013 County of Dorset
1014 County of Glamorgan
1015 County of Gloucester
1016 County of Hants
1017 County of Hereford
1018 County of Leicester
1019 County of Merioneth
1020 County of Monmouth
1021 County of Montgomery
1022 County of Northampton
1023 County of Oxford
1024 County of Pembroke
1025 County of Radnor
1026 County of Salop
1027 County of Stafford
1028 County of Warwick
1029 County of Worcester

0-4-0T   1101 Class

1101	1103	1105
1102	1104	1106

0-4-0ST   SHT

1140	1143	1145
1142	1144	

1151—2158

0-4-0ST   PM

1151   1152

0-4-0ST   Car. R.

1338

0-6-0ST   1361 Class

| 1361 | 1363 | 1365 |
| 1362 | 1364 | |

0-6-0PT   1366 Class

| 1366 | 1368 | 1370 |
| 1367 | 1369 | 1371 |

0-4-2T   1400 Class

1400	1424	1443	1462
1401	1426	1444	1463
1403	1427	1445	1464
1405	1428	1446	1465
1406	1429	1447	1466
1407	1430	1448	1467
1408	1431	1449	1468
1409	1432	1450	1469
1410	1433	1451	1470
1412	1434	1452	1471
1414	1435	1453	1472
1417	1436	1454	1473
1418	1437	1455	1474
1419	1438	1456	
1420	1439	1457	
1421	1440	1458	
1422	1441	1459	
1423	1442	1461	

0-6-0PT   1500 Class

1500	1503	1506	1509
1501	1504	1507	
1502	1505	1508	

0-6-0PT   1600 Class

1600	1618	1636	1654
1601	1619	1637	1655
1602	1620	1638	1656
1603	1621	1639	1657
1604	1622	1640	1658
1605	1623	1641	1659
1606	1624	1642	1660
1607	1625	1643	1661
1608	1626	1644	1662
1609	1627	1645	1663
1610	1628	1646	1664
1611	1629	1647	1665
1612	1630	1648	1666
1613	1631	1649	1667
1614	1632	1650	1668
1615	1633	1651	1669
1616	1634	1652	
1617	1635	1653	

0-6-0PT   850 Class

2008   2012

0-6-0PT   2021 Class

2069   2134   2160

0-6-0T   BPGV Rly.

2198

26

0-6-0   2251 Class

2200	2225	2250	2275
2201	2226	2251	2276
2202	2227	2252	2277
2203	2228	2253	2278
2204	2229	2254	2279
2205	2230	2255	2280
2206	2231	2256	2281
2207	2232	2257	2282
2208	2233	2258	2283
2209	2234	2259	2284
2210	2235	2260	2285
2211	2236	2261	2286
2212	2237	2262	2287
2213	2238	2263	2288
2214	2239	2264	2289
2215	2240	2265	2290
2216	2241	2266	2291
2217	2242	2267	2292
2218	2243	2268	2293
2219	2244	2269	2294
2220	2245	2270	2295
2221	2246	2271	2296
2222	2247	2272	2297
2223	2248	2273	2298
2224	2249	2274	2299

2828	2846	2864	2882
2829	2847	2865	2883
2830	2848	2866	2884
2831	2849	2867	2885
2832	2850	2868	2886
2833	2851	2869	2887
2834	2852	2870	2888
2835	2853	2871	2889
2836	2854	2872	2890
2837	2855	2873	2891
2838	2856	2874	2892
2839	2857	2875	2893
2840	2858	2876	2894
2841	2859	2877	2895
2842	2860	2878	2896
2843	2861	2879	2897
2844	2862	2880	2898
2845	2863	2881	2899

2-8-0   R.O.D. Class

3011	3024	3036	3041
3015			

0-6-0   2301 Class

2538

2-8-0   2800 Class

2800	2807	2814	2821
2801	2808	2815	2822
2802	2809	2816	2823
2803	2810	2817	2824
2804	2811	2818	2825
2805	2812	2819	2826
2806	2813	2820	2827

2-6-2T   3100 Class

3100	3102	3103	3104
3101			

2-6-2T   3150 Class

3150	3172	3180	3190
3163	3174	3183	
3170	3176	3186	
3171	3177	3187	

0-6-0   2251 Class

3200	3205	3210	3215
3201	3206	3211	3216
3202	3207	3212	3217
3203	3208	3213	3218
3204	3209	3214	3219

0-6-0PT   9400 Class

3400	3403	3406	3408
3401	3404	3407	3409
3402	3405		

4-4-0   "City" Class

3440 City of Truro

0-6-0PT   5700 Class

3600	3617	3634	3651
3601	3618	3635	3652
3602	3619	3636	3653
3603	3620	3637	3654
3604	3621	3638	3655
3605	3622	3639	3656
3606	3623	3640	3657
3607	3624	3641	3658
3608	3625	3642	3659
3609	3626	3643	3660
3610	3627	3644	3661
3611	3628	3645	3662
3612	3629	3646	3663
3613	3630	3647	3664
3614	3631	3648	3665
3615	3632	3649	3666
3616	3633	3650	3667

3668	3701	3734	3767
3669	3702	3735	3768
3670	3703	3736	3769
3671	3704	3737	3770
3672	3705	3738	3771
3673	3706	3739	3772
3674	3707	3740	3773
3675	3708	3741	3774
3676	3709	3742	3775
3677	3710	3743	3776
3678	3711	3744	3777
3679	3712	3745	3778
3680	3713	3746	3779
3681	3714	3747	3780
3682	3715	3748	3781
3683	3716	3749	3782
3684	3717	3750	3783
3685	3718	3751	3784
3686	3719	3752	3785
3687	3720	3753	3786
3688	3721	3754	3787
3689	3722	3755	3788
3690	3723	3756	3789
3691	3724	3757	3790
3692	3725	3758	3791
3693	3726	3759	3792
3694	3727	3760	3793
3695	3728	3761	3794
3696	3729	3762	3795
3697	3730	3763	3796
3698	3731	3764	3797
3699	3732	3765	3798
3700	3733	3766	3799

2-8-0   2800 Class

3800	3811	3822	3833
3801	3812	3823	3834
3802	3813	3824	3835
3803	3814	3825	3836
3804	3815	3826	3837
3805	3816	3827	3838
3806	3817	3828	3839
3807	3818	3829	3840
3808	3819	3830	3841
3809	3820	3831	3842
3810	3821	3832	3843

3844	3850	3856	3862
3845	3851	3857	3863
3846	3852	3858	3864
3847	3853	3859	3865
3848	3854	3860	3866
3849	3855	3861	

4096 Highclere Castle
4097 Kenilworth Castle
4098 Kidwelly Castle
4099 Kilgerran Castle

4-6-0   4073 Class
" Castle "

4000 North Star
4037 The South Wales Borderers

4-6-0   4000 Class
" Star "

4056 Princess Margaret
4061 Glastonbury Abbey

4-6-0   4073 Class
" Castle "

4073 Caerphilly Castle
4074 Caldicot Castle
4075 Cardiff Castle
4076 Carmarthen Castle
4077 Chepstow Castle
4078 Pembroke Castle
4079 Pendennis Castle
4080 Powderham Castle
4081 Warwick Castle
4082 Windsor Castle
4083 Abbotsbury Castle
4084 Aberystwyth Castle
4085 Berkeley Castle
4086 Builth Castle
4087 Cardigan Castle
4088 Dartmouth Castle
4089 Donnington Castle
4090 Dorchester Castle
4091 Dudley Castle
4092 Dunraven Castle
4093 Dunster Castle
4094 Dynevor Castle
4095 Harlech Castle

2-6-2T   5100 Class

4100	4120	4140	4160
4101	4121	4141	4161
4102	4122	4142	4162
4103	4123	4143	4163
4104	4124	4144	4164
4105	4125	4145	4165
4106	4126	4146	4166
4107	4127	4147	4167
4108	4128	4148	4168
4109	4129	4149	4169
4110	4130	4150	4170
4111	4131	4151	4171
4112	4132	4152	4172
4113	4133	4153	4173
4114	4134	4154	4174
4115	4135	4155	4175
4116	4136	4156	4176
4117	4137	4157	4177
4118	4138	4158	4178
4119	4139	4159	4179

2-8-0T   4200 Class

4200	4226	4250	4268
4201	4227	4251	4269
4203	4228	4252	4270
4206	4229	4253	4271
4207	4230	4254	4272
4208	4231	4255	4273
4211	4232	4256	4274
4212	4233	4257	4275
4213	4235	4258	4276
4214	4236	4259	4277
4215	4237	4260	4278
4217	4238	4261	4279
4218	4241	4262	4280
4221	4242	4263	4281
4222	4243	4264	4282
4223	4246	4265	4283
4224	4247	4266	4284
4225	4248	4267	4285

4286	4290	4294	4298
4287	4291	4295	4299
4288	4292	4296	
4289	4293	4297	

2-6-0   4300 Class

4326	4358	4375	4377

2-6-2T   4500 Class

4505	4552	4568	4584
4507	4553	4569	4585
4508	4554	4570	4587
4519	4555	4571	4588
4524	4556	4572	4589
4526	4557	4573	4590
4536	4558	4574	4591
4538	4559	4575	4592
4540	4560	4576	4593
4545	4561	4577	4594
4546	4562	4578	4595
4547	4563	4579	4596
4548	4564	4580	4597
4549	4565	4581	4599
4550	4566	4582	
4551	4567	4583	

0-6-0PT   5700 Class

4600	4610	4620	4630
4601	4611	4621	4631
4602	4612	4622	4632
4603	4613	4623	4633
4604	4614	4624	4634
4605	4615	4625	4635
4606	4616	4626	4636
4607	4617	4627	4637
4608	4618	4628	4638
4609	4619	4629	4639

4640	4655	4670	4685
4641	4656	4671	4686
4642	4657	4672	4687
4643	4658	4673	4688
4644	4659	4674	4689
4645	4660	4675	4690
4646	4661	4676	4691
4647	4662	4677	4692
4648	4663	4678	4693
4649	4664	4679	4694
4650	4665	4680	4695
4651	4666	4681	4696
4652	4667	4682	4697
4653	4668	4683	4698
4654	4669	4684	4699

2-8-0   4700 Class

4700	4703	4705	4707
4701	4704	4706	4708
4702			

4-6-0 " Hall " 4900 Class

4900 Saint Martin
4901 Adderley Hall
4902 Aldenham Hall
4903 Astley Hall
4904 Binnegar Hall
4905 Barton Hall
4906 Bradfield Hall
4907 Broughton Hall
4908 Broome Hall
4909 Blakesley Hall
4910 Blaisdon Hall
4912 Berrington Hall
4913 Baglan Hall
4914 Cranmore Hall
4915 Condover Hall
4916 Crumlin Hall
4917 Crosswood Hall
4918 Dartington Hall
4919 Donnington Hall
4920 Dumbleton Hall
4921 Eaton Hall

4922 Enville Hall
4923 Evenley Hall
4924 Eydon Hall
4925 Eynsham Hall
4926 Fairleigh Hall
4927 Farnborough Hall
4928 Gatacre Hall
4929 Goytrey Hall
4930 Hagley Hall
4931 Hanbury Hall
4932 Hatherton Hall
4933 Himley Hall
4934 Hindlip Hall
4935 Ketley Hall
4936 Kinlet Hall
4937 Lanelay Hall
4938 Liddington Hall
4939 Littleton Hall
4940 Ludford Hall
4941 Llangedwyn Hall
4942 Maindy Hall
4943 Marrington Hall
4944 Middleton Hall
4945 Milligan Hall
4946 Moseley Hall
4947 Nanhoran Hall
4948 Northwick Hall
4949 Packwood Hall
4950 Patshull Hall
4951 Pendeford Hall
4952 Peplow Hall
4953 Pitchford Hall
4954 Plaish Hall
4955 Plaspower Hall
4956 Plowden Hall
4957 Postlip Hall
4958 Priory Hall
4959 Purley Hall
4960 Pyle Hall
4961 Pyrland Hall
4962 Ragley Hall
4963 Rignall Hall
4964 Rodwell Hall
4965 Rood Ashton Hall
4966 Shakenhurst Hall
4967 Shirenewton Hall
4968 Shotton Hall
4969 Shrugborough Hall

4970 Sketty Hall
4971 Stanway Hall
4972 Saint Brides Hall
4973 Sweeney Hall
4974 Talgarth Hall
4975 Umberslade Hall
4976 Warfield Hall
4977 Watcombe Hall
4978 Westwood Hall
4979 Wootton Hall
4980 Wrottesley Hall
4981 Abberley Hall
4982 Acton Hall
4983 Albert Hall
4984 Albrighton Hall
4985 Allesley Hall
4986 Aston Hall
4987 Brockley Hall
4988 Bulwell Hall
4989 Cherwell Hall
4990 Clifton Hall
4991 Cobham Hall
4992 Crosby Hall
4993 Dalton Hall
4994 Downton Hall
4995 Easton Hall
4996 Eden Hall
4997 Elton Hall
4998 Eyton Hall
4999 Gopsal Hall

4-6-0 "Castle" 4073 Class

5000 Launceston Castle
5001 Llandovery Castle
5002 Ludlow Castle
5003 Lulworth Castle
5004 Llanstephan Castle
5005 Manorbier Castle
5006 Tregenna Castle
5007 Rougemont Castle
5008 Raglan Castle
5009 Shrewsbury Castle
5010 Restormel Castle
5011 Tintagel Castle
5012 Berry Pomeroy Castle

5013 Abergavenny Castle
5014 Goodrich Castle
5015 Kingswear Castle
5016 Montgomery Castle
5017 The Gloucestershire
     Regiment 28th, 61st
5018 St. Mawes Castle
5019 Treago Castle
5020 Trematon Castle
5021 Whittington Castle
5022 Wigmore Castle
5023 Brecon Castle
5024 Carew Castle
5025 Chirk Castle
5026 Criccieth Castle
5027 Farleigh Castle
5028 Llantilio Castle
5029 Nunney Castle
5030 Shirburn Castle
5031 Totnes Castle
5032 Usk Castle
5033 Broughton Castle
5034 Corfe Castle
5035 Coity Castle
5036 Lyonshall Castle
5037 Monmouth Castle
5038 Morlais Castle
5039 Rhuddlan Castle
5040 Stokesay Castle
5041 Tiverton Castle
5042 Winchester Castle
5043 Earl of Mount Edgcumbe
5044 Earl of Dunraven
5045 Earl of Dudley
5046 Earl Cawdor
5047 Earl of Dartmouth
5048 Earl of Devon
5049 Earl of Plymouth
5050 Earl of St. Germans
5051 Earl Bathurst
5052 Earl of Radnor
5053 Earl Cairns
5054 Earl of Ducie
5055 Earl of Eldon
5056 Earl of Powis
5057 Earl Waldegrave
5058 Earl of Clancarty
5059 Earl St. Aldwyn

5060 Earl of Berkeley
5061 Earl of Birkenhead
5062 Earl of Shaftesbury
5063 Earl Baldwin
5064 Bishop's Castle
5065 Newport Castle
5066 Sir Felix Pole
5067 St. Fagans Castle
5068 Beverston Castle
5069 Isambard Kingdom Brunel
5070 Sir Daniel Gooch
5071 Spitfire
5072 Hurricane
5073 Blenheim
5074 Hampden
5075 Wellington
5076 Gladiator
5077 Fairey Battle
5078 Beaufort
5079 Lysander
5080 Defiant
5081 Lockheed Hudson
5082 Swordfish
5083 Bath Abbey
5084 Reading Abbey
5085 Evesham Abbey
5086 Viscount Horne
5087 Tintern Abbey
5088 Llanthony Abbey
5089 Westminster Abbey
5090 Neath Abbey
5091 Cleeve Abbey
5092 Tresco Abbey
5093 Upton Castle
5094 Tretower Castle
5095 Barbury Castle
5096 Bridgwater Castle
5097 Sarum Castle
5098 Clifford Castle
5099 Compton Castle

2-6-2T   5100 Class

| 5101 | 5103 | 5105 | 5107 |
| 5102 | 5104 | 5106 | 5108 |

5109	5162	5176	5190
5110	5163	5177	5191
5148	5164	5178	5192
5150	5165	5179	5193
5151	5166	5180	5194
5152	5167	5181	5195
5153	5168	5182	5196
5154	5169	5183	5197
5155	5170	5184	5198
5156	5171	5185	5199
5157	5172	5186	
5158	5173	5187	
5160	5174	5188	
5161	5175	5189	

5371	5379	5386	5394
5372	5380	5388	5396
5375	5381	5390	5397
5376	5382	5391	5398
5377	5384	5392	5399
5378	5385	5393	

2-8-0T 4200 Class

5200	5217	5234	5251
5201	5218	5235	5252
5202	5219	5236	5253
5203	5220	5237	5254
5204	5221	5238	5255
5205	5222	5239	5256
5206	5223	5240	5257
5207	5224	5241	5258
5208	5225	5242	5259
5209	5226	5243	5260
5210	5227	5244	5261
5211	5228	5245	5262
5212	5229	5246	5263
5213	5230	5247	5264
5214	5231	5248	
5215	5232	5249	
5216	5233	5250	

0-6-0PT 5400 Class

5400	5407	5414	5420
5402	5409	5415	5421
5403	5410	5416	5422
5404	5411	5417	5423
5405	5412	5418	5424
5406	5413	5419	

2-6-0 4300 Class

5306	5323	5336	5355
5310	5324	5337	5356
5311	5325	5338	5357
5312	5326	5339	5358
5313	5328	5341	5360
5314	5330	5344	5361
5315	5331	5345	5362
5318	5332	5347	5367
5319	5333	5350	5368
5321	5334	5351	5369
5322	5335	5353	5370

2-6-2T 4500 Class

5500	5520	5539	5558
5501	5521	5540	5559
5502	5522	5541	5560
5503	5523	5542	5561
5504	5524	5543	5562
5505	5525	5544	5563
5506	5526	5545	5564
5507	5527	5546	5565
5508	5528	5547	5566
5509	5529	5548	5567
5510	5530	5549	5568
5511	5531	5550	5569
5513	5532	5551	5570
5514	5533	5552	5571
5515	5534	5553	5572
5516	5535	5554	5573
5517	5536	5555	5574
5518	5537	5556	
5519	5538	5557	

0-6-2T 5600 Class

5600	5602	5604	5606
5601	5603	5605	5607

5608	5631	5654	5677
5609	5632	5655	5678
5610	5633	5656	5679
5611	5634	5657	5680
5612	5635	5658	5681
5613	5636	5659	5682
5614	5637	5660	5683
5615	5638	5661	5684
5616	5639	5662	5685
5617	5640	5663	5686
5618	5641	5664	5687
5619	5642	5665	5688
5620	5643	5666	5689
5621	5644	5667	5690
5622	5645	5668	5691
5623	5646	5669	5692
5624	5647	5670	5693
5625	5648	5671	5694
5626	5649	5672	5695
5627	5650	5673	5696
5628	5651	5674	5697
5629	5652	5675	5698
5630	5653	5676	5699

0-6-0PT   5700 Class

5701	5722	5743	5767
5702	5723	5744	5768
5703	5724	5745	5769
5704	5725	5747	5770
5705	5726	5748	5771
5706	5727	5749	5772
5707	5728	5750	5773
5708	5729	5751	5774
5709	5730	5753	5775
5710	5731	5754	5776
5711	5732	5755	5777
5712	5733	5756	5778
5713	5734	5757	5779
5714	5735	5758	5780
5715	5736	5759	5781
5716	5737	5760	5782
5717	5738	5761	5783
5718	5739	5763	5784
5719	5740	5764	5785
5720	5741	5765	5786
5721	5742	5766	5787

5788	5791	5795	5798
5789	5793	5796	5799
5790	5794	5797	

0-4-2T   5800 Class

5800	5805	5811	5816
5801	5806	5812	5817
5802	5807	5813	5818
5803	5809	5814	5819
5804	5810	5815	

4-6-0   4900 Class
" Hall "

5900 Hinderton Hall
5901 Hazel Hall
5902 Howick Hall
5903 Keele Hall
5904 Kelham Hall
5905 Knowsley Hall
5906 Lawton Hall
5907 Marble Hall
5908 Moreton Hall
5909 Newton Hall
5910 Park Hall
5911 Preston Hall
5912 Queen's Hall
5913 Rushton Hall
5914 Ripon Hall
5915 Trentham Hall
5916 Trinity Hall
5917 Westminster Hall
5918 Walton Hall
5919 Worsley Hall
5920 Wycliffe Hall
5921 Bingley Hall
5922 Caxton Hall
5923 Colston Hall
5924 Dinton Hall
5925 Eastcote Hall
5926 Grotrian Hall
5927 Guild Hall
5928 Haddon Hall
5929 Hanham Hall
5930 Hannington Hall
5931 Hatherley Hall

5932 Haydon Hall
5933 Kingsway Hall
5934 Kneller Hall
5935 Norton Hall
5936 Oakley Hall
5937 Stanford Hall
5938 Stanley Hall
5939 Tangley Hall
5940 Whitbourne Hall
5941 Campion Hall
5942 Doldowlod Hall
5943 Elmdon Hall
5944 Ickenham Hall
5945 Leckhampton Hall
5946 Marwell Hall
5947 Saint Benet's Hall
5948 Siddington Hall
5949 Trematon Hall
5950 Wardley Hall
5951 Clyffe Hall
5952 Cogan Hall
5953 Dunley Hall
5954 Faendre Hall
5955 Garth Hall
5956 Horsley Hall
5957 Hutton Hall
5958 Knolton Hall
5959 Mawley Hall
5960 Saint Edmund Hall
5961 Toynbee Hall
5962 Wantage Hall
5963 Wimpole Hall
5964 Wolseley Hall
5965 Woollas Hall
5966 Ashford Hall
5967 Bickmarsh Hall
5968 Cory Hall
5969 Honington Hall
5970 Hengrave Hall
5971 Merevale Hall
5972 Olton Hall
5973 Rolleston Hall
5974 Wallsworth Hall
5975 Winslow Hall
5976 Ashwicke Hall
5977 Beckford Hall
5978 Bodinnick Hall
5979 Cruckton Hall

5980 Dingley Hall
5981 Frensham Hall
5982 Harrington Hall
5983 Henley Hall
5984 Linden Hall
5985 Mostyn Hall
5986 Arbury Hall
5987 Brocket Hall
5988 Bostock Hall
5989 Cransley Hall
5990 Dorford Hall
5991 Gresham Hall
5992 Horton Hall
5993 Kirby Hall
5994 Roydon Hall
5995 Wick Hall
5996 Mytton Hall
5997 Sparkford Hall
5998 Trevor Hall
5999 Wollaton Hall

4-6-0   6000 Class
" King "

6000 King George V
6001 King Edward VII
6002 King William IV
6003 King George IV
6004 King George III
6005 King George II
6006 King George I
6007 King William III
6008 King James II
6009 King Charles II
6010 King Charles I
6011 King James I
6012 King Edward VI
6013 King Henry VIII
6014 King Henry VII
6015 King Richard III
6016 King Edward V
6017 King Edward IV
6018 King Henry VI
6019 King Henry V
6020 King Henry IV

6021 King Richard II
6022 King Edward III
6023 King Edward II
6024 King Edward I
6025 King Henry III
6026 King John
6027 King Richard I
6028 King George VI
6029 King Edward VIII

6354	6366	6378	6391
6355	6367	6379	6392
6356	6368	6380	6393
6357	6369	6381	6394
6358	6370	6382	6395
6359	6371	6384	6396
6360	6372	6385	6397
6361	6373	6386	6398
6362	6374	6387	6399
6363	6375	6388	
6364	6376	6389	
6365	6377	6390	

2-6-2T   6100 Class

6100	6118	6136	6153
6101	6119	6137	6154
6102	6120	6138	6155
6103	6121	6139	6156
6104	6122	6140	6157
6105	6123	6141	6158
6106	6124	6142	6159
6107	6125	6143	6160
6108	6126	6144	6161
6109	6127	6145	6162
6110	6128	6146	6163
6111	6129	6147	6164
6112	6130	6148	6165
6113	6131	6149	6166
6114	6132	6150	6167
6115	6133	6151	6168
6116	6134	6152	6169
6117	6135		

0-6-0PT   6400 Class

6400	6410	6420	6430
6401	6411	6421	6431
6402	6412	6422	6432
6403	6413	6423	6433
6404	6414	6424	6434
6405	6415	6425	6435
6406	6416	6426	6436
6407	6417	6427	6437
6408	6418	6428	6438
6409	6419	6429	6439

2-6-0   4300 Class

6300	6313	6328	6341
6301	6314	6329	6342
6302	6316	6330	6343
6303	6317	6331	6344
6304	6318	6332	6345
6305	6319	6333	6346
6306	6320	6334	6347
6307	6322	6335	6348
6308	6323	6336	6349
6309	6324	6337	6350
6310	6325	6338	6351
6311	6326	6339	6352
6312	6327	6340	6353

0-6-2T   5600 Class

6600	6620	6640	6660
6601	6621	6641	6661
6602	6622	6642	6662
6603	6623	6643	6663
6604	6624	6644	6664
6605	6625	6645	6665
6606	6626	6646	6666
6607	6627	6647	6667
6608	6628	6648	6668
6609	6629	6649	6669
6610	6630	6650	6670
6611	6631	6651	6671
6612	6632	6652	6672
6613	6633	6653	6673
6614	6634	6654	6674
6615	6635	6655	6675
6616	6636	6656	6676
6617	6637	6657	6677
6618	6638	6658	6678
6619	6639	6659	6679

6680	6685	6690	6695
6681	6686	6691	6696
6682	6687	6692	6697
6683	6688	6693	6698
6684	6689	6694	6699

0-6-0PT   5700 Class

6700	6720	6740	6760
6701	6721	6741	6761
6702	6722	6742	6762
6703	6723	6743	6763
6704	6724	6744	6764
6705	6725	6745	6765
6706	6726	6746	6766
6707	6727	6747	6767
6708	6728	6748	6768
6709	6729	6749	6769
6710	6730	6750	6770
6711	6731	6751	6771
6712	6732	6752	6772
6713	6733	6753	6773
6714	6734	6754	6774
6715	6735	6755	6775
6716	6736	6756	6776
6717	6737	6757	6777
6718	6738	6758	6778
6719	6739	6759	6779

4-6-0   6800 Class
" Grange "

6800 Arlington Grange
6801 Aylburton Grange
6802 Bampton Grange
6803 Bucklebury Grange
6804 Brockington Grange
6805 Broughton Grange
6806 Blackwell Grange
6807 Birchwood Grange
6808 Beenham Grange
6809 Burghclere Grange
6810 Blakemere Grange
6811 Cranbourne Grange
6812 Chesford Grange
6813 Eastbury Grange

6814 Enborne Grange
6815 Frilford Grange
6816 Frankton Grange
6817 Gwenddwr Grange
6818 Hardwick Grange
6819 Highnam Grange
6820 Kingstone Grange
6821 Leaton Grange
6822 Manton Grange
6823 Oakley Grange
6824 Ashley Grange
6825 Llanvair Grange
6826 Nannerth Grange
6827 Llanfrechfa Grange
6828 Trellech Grange
6829 Burmington Grange
6830 Buckenhill Grange
6831 Bearley Grange
6832 Brockton Grange
6833 Calcot Grange
6834 Dummer Grange
6835 Eastham Grange
6836 Estevarney Grange
6837 Forthampton Grange
6838 Goodmoor Grange
6839 Hewell Grange
6840 Hazeley Grange
6841 Marlas Grange
6842 Nunhold Grange
6843 Poulton Grange
6844 Penhydd Grange
6845 Paviland Grange
6846 Ruckley Grange
6847 Tidmarsh Grange
6848 Toddington Grange
6849 Walton Grange
6850 Cleeve Grange
6851 Hurst Grange
6852 Headbourne Grange
6853 Morehampton Grange
6854 Roundhill Grange
6855 Saighton Grange
6856 Stowe Grange
6857 Tudor Grange
6858 Woolston Grange
6859 Yiewsley Grange
6860 Aberporth Grange
6861 Crynant Grange

6862 Derwent Grange
6863 Dolhywel Grange
6864 Dymock Grange
6865 Hopton Grange
6866 Morfa Grange
6867 Peterston Grange
6868 Penrhos Grange
6869 Resolven Grange
6870 Bodicote Grange
6871 Bourton Grange
6872 Crawley Grange
6873 Caradoc Grange
6874 Haughton Grange
6875 Hindford Grange
6876 Kingsland Grange
6877 Llanfair Grange
6878 Longford Grange
6879 Overton Grange

4-6-0   4900 Class
" Hall "

6900 Abney Hall
6901 Arley Hall
6902 Butlers Hall
6903 Belmont Hall
6904 Charfield Hall
6905 Claughton Hall
6906 Chicheley Hall
6907 Davenham Hall
6908 Downham Hall
6909 Frewin Hall
6910 Gossington Hall
6911 Holker Hall
6912 Helmster Hall
6913 Levens Hall
6914 Langton Hall
6915 Mursley Hall
6916 Misterton Hall
6917 Oldlands Hall
6918 Sandon Hall
6919 Tylney Hall
6920 Barningham Hall
6921 Borwick Hall
6922 Burton Hall
6923 Croxteth Hall

6924 Grantley Hall
6925 Hackness Hall
6926 Holkham Hall
6927 Lilford Hall
6928 Underley Hall
6929 Whorlton Hall
6930 Aldersey Hall
6931 Aldborough Hall
6932 Burwarton Hall
6933 Birtles Hall
6934 Beachamwell Hall
6935 Browsholme Hall
6936 Breccles Hall
6937 Conyngham Hall
6938 Corndean Hall
6939 Calveley Hall
6940 Didlington Hall
6941 Fillongley Hall
6942 Eshton Hall
6943 Farnley Hall
6944 Fledborough Hall
6945 Glasfryn Hall
6946 Heatherden Hall
6947 Helmingham Hall
6948 Holbrooke Hall
6949 Haberfield Hall
6950 Kingsthorpe Hall
6951 Impney Hall
6952 Kimberley Hall
6953 Leighton Hall
6954 Lotherton Hall
6955 Lydcott Hall
6956 Mottram Hall
6957 Norcliffe Hall
6958 Oxburgh Hall

4-6-0   6959 Class
" Modified Hall "

6959 Peatling Hall
6960 Raveningham Hall
6961 Stedham Hall
6962 Soughton Hall
6963 Throwley Hall
6964 Thornbridge Hall
6965 Thirlestaine Hall
6966 Witchingham Hall

6967 Willesley Hall	7009 Athelney Castle
6968 Woodcock Hall	7010 Avondale Castle
6969 Wraysbury Hall	7011 Banbury Castle
6970 Whaddon Hall	7012 Barry Castle
6971 Athelhampton Hall	7013 Bristol Castle
6972 Beningbrough Hall	7014 Caerhays Castle
6973 Bricklehampton Hall	7015 Carn Brea Castle
6974 Bryngwyn Hall	7016 Chester Castle
6975 Capesthorne Hall	7017 G. J. Churchward
6976 Graythwaite Hall	7018 Drysllwyn Castle
6977 Grundisburgh Hall	7019 Fowey Castle
6978 Haroldstone Hall	7020 Gloucester Castle
6979 Helperly Hall	7021 Haverfordwest Castle
6980 Llanrumney Hall	7022 Hereford Castle
6981 Marbury Hall	7023 Penrice Castle
6982 Melmerby Hall	7024 Powis Castle
6983 Otterington Hall	7025 Sudeley Castle
6984 Owsden Hall	7026 Tenby Castle
6985 Parwick Hall	7027 Thornbury Castle
6986 Rydal Hall	7028 Cadbury Castle
6987 Shervington Hall	7029 Clun Castle
6988 Swithland Hall	7030 Cranbrook Castle
6989 Wightwick Hall	7031 Cromwell's Castle
6990 Witherslack Hall	7032 Denbigh Castle
6991 Acton Burnell Hall	7033 Hartlebury Castle
6992 Arborfield Hall	7034 Ince Castle
6993 Arthog Hall	7035 Ogmore Castle
6994 Baggrave Hall	7036 Taunton Castle
6995 Benthall Hall	7037 Swindon
6996 Blackwell Hall	
6997 Bryn-Ivor Hall	
6998 Burton Agnes Hall	
6999 Capel Dewi Hall	

4-6-0   4073 Class
" Castle "

7000 Viscount Portal
7001 Sir James Milne
7002 Devizes Castle
7003 Elmley Castle
7004 Eastnor Castle
7005 Lamphey Castle
7006 Lydford Castle
7007 Great Western
7008 Swansea Castle

2-8-2T   7200 Class

7200	7214	7228	7242
7201	7215	7229	7243
7202	7216	7230	7244
7203	7217	7231	7245
7204	7218	7232	7246
7205	7219	7233	7247
7206	7220	7234	7248
7207	7221	7235	7249
7208	7222	7236	7250
7209	7223	7237	7251
7210	7224	7238	7252
7211	7225	7239	7253
7212	7226	7240	
7213	7227	7241	

2-6-0   4300 Class

7300	7307	7314	7321
7301	7308	7315	7323
7302	7309	7316	7329
7303	7310	7317	7339
7304	7311	7318	
7305	7312	7319	
7306	7313	7320	

0-6-0PT   7400 Class

7400	7413	7426	7438
7401	7414	7427	7439
7402	7415	7428	7440
7403	7416	7429	7441
7404	7417	7430	7442
7405	7418	7431	7443
7406	7419	7432	7444
7407	7420	7433	7445
7408	7421	7434	7446
7409	7422	7435	7447
7410	7423	7436	7448
7411	7424	7437	7449
7412	7425		

0-6-0PT   5700 Class

7700	7722	7743	7764
7701	7723	7744	7765
7702	7724	7745	7766
7703	7725	7746	7767
7704	7726	7747	7768
7705	7727	7748	7769
7706	7728	7749	7770
7707	7729	7750	7771
7708	7730	7751	7772
7709	7731	7752	7773
7710	7732	7753	7774
7712	7734	7754	7775
7713	7734	7755	7776
7714	7735	7756	7777
7715	7736	7757	7778
7716	7737	7758	7779
7717	7738	7759	7780
7718	7739	7760	7781
7719	7740	7761	7782
7720	7741	7762	7783
7721	7742	7763	7784

7785	7789	7793	7797
7786	7790	7794	7798
7787	7791	7795	7799
7788	7792	7796	

4-6-0   7800 Class
" Manor "

7800 Torquay Manor
7801 Anthony Manor
7802 Bradley Manor
7803 Barcote Manor
7804 Baydon Manor
7805 Broome Manor
7806 Cockington Manor
7807 Compton Manor
7808 Cookham Manor
7809 Childrey Manor
7810 Draycott Manor
7811 Dunley Manor
7812 Erlestoke Manor
7813 Freshford Manor
7814 Fringford Manor
7815 Fritwell Manor
7816 Frilsham Manor
7817 Garsington Manor
7818 Granville Manor
7819 Hinton Manor
7820 Dinmore Manor
7821 Ditcheat Manor
7822 Foxcote Manor
7823 Hook Norton Manor
7824 Iford Manor
7825 Lechlade Manor
7826 Longworth Manor
7827 Lydham Manor
7828 Odney Manor
7829 Ramsbury Manor

4-6-0   6959 Class
" Modified Hall "

7900 Saint Peter's Hall
7901 Dodington Hall
7902 Eaton Mascot Hall
7903 Foremarke Hall
7904 Fountains Hall

1000 Class 4-6-0 No. 1009 *County of Carmarthen* (with double chimney) [*G. Wheeler*

000 Class 4-6-0 No. 1028 *County of Warwick* [*G. Wheeler*

7800 Class 4-6-0 No. 7812 *Erlestoke Manor* [*P. J. Sharpe*

4900 Class 4-6-0 No. 5919 *Worsley Hall*   [G. Wheeler

6959 Class 4-6-0 No. 7912 *Little Linford Hall*   [G. Wheeler

6800 Class 4-6-0 No. 6843 *Poulton Grange*   [P. H. Groom

9000 Class 4-4-0 No. 9005   [A. A. Cameron

" City " Class 4-4-0 No. 3440 City of Truro   [Locomotive Publishing Co.

2301 Class 0-6-0 No. 2538   [Brian Hilton

Top: 3150 Class 2-6-2T No. 3186 [T. K. Widd

Centre: 5100 Class 2-6-2T No. 5148 [R. S. Potts

Left: 3100 Class 2-6-2T No. 3101 [G. Wheeler

Top: 4500 Class 2-6-2T
No. 4573
[C. G. Pearson

Centre: 4500 Class
2-6-2T No. 5563 (with
sloping side-tanks)
[R. C. Blake

Right: 7200 Class 2-8-2T
No. 7225 [R. E. Vincent

7200 Class 2-8-2T No. 7213 (with raised footplating over cylinders [H. Gordon Tidey

4200 Class 2-8-0T No. 4254 [A. R. Carpenter

4200 Class 2-8-0T No. 4228 (with raised footplating over cylinders)
[A. A. Cameron

Class 3 2-6-2T No. 82022

[I. S. Swanson

Class 4 4-6-0 No. 75038

[A. E. Brown

Class 9F 2-10-0 No. 92052

[P. H. Groom

Class 5 4-6-0 No. 73004   [*J. G. Ballantyne*

Class 5 4-6-0 No. 73128 (with Caprotti valve gear)   [*W. H. Whitworth*

Class 7P6F 4-6-2 No. 70052 *Firth of Tay*   [*David A. Anderson*

7905 Fowey Hall			
7906 Fron Hall			
7907 Hart Hall			
7908 Henshall Hall			
7909 Heveningham Hall			
7910 Hown Hall			
7911 Lady Margaret Hall			
7912 Little Linford Hall			
7913 Little Wyrley Hall			
7914 Lleweni Hall			
7915 Mere Hall			
7916 Mobberley Hall			
7917 North Aston Hall			
7918 Rhose Wood Hall			
7919 Runter Hall			
7920 Coney Hall			
7921 Edstone Hall			
7922 Salford Hall			
7923 Speke Hall			
7924 Thornycroft Hall			
7925 Westol Hall			
7926 Willey Hall			
7927 Willington Hall			
7928 Wolf Hall			
7929 Wyke Hall			

8456	8467	8478	8489
8457	8468	8479	8490
8458	8469	8480	8491
8459	8470	8481	8492
8460	8471	8482	8493
8461	8472	8483	8494
8462	8473	8484	8495
8463	8474	8485	8496
8464	8475	8486	8497
8465	8476	8487	8498
8466	8477	8488	8499

2-6-2T   8100 Class

8100	8103	8106	8108
8101	8104	8107	8109
8102	8105		

0-6-0PT   9400 Class

8400	8414	8428	8442
8401	8415	8429	8443
8402	8416	8430	8444
8403	8417	8431	8445
8404	8418	8432	8446
8405	8419	8433	8447
8406	8420	8434	8448
8407	8421	8435	8449
8408	8422	8436	8450
8409	8423	8437	8451
8410	8424	8438	8452
8411	8425	8439	8453
8412	8426	8440	8454
8413	8427	8441	8455

0-6-0PT   5700 Class

8700	8725	8750	8775
8701	8726	8751	8776
8702	8727	8752	8777
8703	8728	8753	8778
8704	8729	8754	8779
8705	8730	8755	8780
8706	8731	8756	8781
8707	8732	8757	8782
8708	8733	8758	8783
8709	8734	8759	8784
8710	8735	8760	8785
8711	8736	8761	8786
8712	8737	8762	8787
8713	8738	8763	8788
8714	8739	8764	8789
8715	8740	8765	8790
8716	8741	8766	8791
8717	8742	8767	8792
8718	8743	8768	8793
8719	8744	8769	8794
8720	8745	8770	8795
8721	8746	8771	8796
8722	8747	8772	8797
8723	8748	8773	8798
8724	8749	8774	8799

4-4-0   9000 Class

9004	9012	9018	9025
9005	9013	9020	9026
9008	9014	9021	9027
9009	9015	9022	9028
9010	9016	9023	
9011	9017	9024	

2-6-0   4300 Class

9300	9306	9312	9318
9302	9308	9313	9319
9303	9309	9314	
9304	9310	9315	
9305	9311	9316	

0-6-0PT   9400 Class

9400	9425	9450	9475
9401	9426	9451	9476
9402	9427	9452	9477
9403	9428	9453	9478
9404	9429	9454	9479
9405	9430	9455	9480
9406	9431	9456	9481
9407	9432	9457	9482
9408	9433	9458	9483
9409	9434	9459	9484
9410	9435	9460	9485
9411	9436	9461	9486
9412	9437	9462	9487
9413	9438	9463	9488
9414	9439	9464	9489
9415	9440	9465	9490
9416	9441	9466	9491
9417	9442	9467	9492
9418	9443	9468	9493
9419	9444	9469	9494
9420	9445	9470	9495
9421	9446	9471	9496
9422	9447	9472	9497
9423	9448	9473	9498
9424	9449	9474	9499

0-6-0PT   5700 Class

9600	9610	9620	9630
9601	9611	9621	9631
9602	9612	9622	9632
9603	9613	9623	9633
9604	9614	9624	9634
9605	9615	9625	9635
9606	9616	9626	9636
9607	9617	9627	9637
9608	9618	9628	9638
9609	9619	9629	9639

9640	9676	9729	9765
9641	9677	9730	9766
9642	9678	9731	9767
9643	9679	9732	9768
9644	9680	9733	9769
9645	9681	9734	9770
9646	9682	9735	9771
9647	9700	9736	9772
9648	9701	9737	9773
9649	9702	9738	9774
9650	9703	9739	9775
9651	9704	9740	9776
9652	9705	9741	9777
9653	9706	9742	9778
9654	9707	9743	9779
9655	9708	9744	9780
9656	9709	9745	9781
9657	9710	9746	9782
9658	9711	9747	9783
9659	9712	9748	9784
9660	9713	9749	9785
9661	9714	9750	9786
9662	9715	9751	9787
9663	9716	9752	9788
9664	9717	9753	9789
9665	9718	9754	9790
9666	9719	9755	9791
9667	9720	9756	9792
9668	9721	9757	9793
9669	9722	9758	9794
9670	9723	9759	9795
9671	9724	9760	9796
9672	9725	9761	9797
9673	9726	9762	9798
9674	9727	9763	9799
9675	9728	9764	

SERVICE LOCOMOTIVES

Diesel Mechanised

20

           Total 1

Petrol

22, 23, 24, 26 and 27

           Total 5

BRITISH RAILWAYS STANDARD LOCOMOTIVES

Chief Officer (Mechanical Engineering)

R. C. BOND

4-6-2　　　　　**7P6F**

Introduced 1951. Designed at Derby.

Weight: Loco. 94 tons 0 cwt.
Tender (see page 58).

Pressure: 250 lb. Su.

Cyls.: (O) 20″ × 28″.

Driving Wheels: 6′ 2″.

T.E.: 32,150 lb.

Walschaerts valve gear.　P.V.

70000	Britannia
70001	Lord Hurcomb
70002	Geoffrey Chaucer
70003	John Bunyan
70004	William Shakespeare
70005	John Milton
70006	Robert Burns
70007	Coeur-de-Lion
70008	Black Prince
70009	Alfred the Great
70010	Owen Glendower
70011	Hotspur
70012	John of Gaunt
70013	Oliver Cromwell
70014	Iron Duke
70015	Apollo
70016	Ariel
70017	Arrow
70018	Flying Dutchman
70019	Lightning
70020	Mercury
70021	Morning Star
70022	Tornado
70023	Venus
70024	Vulcan
70025	Western Star
70026	Polar Star
70027	Rising Star
70028	Royal Star
70029	Shooting Star
70030	William Wordsworth

70031	Byron
70032	Tennyson
70033	Charles Dickens
70034	Thomas Hardy
70035	Rudyard Kipling
70036	Boadicea
70037	Hereward the Wake
70038	Robin Hood
70039	Sir Christopher Wren
70040	Clive of India
70041	Sir John Moore
70042	Lord Roberts
70043	
70044	Earl Haig
70045	
70046	
70047	
70048	
70049	
70050	Firth of Clyde
70051	Firth of Forth
70052	Firth of Tay
70053	Moray Firth
70054	Dornoch Firth

Total 55

4-6-2　　　　　**8P**

Introduced 1954. Designed at Derby.

Weight: Loco. 101 tons 5 cwt.
Tender (see page 58).

Pressure: 250 lb. Su.

Cyls.: (3) 18″ × 28″.

Driving Wheels: 6′ 2″.

T.E.: 39,080 lb.

Caprotti valve gear.

71000 Duke of Gloucester

Total 1

4-6-2   6P5F

Introduced 1952. Designed at Derby.
Weight: Loco. 86 tons 19 cwt.
       Tender (see page 58).
Pressure: 225 lb. Su.
Cyls.: (O) 19½" × 28".
Driving Wheels: 6' 2".
T.E.: 27,520 lb.
Walschaerts valve gear. P.V.

72000	Clan Buchanan
72001	Clan Cameron
72002	Clan Campbell
72003	Clan Fraser
72004	Clan Macdonald
72005	Clan Macgregor
72006	Clan Mackenzie
72007	Clan Mackintosh
72008	Clan Macleod
72009	Clan Stewart

Total 10

4-6-0   5

Introduced 1951. Designed at Doncaster.
Introduced 1956. Fitted with Caprotti valve gear.
Weight: Loco. 76 tons 4 cwt.
       Tender (see page 58).
Pressure: 225 lb. Su.
Cyls.: (O) 19" × 28".
Driving Wheels: 6' 2".
T.E.: 26,120 lb.
Walschaerts valve gear. P.V.

73000	73014	73028	73042
73001	73015	73029	73043
73002	73016	73030	73044
73003	73017	73031	73045
73004	73018	73032	73046
73005	73019	73033	73047
73006	73020	73034	73048
73007	73021	73035	73049
73008	73022	73036	73050
73009	73023	73037	73051
73010	73024	73038	73052
73011	73025	73039	73053
73012	73026	73040	73054
73013	73027	73041	73055

73056	73085	73114	73143*
73057	73086	73115	73144*
73058	73087	73116	73145*
73059	73088	73117	73146*
73060	73089	73118	73147*
73061	73090	73119	73148*
73062	73091	73120	73149*
73063	73092	73121	73150*
73064	73093	73122	73151*
73065	73094	73123	73152*
73066	73095	73124	73153*
73067	73096	73125*	73154*
73068	73097	73126*	73155
73069	73098	73127*	73156
73070	73099	73128*	73157
73071	73100	73129*	73158
73072	73101	73130*	73159
73073	73102	73131*	73160
73074	73103	73132*	73161
73075	73104	73133*	73162
73076	73105	73134*	73163
73077	73106	73135*	73164
73078	73107	73136*	73165
73079	73108	73137*	73166
73080	73109	73138*	73167
73081	73110	73139*	73168
73082	73111	73140*	73169
73083	73112	73141*	73170
73084	73113	73142*	73171

Engines of this class are still being delivered.

4-6-0   4

Introduced 1951. Designed at Brighton.
Weight: Loco. 69 tons 0 cwt.
       Tender (see page 58).
Pressure: 225 lb. Su.
Cyls.: (O) 18" × 28".
Driving Wheels: 5' 8".
T.E.: 25,100 lb.
Walschaerts valve gear. P.V.

75000	75008	75016	75024
75001	75009	75017	75025
75002	75010	75018	75026
75003	75011	75019	75027
75004	75012	75020	75028
75005	75013	75021	75029
75006	75014	75022	75030
75007	75015	75023	75031

75032	75047	75062	75077
75033	75048	75063	75078
75034	75049	75064	75079
75035	75050	75065	75080
75036	75051	75066	75081
75037	75052	75067	75032
75038	75053	75068	75083
75039	75054	75069	75084
75040	75055	75070	75085
75041	75056	75071	75086
75042	75057	75072	75087
75043	75058	75073	75088
75044	75059	75074	75089
75045	75060	75075	
75046	75061	75076	

Engines of this class are still being delivered.

2-6-0   4

Introduced 1953. Designed at Don-caster.
Weight: Loco. 59 tons 2 cwt.
       Tender (see page 58).
Pressure: 225 lb. Su.
Cyls.: (O) 17½″ × 26″.
Driving Wheels: 5′ 3″.
T.E.: 24,170 lb.
Walschaerts valve gear. P.V.

76000	76020	76040	76060
76001	76021	76041	76061
76002	76022	76042	76062
76003	76023	76043	76063
76004	76024	76044	76064
76005	76025	76045	76065
76006	76026	76046	76066
76007	76027	76047	76067
76008	76028	76048	76068
76009	76029	76049	76069
76010	76030	76050	76070
76011	76031	76051	76071
76012	76032	76052	76072
76013	76033	76053	76073
76014	76034	76054	76074
76015	76035	76055	76075
76016	76036	76056	76076
76017	76037	76057	76077
76018	76038	76058	76078
76019	76039	76059	76079

76080	76089	76098	76107
76081	76090	76099	76108
76082	76091	76100	76109
76083	76092	76101	76110
76084	76093	76102	76111
76085	76094	76103	76112
76086	76095	76104	76113
76087	76096	76105	76114
76088	76097	76106	

Engines of this class are still being delivered.

2-6-0   3

Introduced 1954. Designed at Swindon
Weight: Loco. 57 tons 9 cwt.
        Tender (see page 58).
Pressure: 200 lb. Su.
Cyls.: (O) 17½″ × 26″.
Driving Wheels: 5′ 3″.
T.E.: 21,490 lb.
Walschaerts valve gear. P.V.

77000	77007	77014	77021
77001	77008	77015	77022
77002	77009	77016	77023
77003	77010	77017	77024
77004	77011	77018	
77005	77012	77019	
77006	77013	77020	

Engines of this class are still being delivered.

2-6-0   2

Introduced 1953. Designed at Derby.
Weight: Loco. 49 tons 5 cwt.
        Tender (see page 58).
Pressure: 200 lb. Su.
Cyls.: (O) 16½″ × 24″.
Driving Wheels: 5′ 0″.
T.E.: 18,515 lb.
Walschaerts valve gear. P.V.

78000	78007	78014	78021
78001	78008	78015	78022
78002	78009	78016	78023
78003	78010	78017	78024
78004	78011	78018	78025
78005	78012	78019	78026
78006	78013	78020	78027

78028	78038	78048	78058
78029	78039	78049	78059
78030	78040	78050	78060
78031	78041	78051	78061
78032	78042	78052	78062
78033	78043	78053	78063
78034	78044	78054	78064
78035	78045	78055	
78036	78046	78056	
78037	78047	78057	

Total 65

2-6-4T   4

Introduced 1951. Designed at Brighton.
Weight: 88 tons 10 cwt.
Pressure: 225 lb. Su.
Cyls.: (O) 18″ × 28″.
Driving Wheels: 5′ 8″.
T.E.: 25,100 lb.
Walschaerts valve gear. P.V.

80000	80026	80052	80078
80001	80027	80053	80079
80002	80028	80054	80080
80003	80029	80055	80081
80004	80030	80056	80082
80005	80031	80057	80083
80006	80032	80058	80084
80007	80033	80059	80085
80008	80034	80060	80086
80009	80035	80061	80087
80010	80036	80062	80088
80011	80037	80063	80089
80012	80038	80064	80090
80013	80039	80065	80091
80014	80040	80066	80092
80015	80041	80067	80093
80016	80042	80068	80094
80017	80043	80069	80095
80018	80044	80070	80096
80019	80045	80071	80097
80020	80046	80072	80098
80021	80047	80073	80099
80022	80048	80074	80100
80023	80049	80075	80101
80024	80050	80076	80102
80025	80051	80077	80103

80104	80117	80130	80143
80105	80118	80131	80144
80106	80119	80132	80145
80107	80120	80133	80146
80108	80121	80134	80147
80109	80122	80135	80148
80110	80123	80136	80149
80111	80124	80137	80150
80112	80125	80138	80151
80113	80126	80139	80152
80114	80127	80140	80153
80115	80128	80141	80154
80116	80129	80142	

Total 155

2-6-2T   Class 3

Introduced 1952. Designed at Swindon.
Weight: 73 tons 10 cwt.
Pressure: 200 lb. Su.
Cyls.: (O) 17½″ × 26″.
Driving Wheels: 5′ 3″.
T.E.: 21,490 lb.
Walschaerts valve gear. P.V.

82000	82012	82024	82036
82001	82013	82025	82037
82002	82014	82026	82038
82003	82015	82027	82039
82004	82016	82028	82040
82005	82017	82029	82041
82006	82018	82030	82042
82007	82019	82031	82043
82008	82020	82032	82044
82009	82021	82033	
82010	82022	82034	
82011	82023	82035	

Total 45

2-6-2T   2

Introduced 1953. Designed at Derby.
Weight: 63 tons 5 cwt.
Pressure: 200 lb. Su.
Cyls.: (O) 16½″ × 24″.
Driving Wheels: 5′ 0″.
T.E.: 18,515 lb.
Walschaerts valve gear. P.V.

84000	84002	84004	84006
84001	84003	84005	84007

84008	84014	84020	84026
84009	84015	84021	84027
84010	84016	84022	84028
84011	84017	84023	84029
84012	84018	84024	
84013	84019	84025	

Engines of this class are still being delivered.

2-8-0   8F   **WD**

Ministry of Supply " Austerity " 2-8-0 locomotives purchased by British Railways, 1948.

Introduced 1943. Riddles M.o.S. design.

Weight: Loco.   70 tons 5 cwt.
         Tender   55 tons 10 cwt.

Pressure: 225 lb. Su.

Cyls.: (O) 19″ × 28″.

Driving Wheels: 4′ 8½″.

T.E.: 34,215 lb.

Walschaerts valve gear.   P.V.

90000	90026	90052	90078
90001	90027	90053	90079
90002	90028	90054	90080
90003	90029	90055	90081
90004	90030	90056	90082
90005	90031	90057	90083
90006	90032	90058	90084
90007	90033	90059	90085
90008	90034	90060	90086
90009	90035	90061	90087
90010	90036	90062	90088
90011	90037	90063	90089
90012	90038	90064	90090
90013	90039	90065	90091
90014	90040	90066	90092
90015	90041	90067	90093
90016	90042	90068	90094
90017	90043	90069	90095
90018	90044	90070	90096
90019	90045	90071	90097
90020	90046	90072	90098
90021	90047	90073	90099
90022	90048	90074	90100
90023	90049	90075	90101
90024	90050	90076	90102
90025	90051	90077	90103

90104	90152	90200	90248
90105	90153	90201	90249
90106	90154	90202	90250
90107	90155	90203	90251
90108	90156	90204	90252
90109	90157	90205	90253
90110	90158	90206	90254
90111	90159	90207	90255
90112	90160	90208	90256
90113	90161	90209	90257
90114	90162	90210	90258
90115	90163	90211	90259
90116	90164	90212	90260
90117	90165	90213	90261
90118	90166	90214	90262
90119	90167	90215	90263
90120	90168	90216	90264
90121	90169	90217	90265
90122	90170	90218	90266
90123	90171	90219	90267
90124	90172	90220	90268
90125	90173	90221	90269
90126	90174	90222	90270
90127	90175	90223	90271
90128	90176	90224	90272
90129	90177	90225	90273
90130	90178	90226	90274
90131	90179	90227	90275
90132	90180	90228	90276
90133	90181	90229	90277
90134	90182	90230	90278
90135	90183	90231	90279
90136	90184	90232	90280
90137	90185	90233	90281
90138	90186	90234	90282
90139	90187	90235	90283
90140	90188	90236	90284
90141	90189	90237	90285
90142	90190	90238	90286
90143	90191	90239	90287
90144	90192	90240	90288
90145	90193	90241	90289
90146	90194	90242	90290
90147	90195	90243	90291
90148	90196	90244	90292
90149	90197	90245	90293
90150	90198	90246	90294
90151	90199	90247	90295

90296	90344	90392	90440	90488	90536	90584	90632
90297	90345	90393	90441	90489	90537	90585	90633
90298	90346	90394	90442	90490	90538	90586	90634
90299	90347	90395	90443	90491	90539	90587	90635
90300	90348	90396	90444	90492	90540	90588	90636
90301	90349	90397	90445	90493	90541	90589	90637
90302	90350	90398	90446	90494	90542	90590	90638
90303	90351	90399	90447	90495	90543	90591	90639
90304	90352	90400	90448	90496	90544	90592	90640
90305	90353	90401	90449	90497	90545	90593	90641
90306	90354	90402	90450	90498	90546	90594	90642
90307	90355	90403	90451	90499	90547	90595	90643
90308	90356	90404	90452	90500	90548	90596	90644
90309	90357	90405	90453	90501	90549	90597	90645
90310	90358	90406	90454	90502	90550	90598	90646
90311	90359	90407	90455	90503	90551	90599	90647
90312	90360	90408	90456	90504	90552	90600	90648
90313	90361	90409	90457	90505	90553	90601	90649
90314	90362	90410	90458	90506	90554	90602	90650
90315	90363	90411	90459	90507	90555	90603	90651
90316	90364	90412	90460	90508	90556	90604	90652
90317	90365	90413	90461	90509	90557	90605	90653
90318	90366	90414	90462	90510	90558	90606	90654
90319	90367	90415	90463	90511	90559	90607	90655
90320	90368	90416	90464	90512	90560	90608	90656
90321	90369	90417	90465	90513	90561	90609	90657
90322	90370	90418	90466	90514	90562	90610	90658
90323	90371	90419	90467	90515	90563	90611	90659
90324	90372	90420	90468	90516	90564	90612	90660
90325	90373	90421	90469	90517	90565	90613	90661
90326	90374	90422	90470	90518	90566	90614	90662
90327	90375	90423	90471	90519	90567	90615	90663
90328	90376	90424	90472	90520	90568	90616	90664
90329	90377	90425	90473	90521	90569	90617	90665
90330	90378	90426	90474	90522	90570	90618	90666
90331	90379	90427	90475	90523	90571	90619	90667
90332	90380	90428	90476	90524	90572	90620	90668
90333	90381	90429	90477	90525	90573	90621	90669
90334	90382	90430	90478	90526	90574	90622	90670
90335	90383	90431	90479	90527	90575	90623	90671
90336	90384	90432	90480	90528	90576	90624	90672
90337	90385	90433	90481	90529	90577	90625	90673
90338	90386	90434	90482	90530	90578	90626	90674
90339	90387	90435	90483	90531	90579	90627	90675
90340	90388	90436	90484	90532	90580	90628	90676
90341	90389	90437	90485	90533	90581	90629	90677
90342	90390	90438	90486	90534	90582	90630	90678
90343	90391	90439	90487	90535	90583	90631	90679

90680	90694	90708	90722
90681	90695	90709	90723
90682	90696	90710	90724
90683	90697	90711	90725
90684	90698	90712	90726
90685	90699	90713	90727
90686	90700	90714	90728
90687	90701	90715	90729
90688	90702	90716	90730
90689	90703	90717	90731
90690	90704	90718	90732
90691	90705	90719	Vulcan
90692	90706	90720	
90693	90707	90721	

Total 733

2-10-0   8F   WD

Ministry of Supply "Austerity" 2-10-0 locomotives purchased by British Railways, 1948.

Introduced 1943, Riddles M.o.S. design.

Weight: Loco.   78 tons 6 cwt.
        Tender 55 tons 10 cwt.

Pressure: 225 lb. Su.

Cyls.: (O) 19″ × 28″.

Driving Wheels: 4′ 8½″.

T.E.: 34,215 lb.

Walschaerts valve gear.   P.V.

90750	90757	90764	90771
90751	90758	90765	90772
90752	90759	90766	90773
90753	90760	90767	90774
90754	90761	90768	
90755	90762	90769	
90756	90763	90770	

Total 25

2-10-0   9F

Introduced 1954. Designed at Brighton.

*Introduced 1955. Fitted with Crosti boiler.

Weight: Loco. { 86 tons 14 cwt.
                { 90 tons 4 cwt.*
        Tender (see page 58).

Pressure: 250 lb. Su.

Cyls.: (O) 20″ × 28″.

Driving Wheels: 5′ 0″.

T.E.: 39,670 lb.

Walschaerts valve gear.   P.V.

92000	92043	92086	92129
92001	92044	92087	92130
92002	92045	92088	92131
92003	92046	92089	92132
92004	92047	92090	92133
92005	92048	92091	92134
92006	92049	92092	92135
92007	92050	92093	92136
92008	92051	92094	92137
92009	92052	92095	92138
92010	92053	92096	92139
92011	92054	92097	92140
92012	92055	92098	92141
92013	92056	92099	92142
92014	92057	92100	92143
92015	92058	92101	92144
92016	92059	92102	92145
92017	92060	92103	92146
92018	92061	92104	92147
92019	92062	92105	92148
92020*	92063	92106	92149
92021*	92064	92107	92150
92022*	92065	92108	92151
92023*	92066	92109	92152
92024*	92067	92110	92153
92025*	92068	92111	92154
92026*	92069	92112	92155
92027*	92070	92113	92156
92028*	92071	92114	92157
92029*	92072	92115	92158
92030	92073	92116	92159
92031	92074	92117	92160
92032	92075	921 8	92161
92033	92076	92119	92162
92034	92077	92120	92163
92035	92078	92121	92164
92036	92079	92122	92165
92037	92080	92123	92166
92038	92081	92124	92167
92039	92082	92125	92168
92040	92083	92126	92169
92041	92084	92127	92170
92042	92085	92128	92171

92172	92177	92182	92187		92192	92195	92198	92201
92173	92178	92183	92188		92193	92196	92199	92202
92174	92179	92184	92189		92194	92197	92200	
92175	92180	92185	92190					
92176	92181	92186	92191					

Engines of this class are still being delivered.

BRITISH RAILWAYS STANDARD TENDERS

N.B.—These pairings are not permanent and are liable to alteration with changed operating conditions.

| Type | Capacity | | Weight in Full W.O. | | Locos to which Allocated |
	Water galls.	Coal tons	tons	cwt.	
BRI	4,250	7	49	3	70000–24/30-44 72000–9 73000–49
BRIA	5,000	7	52	10	70025–29
BRIB	4,725	7	50	5	73080–89 73100–09/20-34 73145–71 75065–79 76053–69 92020–29/60-6 92097–9
BRIC	4,725	9	53	5	73065–79/90-9 73135–44 92015–9/45-59 92077–86 92100–39/50-67
BRID	4,725	9	54	10	70045–54
BRIE	4,725	10	55	10	71000
BRIF	5,625	7	55	5	73110–19 92010–14/30-44 92067–76 92087–96 92140–9 92168–92202
BRIG	5,000	7	52	10	73050–52 92000–9
BRIH	4,250	7	49	3	73053–64
BR2	3,500	6	42	3	75000–49 76000–44
BR2A	3,500	6	42	3	75050–64/80-9 76045–52 76070–76114 77000–24
BR3	3,000	4	36	17	78000–64

POWER AND WEIGHT CLASSIFICATION

Since 1920 Western Region locomotives have been classified for power and weight by a letter on a coloured disc on the cab side. The letter represents the power of the locomotive, and is approximately proportional to the tractive effort as under :

Power class	Tractive effort lb.	Power class	Tractive effort lb.
Special	Over 38,000	B	18,501–20,500
E	33,001–38,000	A	16,500–18,500
D	25,001–33,000	Un-	
C	20,501–25,000	grouped	Below 16,500

The colour of the circle represents the routes over which the engine may work. Red engines are limited to the main lines and lines capable of carrying the heaviest locomotives ; blue engines are allowed over additional routes, yellow engines over nearly the whole system and uncoloured engines are more or less unrestricted. The double red circles on the " King " class represent special restrictions for these engines.

Class	Power Class	Route Restriction Colour	Class	Power Class	Route Restriction Colour
4-6-0			**0-6-2T**		
1000	D	Red	5600	D	Red
4000	D	Red	(35)	D	Red
4073	D	Red	(304)	C	Red
4900	D	Red			
6000	Special	Double Red			
6800	D	Red	**0-6-0T**		
6959	D	Red	850	—	—
7800	D	Blue	1361	—	—
4-4-0			1366	—	—
9000	B	Yellow	1500	C	Red
2-8-0			1600	A	—
2800	E	Blue	2021	A	—
R.O.D.	D	Blue	5400	—	Yellow
4700	D	Red	5700	C	Yellow
2-6-0			9700–10	C	Blue
4300	D	Blue	6400	A	Yellow
7323/9/39 } D		Red	7400	A	Yellow
9300–19 }			9400	C	Red
0-6-0			(2198)	—	—
2251	B	Yellow			
2301	A	—	**0-4-2T**		
2-8-2T			1400	—	—
7200	E	Red	5800	—	—
2-8-0T					
4200	E	Red	**0-4-0T**		
2-6-2T			1101	B	Red
3100	D	Red	(1333)	—	—
4500	C	Yellow	(1151)	—	—
5100	D	Blue	(1140)	—	—
6100	D	Blue	(1143)	—	Blue
8100	D	Blue	(1144)	—	Yellow
(7)	—	—	(1142)	A	Yellow

WESTERN REGION PASSENGER TRAIN REPORTING NUMBERS
SUMMER

CERTAIN passenger trains, and any relief trains run thereto, bear a number for identification purposes for the whole or part of the journey over the Western Region, as shown in the following list. In a few instances through trains to and from the Southern Region carry the identification number during their journey over that Region also.

The number allotted to each train is displayed in a metal frame carried on the smokebox of the engine.

The numbers shown in this list refer to ordinary trains only: those carried by relief or duplicate trains are shown only in the Western Region's official working notices, as required, and do not appear in this list.

Train No.	Time	From	To
038	10.50 a.m.‡‡	Manchester (L.R.)	Cardiff
100	5.30 a.m.**	Paddington	Penzance
	5.30 a.m.†	"	Minehead
102	6.55 a.m.†	"	Penzance
103	7. 0 a.m.†	"	Kingswear
105	7. 5 a.m.†	"	Penzance
107	7.25 a.m.†	Ealing Bdy.	Paignton
	7.30 a.m.§	Paddington	"
108	7.40 a.m.†	"	Paignton
110	8.10 a.m.†	"	"
113	8.20 a.m.†	"	Weymouth
114	8.25 a.m.†	"	Penzance
115	8.20 a.m.*	"	Weymouth
116	8.30 a.m.	"	Bristol
117	8.45 a.m.†	"	Paignton
119	8.50 a.m.†	"	Bristol
120	9. 5 a.m.§	"	Durston
122	9.15 a.m.†	"	Falmouth
	9.30 a.m.†	"	Newquay
123	9.30 a.m.†	"	Minehead
125	9.35 a.m.†	"	Paignton
128	9.40 a.m.†	"	Kingswear
130	10.20 a.m.†	"	Penzance
131	10.30 a.m.§	"	"
	10.35 a.m.**	"	"
133	10.35 a.m.	"	Paignton
135	10.40 a.m.†	Swindon	Sheffield
136	11. 5 a.m.†	Paddington	Penzance
138	11. 0 a.m.†	"	"

Train No.	Time	From	To
010	9.50 p.m.†	Paddington	Penzance
011	10.12 p.m.††	"	"
012	10.35 p.m.†	"	"
013	10.50 p.m.††	"	Newquay
015	11.35 p.m.†	"	Penzance
016	11.50 p.m.†	"	"
018	12.30 a.m.†	"	"
	(News)	"	"
019	12.35 a.m.†	"	"

§ Every weekday. * Sats. exc. † Sats. only. ‡ Fris. only. ¶ Sats. & Suns. ‖ Tues. to Sats. or Suns. incl. ** Weekdays and Suns. †† Mons. only. ‡‡ Suns. only

Train No.	Time	From	To
140	11. 5 a.m.†	Paddington	Penzance
142	11.15 a.m.§	"	Weston-s-Mare
144	11.30 a.m.†	"	Penzance
146	11.30 a.m.	"	Minehead
147	12. 0 nn.§	"	Kingswear
148	12. 5 p.m.†	"	Plymouth
149	1.25 p.m.	"	Kingswear
150	1.35 p.m.†	"	Penzance
152	3.20 p.m.†	"	Penzance
153	3.30 p.m.§	"	Kingswear
154	4.15 p.m.§	"	Penzance
155	5. 5 p.m.§	"	Plymouth
156	11. 4 p.m.§	Bournemouth	Weston-s-Mare
157	5.30 p.m.§	Paddington	Sheffield
158	6.15 p.m.†	"	Plymouth
159	6.30 p.m.§	"	Bristol
161	7.55 a.m.†	"	Weston-s-Mare
162	8.50 a.m.†	"	Carmarthen
163	8.55 a.m.§	"	Pembroke Dock
164	9.55 a.m.†	"	"
165	9.55 a.m.§	"	Swansea
166	10.55 a.m.§	"	Neyland
167	11.35 a.m.†	"	Pembroke Dock
168	1.50 p.m.§	"	Neyland
169	3.45 p.m.§	"	Pembroke Dock
170	3.55 p.m.§	"	Carmarthen
171	4.55 p.m.§	"	Pembroke Dock
172	5.55 p.m.§	"	Fishguard Harbour
173	5.50 p.m.§	"	Neyland
174	5.50 p.m.§	"	Carmarthen
175	5.50 p.m.§	"	Swansea
176	6.35 p.m.§	"	Cheltenham

Train No.	Time	From	To
178	6.55 p.m.§	Paddington	Fishguard Harbour
179	7.15 p.m.†	"	Birkenhead
180	9.10 a.m.	"	Wolverhampton
181	9. 0 a.m.§	"	Pwllheli
...	9.10 a.m.†	"	Aberystwyth
183	10.10 a.m.†	"	Hereford
185	11.45 a.m.§	"	
186	1.45 p.m.	"	Birkenhead
187	4.10 p.m.	"	Hereford
189	4.45 p.m.§	"	Wolverhampton
192	5.10 p.m.*	"	Birkenhead
195	6.10 p.m.§	"	Hereford
198	6.45 p.m.§	"	Birkenhead
201	10.22 p.m.‡	York	Swindon
202	11.35 p.m.‡	Liverpool	Penzance
204	8.10 a.m.†	Manchester (L.R.)	Newcastle
205	11.16 a.m.§	Bournemouth	Newcastle
206	12. 0 nn.§	Penzance	Crewe
208	8. 5 a.m.†	Bournemouth	Newcastle
...	9.10 a.m.†	Liverpool	Plymouth
...	9.15 a.m.§	"	
...	10.40 a.m.‡‡	Swindon	York
210	9.40 p.m.§	Manchester (L.R.)	Swansea
212	9.25 a.m.§	"	Plymouth
...	9.10 a.m.†	"	Paignton
214	5.30 p.m.‡	Glasgow	Plymouth
215	12. 5 a.m.**	Cardiff	Liverpool
216	9. 5 a.m.†	Birkenhead	Plymouth
217	12.10 a.m.‡‡	Bristol	Plymouth
221	4.45 p.m.§	Penzance	Manchester (L.R.)
...	7. 5 p.m.†	"	" (V.)
223	9. 0 a.m.†	Exmouth	" (L.R.)

Train No.	Time	From	To
227	8.20 a.m.†	Cardiff	Manchester (May.)
228	11.55 a.m.§	Manchester (L.R.)	Plymouth
230	12.15 a.m.†		Paignton
232	12.40 p.m.†	Cardiff	Manchester (Ex.)
234	3. 0 p.m.*	Liverpool	Cardiff
..	3. 5 p.m.††		
239	10.15 a.m.†	Bradford (Exch.)	Poole
240	3.10 p.m.†	Manchester (L.R.)	Plymouth
..	3.15 p.m.††		Bristol
241	8.55 a.m.†	Cardiff	Manchester (L.R.)
243	10.25 p.m.†	Derby	Bournemouth
244	11.45 a.m.†	Ilfracombe	Manchester (Ex.)
246	8.33 p.m.§	Crewe	Cardiff
248	8.20 p.m.§		Bristol
252	9.25 p.m.†	Manchester (L.R.)	Newquay
257	4.40 p.m.†	Cardiff	Manchester (L.R.)
258	10.35 p.m.§	Manchester (V.)	Paignton
262	12.35 a.m.†	" (L.R.)	Plymouth
263	1.40 a.m.††	Crewe	
..	8. 0 a.m.††	Plymouth	Crewe
265	8.45 a.m.†		
..	12.40 p.m.††	Cardiff	Manchester (L.R.)
..	11.15 a.m.†	Swansea	
..	11.50 a.m.*		
268	11.15 p.m.†	Manchester (V.)	Paignton
273	7.30 a.m.†	Penzance	Crewe
..	7.50 a.m.†	Newquay	Manchester (L.R.)
280	1.25 a.m.**	Crewe	Cardiff
283	8.15 a.m.†	Bristol	Manchester (L.R.)
..	8.15 a.m.†		Liverpool
284	8.45 a.m.†	Liverpool	Penzance
285	10. 5 a.m.§	Penzance	Liverpool
289	6. 5 p.m.‡‡	Cardiff	Crewe
292	11.15 p.m.†	Manchester (L.R.)	Penzance

Train No.	Time	From	To
297	7.35 a.m.†	Cardiff	Blackpool
303	9.15 a.m.†	Blackpool	Cardiff
301	5.40 p.m.††		Crewe
305	8. 0 p.m.†	Penzance	Manchester (V.)
314	12. 0 nn.†	Manchester (L.R.)	Cardiff
329	4.40 p.m.†	Penzance	Manchester (L.R.)
334	9.10 p.m.†	Manchester (V.)	Paignton
341	9. 8 p.m.†	"	Penzance
350	4.40 p.m.†	Penzance	Manchester (L.R.)
353	6.45 a.m.§	Wolverhampton	Paddington
355	7.30 a.m.§	Shrewsbury	"
360	6.35 a.m.§	Hereford	"
363	8.19 a.m.§	Kidderminster	"
365	7.25 a.m.*	Wolverhampton	"
375	11.15 a.m.*	Aberystwyth	"
376	4.35 p.m.*	Wolverhampton	"
375	2.40 p.m.§	Birkenhead	"
380	5.20 p.m.††	Wolverhampton	"
383	9.25 a.m.†	Weymouth	Wolverhampton
384	10.20 a.m.†		Birmingham
385	10.20 a.m.†		Wolverhampton
387	11.12 a.m.†		Paddington
388	3.40 p.m.§		
389	4.10 p.m.†		
390	4.18 p.m.†		
391	9. 0 a.m.†	Bournemouth	Cardiff
392	8.50 a.m.†	New Milton	
395	9. 0 a.m.†	Portsmouth	Swansea
396	9.33 a.m.†		Cardiff
397	10.34 a.m.†		"
399	11.37 a.m.†		"
400	11. 0 a.m.†	Brighton	"
399	3.57 p.m.††	Newcastle	Penzance
403	7.14 p.m.†	Sheffield	Newquay

Train No.	Time	From	To
405	1. 5 a.m.†	Bristol	Penzance
403	9.12 p.m.†‡	Nottingham	Paignton
410	10.20 p.m.	"	"
413	10.20 p.m.	"	"
415	8.50 p.m.†‡	Sheffield	"
417	10.10 p.m.	Bradford	"
418	9. 5 p.m.†	Hull	"
419	6.25 a.m.*	Newcastle	Plymouth
420	7. 0 a.m.†	Bristol	Penzance
423	8.30 a.m.†	Swindon	Weymouth
425	9.35 a.m.†	Weston-s-Mare	Penzance
430	6.35 a.m.†	Bristol	Kingswear
433	6.40 a.m.†	Walsall	Paignton
435	7.43 a.m.†	Leicester	Plymouth
438	8. 6 a.m.†	Nottingham	Kingswear
440	1.45 p.m.†	Sheffield	Kingswear
442	7.30 a.m.†	Bristol	Penzance
444	9.30 a.m.†	Newcastle	Paignton
446	9.25 a.m.†	Leeds	"
450	7. 0 a.m.§	Bradford	Paddington
455	8.20 a.m.§	Weston-s-Mare	"
457	10.42 a.m.†	"	"
460	11.45 a.m.†	Bristol	"
462	11. 5 a.m.†	Weston-s-Mare	"
463	1.50 p.m.†	Bristol	"
465	1.58 p.m.†	Weston-s-Mare	"
470	4.15 p.m.*	Bristol	"
473	4.30 p.m.*	"	"
475	4.35 p.m.†	Weston-s-Mare	"
480	4.41 p.m.†	"	Birmingham
490	2. 5 p.m.†	"	Swansea
493	1.50 p.m.†	Swindon	Sheffield
500	7.30 p.m.‡	Kingswear	Paddington

Train No.	Time	From	To
503	10.30 p.m.†	Paignton	Nottingham
505	8. 0 a.m.†	Kingswear	Paddington
508	9. 5 a.m.†	Minehead	"
510	10.40 a.m.†	Churston	"
512	9.45 a.m.†	Minehead	"
513	6. 5 a.m.†	Paignton	L.M.R.
515	10.35 a.m.†	Torquay	Paddington
517	11.50 p.m.†	Paignton	Wolverhampton
518	6.30 a.m.†	"	L.M.R.
520	11.20 a.m.†	Kingswear	Paddington
522	11.25 a.m.*	"	"
523	11.55 a.m.†	Minehead	Bradford
525	6.55 a.m.†	Paignton	Birmingham
527	11.30 a.m.†	Torquay	Birmingham
528	10. 0 a.m.†	Paignton	L.M.R.
529	7.10 a.m.†	Newton Abbot	Paddington
530	12.18 p.m.†	Paignton	
533	1.30 p.m.†	Paignton	Newcastle
535	7.45 a.m.†	Kingswear	Paddington
537	1.40 p.m.†	Paignton	Wolverhampton
540	10.35 a.m.†	"	Paddington
542	1.45 p.m.†	Minehead	"
543	2.15 p.m.†	Paignton	Nottingham
545	8.40 a.m.†	Minehead	Paddington
550	2.45 p.m.†	Paignton	"
552	4.15 p.m.†	Teignmouth	Bradford
553	10.15 a.m.†	Paignton	Sheffield
555	8.52 a.m.†	Kingswear	Paddington
557	4.35 p.m.†	Paignton	Wolverhampton
560	12.15 p.m.†	Ilfracombe	Bradford
563	10.55 a.m.†	Kingswear	Manchester (L.R.)
565	8.45 a.m.†	Paignton	Wolverhampton
567	1.55 p.m.‡	"	Wolverhampton

Train No.	Time	From	To
568	6.40 a.m.†	Paignton	Stockport
570	7.45 a.m.†	Newton Abbot	Swansea
573	10.58 a.m.†	Paignton	Nottingham
577	2.55 p.m.†	"	Wolverhampton
578	8. 5 a.m.†	"	Manchester (V.) (L.R.)
579	9. 5 a.m.†	"	"
580	9. 5 a.m.†	Kingswear	Swansea
583	2.25 p.m.†	Paignton	Sheffield
585	10.10 a.m.†	"	Cardiff
587	9.25 a.m.†	Ilfracombe	"
588	3.10 p.m.†	Paignton	Wolverhampton
590	10.20 a.m.†	Kingswear	Crewe
593	12. 5 p.m.†	Paignton	Cardiff
594	5.15 p.m.†	"	Nottingham
595	12.30 p.m.†	"	Manchester (L.R.)
597	3.20 p.m.†	Kingswear	Cardiff
600	10.30 p.m.†	Paignton	Manchester
	7. 0 a.m.*	Plymouth	Paddington
603	7.15 a.m.*	"	"
605	7.25 a.m.†	"	"
608	8.30 a.m.§	Truro	"
610	7.30 a.m.*	Perranporth	"
615	8.15 a.m.†	Falmouth	"
620	11.15 a.m.†	Plymouth	"
623	9.40 a.m.*	Falmouth	"
625	8.20 a.m.†	Penzance	"
630	9.20 a.m.†	St. Ives	"
635	10. 0 a.m.§	Newquay	"
638	10. 0 a.m.†	Penzance	"
640	12.30 p.m.†	"	"
645	11.50 a.m.†	Penzance	"
647	1.50 p.m.†	Newquay	"
649	1.20 p.m.†	Penzance	"

Train No.	Time	From	To
663	10.20 a.m.†	Penzance	Cardiff
666	3.35 p.m.†	Plymouth	Stapleton Road
670	7.40 a.m.†	St. Austell	Birmingham
672	7.30 a.m.†	Penzance	Wolverhampton
675	10.35 a.m.*	"	"
	11.10 a.m.†	"	"
678	11.15 a.m.†	Newquay	Newcastle
683	8. 5 a.m.†	"	York
685	11. 0 a.m.†	"	Sheffield
688	10.45 a.m.†	Penzance	Paignton
700	6.15 a.m.†	Cardiff	"
703	8.10 a.m.†	Newport	Kingswear
704	8. 5 a.m.†	Cardiff	"
705	9. 5 a.m.†	Swansea	"
708	8.17 a.m.†	Carmarthen	Penzance
710	3.35 a.m.‡	Fishguard Harbour	Paddington
	4. 5 a.m.‡	"	"
711	3.55 a.m.‡	"	"
	4.35 a.m.‡	"	"
712	4.25 a.m.||	"	"
715	5. 5 a.m.‡	Swansea	"
716	5.30 a.m.†	Cardiff	"
	7.43 a.m.†	"	"
718	7.50 a.m.||	"	"
	4.55 a.m.††	Fishguard Harbour	"
719	8.15 a.m.††	Cardiff	"
720	8.20 a.m.†	Swansea	"
722	9.45 a.m.†	Cardiff	"
724	7.30 a.m.§	Carmarthen	"
725	9.55 a.m.†	Cardiff	"
	7. 5 a.m.§	Cardiff	"
730	8. 0 a.m.§	Cheltenham	"
	11.45 a.m.†	"	"
733	7.30 a.m.†	Pembroke Dock	"

THE abc OF
BRITISH RAILWAYS
LOCOMOTIVES

PART 2—Nos. 10000-39999
and
70000-99999

SUMMER
1957
EDITION

LONDON :

Ian Allan Ltd

NOTES ON THE USE OF THIS BOOK

This book lists and describes British Railways locomotives numbered between 10000 and 39999, and between 70000 and 99999. In future, diesel locomotives will be numbered in a separate series commencing at D1. New construction will bear these numbers at the outset and existing locomotives numbered between 10000 and 15236 will be re-numbered. The following notes are a guide to the system of reference marks and other details given in the lists of dimensions shown for each class in the alphabetical list of classes.

(a) In the lists of dimensions " Su " after the boiler pressure details indicates a superheated class.

(b) Locomotives are fitted with two inside cylinders, slide valves and Stephenson link motion, except where otherwise shown, e.g., (O) indicates outside cylinders and " P.V." piston valves.

(c) The letters " DS " preceding a number indicate a Service Locomotive. On the S.R. (only) this marking appears on the locomotive.

(d) (W) before a number indicates an Isle of Wight locomotive. The " W " is no longer painted on the locomotives, but may still be seen on the bunker numberplate of some of them.

(e) The date on which a design of locomotive first appeared or was modified is indicated by " Introduced." Differences between subdivisions of a class can be followed by tracing the appropriate reference mark throughout the details given for that class.

(f) The code given in smaller bold type at the head of each class, e.g., " 2P2F " denotes its British Railways power classification.

The details given in this book are correct to **April 1st, 1957.**

BRITISH RAILWAYS
MOTIVE POWER DEPOTS AND CODES

**ALL B.R LOCOMOTIVES CARRY THE CODE OF THEIR HOME DEPOT
ON A SMALL PLATE AFFIXED TO THE SMOKEBOX DOOR.)**

LONDON MIDLAND REGION

1A	**Willesden**	8A	**Edge Hill**	17C	Coalville
1B	Camden	8B	Warrington	17D	Rowsley
1C	Watford	8C	Speke Junction	17E	Heaton Mersey
1D	Devons Road (Bow)	8E	Brunswick (L'pool)	17F	Trafford Park
1E	Bletchley				
		9A	**Longsight**	18A	**Toton**
		9B	Stockport	18B	Westhouses
2A	**Rugby**		(Edgeley)	18C	Hasland
2B	Nuneaton	9C	Macclesfield	18D	Staveley
2C	Warwick	9D	Buxton		
2D	Coventry	9G	Northwich	19A	**Sheffield**
2E	Northampton			19B	Millhouses
2F	Market Harboro'	10A	**Springs Branch**	19C	Canklow
			(Wigan)		
		10B	Preston	20F	**Skipton**
3A	**Bescot**	10C	Patricroft	20G	Hellifield
3B	Bushbury	10D	Sutton Oak		
3C	Walsall			21A	**Saltley**
3D	Aston	11A	**Carnforth**	21B	Bournville
3E	Monument Lane	11B	Barrow	21C	Bromsgrove
		11C	Oxenholme		
		11D	Tebay	22A	**Bristol**
5A	**Crewe North**	11E	Lancaster	22B	Gloucester
5B	Crewe South				
5C	Stafford	12A	**Carlisle**	24A	**Accrington**
5D	Stoke		**(Upperby)**	24B	Rose Grove
5E	Alsager	12B	Penrith	24C	Lostock Hall
5F	Uttoxeter	12C	Workington	24D	Lower Darwen
				24E	Blackpool
		14A	**Cricklewood**	24F	Fleetwood
6A	**Chester**	14B	Kentish Town		
6B	Mold Junction	14C	St. Albans	26A	**Newton Heath**
6C	Birkenhead			26B	Agecroft
6D	Chester	15A	**Wellingborough**	26C	Bolton
	(Northgate)	15B	Kettering	26D	Bury
6E	Wrexham	15C	Leicester	26E	Lees
6F	Bidston	15D	Bedford		
6G	Llandudno			27A	**Bank Hall**
	Junction	16A	**Nottingham**	27B	Aintree
6H	Bangor	16B	Kirkby	27C	Southport
6J	Holyhead	16C	Mansfield	27D	Wigan (L. & Y.)
6K	Rhyl			27E	Walton
		17A	**Derby**		
		17B	Burton		

EASTERN REGION

30A	**Stratford**	32F	Yarmouth Beach	36D	Barnsley
30B	Hertford East	32G	Melton Constable	36E	Retford
30C	Bishops Stortford	33A	**Plaistow**		
30E	Colchester	33B	Tilbury	38A	**Colwick**
30F	Parkeston	33C	Shoeburyness	38B	Annesley
				38C	Leicester
31A	**Cambridge**	34A	**Kings Cross**	38D	Staveley
31B	March	34B	Hornsey	38E	Woodford Halse
31C	Kings Lynn	34C	Hatfield		
31D	South Lynn	34D	Hitchin	39A	**Gorton**
31E	Bury St. Edmunds	34E	Neasden		
		35A	**New England**	40A	**Lincoln**
32A	**Norwich**	35B	Grantham	40B	Immingham
32B	Ipswich	35C	Peterborough	40D	Tuxford
32C	Lowestoft		(Spital)	40E	Langwith Junction
32D	Yarmouth			40F	Boston
	(South Town)	36A	**Doncaster**		
32E	Yarmouth	36B	Mexborough	41A	**Sheffield**
	(Vauxhall)	36C	Frodingham		(Darnall)

NORTH EASTERN REGION

50A	**York**	52B	Heaton	55A	**Leeds (Holbeck)**
50B	Leeds (Neville Hill)	52C	Blaydon	55B	Stourton
50C	Selby	52D	Tweedmouth	55C	Farnley Junction
50D	Starbeck	52E	Percy Main	55D	Royston
50E	Scarborough	52F	North Blyth	55E	Normanton
50F	Malton			55F	Manningham
50G	Whitby	53A	**Hull**	55G	Huddersfield
51A	**Darlington**		(Dairycoates)		
51B	Newport (Yorks.)	53B	Hull		
51C	West Hartlepool		(Botanic Gardens)		
51D	Middlesbrough	53C	Hull (Springhead)	56A	**Wakefield**
51E	Stockton	53D	Bridlington	56B	Ardsley
51F	West Auckland	53E	Goole	56C	Copley Hill
51G	Haverton Hill			56D	Mirfield
51H	Kirkby Stephen	54A	**Sunderland**	56E	Sowerby Bridge
51J	Northallerton	54B	Tyne Dock	56F	Low Moor
51K	Saltburn	54C	Borough Gardens	56G	Bradford
52A	**Gateshead**	54D	Consett		

SCOTTISH REGION

60A	**Inverness**	64A	**St. Margarets**	65I	Balloch
60B	Aviemore		(Edinburgh)	65J	Fort William
60C	Helmsdale	64B	Haymarket	66A	**Polmadie**
60D	Wick	64C	Dalry Road		(Glasgow)
60E	Forres	64D	Carstairs	66B	Motherwell
		64E	Polmont	66C	Hamilton
61A	**Kittybrewster**	64F	Bathgate	66D	Greenock
61B	Aberdeen	64G	Hawick	67A	**Corkerhill**
	(Ferryhill)				(Glasgow)
61C	Keith	65A	**Eastfield**	67B	Hurlford
62A	**Thornton**		(Glasgow)	67C	Ayr
62B	Dundee	65B	St. Rollox	67D	Ardrossan
	(Tay Bridge)	65C	Parkhead	68A	**Carlisle**
62C	Dunfermline	65D	Dawsholm		(Kingmoor)
63A	**Perth South**	65E	Kipps	68B	Dumfries
63B	Stirling South	65F	Grangemouth	68C	Stranraer
63C	Forfar	65G	Yoker	68D	Beattock
63D	Oban	65H	Helensburgh	68E	Carlisle (Canal)

SOUTHERN REGION

70A	**Nine Elms**	72B	Salisbury
70B	Feltham	72C	Yeovil
70C	Guildford	72D	Plymouth
70D	Basingstoke		Callington
70E	Reading	72E	Barnstaple Junction
70F	Fratton		Ilfracombe
70G	Newport (I.O.W.)		Torrington
70H	Ryde (I.O.W.)	72F	Wadebridge
71A	**Eastleigh**	73A	**Stewarts Lane**
	Andover Junction	73B	Bricklayers Arms
	Lymington	73C	Hither Green
	Winchester	73D	Gillingham (Kent)
71B	Bournemouth	73E	Faversham
	Branksome		
71G	Bath (S. & D.)	74A	**Ashford (Kent)**
	Radstock	74B	Ramsgate
71H	Templecombe	74C	Dover
71I	Southampton Docks		Folkestone
71J	Highbridge	74D	Tonbridge
		74E	St. Leonards
72A	**Exmouth Junction**	75A	**Brighton**
	Bude	75B	Redhill
	Exmouth	75C	Norwood Junction
	Lyme Regis	75D	Horsham
	Okehampton	75E	Three Bridges
	Seaton	75F	Tunbridge Wells West

WESTERN REGION

81A	**Old Oak Common**	84B	Oxley	86J	Aberdare
		84C	Banbury	86K	Tredegar
81B	Slough	84D	Leamington Spa	87A	**Neath**
81C	Southall	84E	Tyseley	87B	Duffryn Yard
81D	Reading	84F	Stourbridge Junc.	87C	Danygraig
81E	Didcot	84G	Shrewsbury	87D	Swansea
81F	Oxford	84H	Wellington (Salop)		(East Dock
82A	**Bristol (Bath Rd.)**	84J	Croes Newydd	87E	Landore
82B	Bristol	84K	Chester	87F	Llanelly
	(St. Philip's Marsh)	85A	**Worcester**	87G	Carmarthen
82C	Swindon	85B	Gloucester	87H	Neyland
82D	Westbury	85C	Hereford	87J	Goodwick
82E	Yeovil	85D	Kidderminster	87K	Swansea (Victoria)
82F	Weymouth	86A	**Newport**	88A	**Cardiff (Cathays)**
83A	**Newton Abbot**		(Ebbw Jcn.)	88B	Cardiff East Dock
83B	Taunton	86B	Newport (Pill)	88C	Barry
83C	Exeter	86C	Cardiff (Canton)	88D	Merthyr
83D	Laira (Plymouth)	86D	Llantrisant	88E	Abercynon
83E	St. Blazey	86E	Severn Tunnel	88F	Treherbert
83F	Truro		Junction	89A	**Oswestry**
83G	Penzance	86F	Tondu	89B	Brecon
84A	**Wolverhampton (Stafford Road)**	86G	Pontypool Road	89C	Machynlleth
		86H	Aberbeeg		

BRITISH RAILWAYS NON-STEAM LOCOMOTIVE CLASSES

INTERNAL COMBUSTION LOCOMOTIVES

1-Co-Co-1 Diesel Electric

To be introduced 1957: B.R. Main Line Type " C " 2,000 h.p., built by English Electric Co.
Weight:
Driving Wheels:
T.E.:

D200	D203	D206	D208
D201	D204	D207	D209
D202	D205		

AIA-AIA Diesel Hydraulic

To be introduced 1957: B.R. Main Line Type " C " 2,000 h.p., built by North British Loco. Co.
Weight:
Driving Wheels:
T.E.:

D600	D602	D603	D604
D601			

AIA-AIA Diesel Hydraulic

To be introduced 1957: B.R. Main Line Type " C " 2,000 h.p., built at Swindon.
Weight:
Driving Wheels:
T.E.:

D800	D801	D802

AIA-AIA Diesel Electric

To be introduced 1957: B.R. Main Line Type " B " 1,250 h.p., built by Brush Traction Ltd.
Weight:
Driving Wheels:
T.E.:

D5500	D5501

Bo-Bo Diesel Hydraulic

To be introduced 1957: B.R. Main Line Type " B " 1,000 h.p., built by North British Loco. Co.
Weight:
Driving Wheels:
T.E.:

D6300	D6302	D6304	D6305
D6301	D6303		

Bo-Bo Diesel Electric

To be introduced 1957: B.R. Main Line Type " A " 1,000 h.p., built by English Electric Co.
Weight:
Driving Wheels:
T.E.:

D8000	D8004	D8008	D8012
D8001	D8005	D8009	D8013
D8002	D8006	D8010	D8014
D8003	D8007	D8011	

Bo-Bo Diesel Electric

To be introduced 1957: B.R. Main Line Type " A " 800 h.p., built by British Thomson-Houston Co.
Weight:
Driving Wheels:
T.E.:

D8200	D8202	D3204	D3206
D8201	D8203	D8205	

Bo-Bo Diesel Electric

To be introduced 1957: B.R. Main Line Type " A " 800 h.p., built by North British Loco. Co.
Weight:
Driving Wheels:
T.E.:

D8400

Diesel
Co-Co 5P/5F Electric

Introduced 1947: English Electric Co. and H. G. Ivatt, main line passenger design for L.M.S.R.
Weight: 121 tons 10 cwt.
Driving Wheels: 3′ 6″.
T.E.: 41,400 lb.
Engine: English Electric Co. 16 cyls. 1,600 h.p.
Motors: Six nose-suspended motors, single reduction gear drive.

| 10000 | 10001 | **Total 2** |

Diesel
2-D-2 6P/5F Mechanical

Introduced 1951: H. G. Ivatt and Fell design for L.M.S.R.
Engines: Four 500 h.p., 12-cylinder.
Transmission: Fell patent differential drive and fluid couplings.
Weight : 120 tons.
Driving Wheels : 4′ 3″.
T.E.: 25,000 lb.

| 10100 | **Total 1** |

Diesel
1-Co-Co-1 { 10201/2 5P/5F } Elec.
{ 10203   6P/6F }

Introduced 1951: English Electric Co. and Bulleid main line passenger design for S.R.
*Introduced 1954: Modernised version of above.
Engine : English Electric Co. 16 cyls. 1,750 h.p. (2,000 h.p.*)
Weight : 135 tons.
Driving Wheels . 3′ 7″.
T.E. : { 48,000 lb.
        { 50,000 lb.*

| 10201 | 10202 | *10203 |

Total 3

Bo-Bo 3 Diesel Electric

Introduced 1950: N.B. Loco. Co., B.T.H. Co. and H. G. Ivatt, branch line design for L.M.S.R.
Weight: 69 tons 16 cwt.
Driving Wheels: 3′ 6″
T.E.: 34,500 lb.
Engine: Davey Paxman 16 cyls. 827 h.p.
Motors: Four nose-suspended motors, single reduction gear drive.

| 10800 | **Total 1** |

0-6-0 Diesel Mechanical

Introduced 1950: Bulleid S.R. design for shunting and transfer work.
Weight: 49 tons 9 cwt.
Driving Wheels: 4′ 6″.
T.E.: 33,500 lb. (max. in low gear).
Engine: Davey Paxman 12 cyls. 500 h.p.
Transmission: S.S.S. Powerflow three-speed gearbox and fluid coupling.

| 11001 | **Total 1** |

0-6-0 Diesel Mechanical

Introduced 1952 : 200 h.p. locomotives. Built by various contractors and at Swindon. On the E. & N.E. Regions these locomotives are classified as follows :
Nos. 11100-15 : Drewry (with 3′ 3″ Driving Wheels) : DJ12/1.
Nos. 11121-35/49-60 : Drewry (with 3′ 6″ Driving Wheels) : DJ12/2.
Nos. 11136-43/61-72 : Hunslet Engineering Co. : DJ13.
Nos. 11177-86 : Andrew Barclay DJ14.

11100	11125	11149	11173
11101	11126	11150	11174
11102	11127	11151	11175
11103	11128	11152	11176
11104	11129	11153	11177
11105	11130	11154	11178
11106	11131	11155	11179
11107	11132	11156	11180
11108	11133	11157	11181
11109	11134	11158	11182
11110	11135	11159	11183
11111	11136	11160	11184
11112	11137	11161	11185
11113	11138	11162	11186
11114	11139	11163	11187
11115	11140	11164	11188
11116	11141	11165	11189
11117	11142	11166	11190
11118	11143	11167	11191
11119	11144	11168	11192
11120	11145	11169	11193
11121	11146	11170	11194
11122	11147	11171	11195
11123	11148	11172	11196
11124			

11197	11207	11217	11227
11198	11208	11218	11228
11199	11209	11219	11229
11200	11210	11220	11230
11201	11211	11221	11231
11202	11212	11222	11232
11203	11213	11223	11233
11204	11214	11224	11234
11205	11215	11225	11235
11206	11216	11226	11236

N.B.—Locos of this type are still being delivered.

0-4-0   Diesel Mechanical

Introduced 1955   153 h.p. locomotives for E.R. Built by Hunslet and classified **DY1** by the E. & N.E.R.
Weight: 22 tons 9 cwt.
Driving Wheels: 3′ 4″.
T.E.: 10,800 lb.

11500	11501	11502

Total 3

0-4-0   Diesel Mechanical

Introduced 1956. 153 h.p. locomotives for E.R. Built by Andrew Barclay, Kilmarnock and classified **DY2** by the E. & N.E.R.
Weight: 28 tons.
Driving Wheels: 3′ 4″.
T.E.: 14,350 lb.

11503	11504	11505	11506

Total 4

0-4-0   Diesel Mechanical

Introduced 1956. 165 h.p. locomotives for E.R. Built by Ruston & Hornsby and classified **DY5** by the E. & N.E.R.
Weight: 25 tons.
Driving Wheels: 3′ 2″.
T.E.: 12,750 lb.

11507	11508

Total 2

0-4-0   Diesel Hydraulic

Introduced 1953: N.B. Loco. Co. 204 h.p. design for N.E. and Scottish Regions and classified **DY11** by the E. & N.E.R.
Weight 32 tons.
Driving Wheels : 3′ 6 .
T.E.: 21,500 lb.

11700	11702	11704	11706
11701	11703	11705	11707

Total 8

0-4-0   Diesel Hydraulic

To be introduced 1957: North British Loco. Co. 204 h.p. design for N.E. and Scottish Regions and classified **DY11** by the E. & N.E.R.
Weight: 36 tons.
Driving Wheels: 3′ 9″
T.E.: 24,190 lb.

11708	11711	11714	11717
11709	11712	11715	11718
11710	11713	11716	11719

0-6-0   Diesel Electric

Introduced 1936: English Electric-Hawthorn Leslie design for L.M.S.R
Weight: 51 tons.
Driving Wheels: 4′ 0½″
T.E.: 30,000 lb.
Engine: English Electric 6 cyls. 350 h.p.
Motors: Two nose-suspended motors single reduction gear drive.

12000	12001	**Total 2**

0-6-0   Diesel Electric

Introduced 1939: English Electric and Stanier design for L.M.S.R., development of previous design with jack-shaft drive.
Weight: 54 tons 16 cwt.
Driving Wheels: 4′ 3″.
T.E.: 33,000 lb.
Engine: English Electric, 6 cyls. 350 h.p.
Motors: Single motor: jackshaft drive.

12003	12011	12019	12027
12004	12012	12020	12028
12005	12013	12021	12029
12006	12014	12022	12030
12007	12015	12023	12031
12008	12016	12024	12032
12009	12017	12025	
12010	12018	12026	

Total 30

0-6-0 Diesel Electric

Introduced 1945: English Electric and Fairburn design for L.M.S.R., development of previous design with double reduction gear drive. Classified **DEJ3** by the E. and N.E.R.
Weight: 50 tons.
Driving Wheels: 4' 0¼".
T.E.: 33,000 lb.
Engine: English Electric, 6 cyls. 350 h.p.
Motors: Two nose-suspended motors double reduction gear drive.

12033	12060	12087	12114
12034	12061	12088	12115
12035	12062	12089	12116
12036	12063	12090	12117
12037	12064	12091	12118
12038	12065	12092	12119
12039	12066	12093	12120
12040	12067	12094	12121
12041	12068	12095	12122
12042	12069	12096	12123
12043	12070	12097	12124
12044	12071	12098	12125
12045	12072	12099	12126
12046	12073	12100	12127
12047	12074	12101	12128
12048	12075	12102	12129
12049	12076	12103	12130
12050	12077	12104	12131
12051	12078	12105	12132
12052	12079	12106	12133
12053	12080	12107	12134
12054	12081	12108	12135
12055	12082	12109	12136
12056	12083	12110	12137
12057	12084	12111	12138
12058	12085	12112	
12059	12086	12113	

Total 106

0-6-0 Diesel Electric

Introduced 1953 and onwards: B.R. standard design.
These locomotives are variously engined and equipped as follows:

Nos. 13000-13116
Nos. 13127-13136
Nos. 13167-13336 } 400 h.p. B.R./English Electric.
Weight: 49 tons.
Driving Wheels: 4' 6".
T.E.: 35,000 lb.
E. & N.E. Regions classify as **DEJ4**

Nos. 13117-13126: 350 h.p. B.R./Crossley Bros./Crompton-Parkinson.
Weight: 47 tons 10 cwt.
Driving Wheels: 4' 6".
T.E.: 35,000 lb.

Nos. 13137-13151: 370 h.p. B.R./Blackstone/General Electric. Dimensions as for Nos. 13117-26.
E. & N.E. Regions classify as **DEJ5**

Nos. 13152-13166: 370 h.p. B.R./Blackstone/British Thomson-Houston.
Weight: 47 tons.
Driving Wheels: 4' 6".
T.E.: 35,000 lb.
E. & N.E. classify as **DEJ6**

Nos. D3419-28/D3439-87: Details not yet available.

Motors: Two nose-suspended motors double reduction gear drive.

13000	13019	13038	13057
13001	13020	13039	13058
13002	13021	13040	13059
13003	13022	13041	13060
13004	13023	13042	13061
13005	13024	13043	13062
13006	13025	13044	13063
13007	13026	13045	13064
13008	13027	13046	13065
13009	13028	13047	13066
13010	13029	13048	13067
13011	13030	13049	13068
13012	13031	13050	13069
13013	13032	13051	13070
13014	13033	13052	13071
13015	13034	13053	13072
13016	13035	13054	13073
13017	13036	13055	13074
13018	13037	13056	13075

13076	13120	13164	13208	13252	13274	13296	13318
13077	13121	13165	13209	13253	13275	13297	13319
13078	13122	13166	13210	13254	13276	13298	13320
13079	13123	13167	13211	13255	13277	13299	13321
13080	13124	13168	13212	13256	13278	13300	13322
13081	13125	13169	13213	13257	13279	13301	13323
13082	13126	13170	13214	13258	13280	13302	13324
13083	13127	13171	13215	13259	13281	13303	13325
13084	13128	13172	13216	13260	13282	13304	13326
13085	13129	13173	13217	13261	13283	13305	13327
13086	13130	13174	13218	13262	13284	13306	13328
13087	13131	13175	13219	13263	13285	13307	13329
13088	13132	13176	13220	13264	13286	13308	13330
13089	13133	13177	13221	13265	13287	13309	13331
13090	13134	13178	13222	13266	13288	13310	13332
13091	13135	13179	13223	13267	13289	13311	13333
13092	13136	13180	13224	13268	13290	13312	13334
13093	13137	13181	13225	13269	13291	13313	13335
13094	13138	13182	13226	13270	13292	13314	13336
13095	13139	13183	13227	13271	13293	13315	
13096	13140	13184	13228	13272	13294	13316	
13097	13141	13185	13229	13273	13295	13317	
13098	13142	13186	13230				
13099	13143	13187	13231				
13100	13144	13188	13232	D3419	D3439	D3456	D3472
13101	13145	13189	13233	D3420	D3440	D3457	D3473
13102	13146	13190	13234	D3421	D3441	D3458	D3474
13103	13147	13191	13235	D3422	D3442	D3459	D3475
13104	13148	13192	13236	D3423	D3443	D3460	D3476
13105	13149	13193	13237	D3424	D3444	D3461	D3477
13106	13150	13194	13238	D3425	D3445	D3462	D3478
13107	13151	13195	13239	D3426	D3446	D3463	D3479
13108	13152	13196	13240	D3427	D3447	D3464	D3480
13109	13153	13197	13241	D3428	D3448	D3465	D3481
13110	13154	13198	13242		D3449	D3466	D3482
13111	13155	13199	13243		D3450	D3467	D3483
13112	13156	13200	13244		D3451	D3468	D3484
13113	13157	13201	13245		D3452	D3469	D3485
13114	13158	13202	13246		D3453	D3470	D3486
13115	13159	13203	13247		D3454	D3471	D3487
13116	13160	13204	13248		D3455		
13117	13161	13205	13249				
13118	13162	13206	13250				
13119	13163	13207	13251				

N.B.—Locos of this class are still
being delivered.

0-6-0   Diesel Electric

Introduced 1944: English Electric and
   Thompson design for L.N.E.R.,
   (L.N.E.R. version of L.M.S. 12033
   series). Classified DEJI by the E. &
   N.E.R.
Weight: 51 tons.
Driving Wheels: 4′ 0″.
T.E.: 32,000 lb.
Engine: English Electric, 6 cyls. 350 h.p.
Motors: Two nose-suspended motors,
   double reduction gear drive.

15000	15001	15002	15003

Total 4

0-6-0   Diesel Electric

Introduced 1949: Brush design for E.R.
   Classified DEJ2 by the E. & N.E.R.
Weight: 51 tons.
Driving Wheels: 4′ 0″.
T.E.: 32,000 lb.
Engine: Petter 4 cyls. 360 h.p.

15004   **Total 1**

0-6-0   Diesel Electric

Introduced 1936: Hawthorn Leslie and
   English Electric design for G.W.R.
   (G.W.R. version of L.M.S.R. Nos.
   12000/1).
Weight: 51 tons 10 cwt.
Driving Wheels: 4′ 1″.
T.E.: 30,000 lb.
Engine: English Electric 6 cyls. 350 h.p.
Motors: Two nose-suspended motors,
   single reduction gear drive

15100   **Total 1**

0-6-0   Diesel Electric

Introduced 1948: English Electric and
   Hawksworth design for Western
   Region (W.R. version of L.M.S.
   12033 series).
Weight: 46 tons 9 cwt.
Driving Wheels: 4′ 0¾″.
T.E.: 33,500 lb.
Engine: English Electric 6 cyls. 350 h.p.
Motors: Two nose-suspended motors,
   single reduction gear drive.

15101	15103	15105
15102	15104	15106

Total 6

0-6-0   Diesel Electric

Introduced 1949: Brush design for
   W.R.

15107   **Total 1**

0-6-0   Diesel Electric

Introduced 1937: English Electric and
   Bulleid design for S.R.
Weight: 55 tons 5 cwt.
Driving Wheels: 4′ 6″.
T.E.: 30,000 lb.
Engine: English Electric 6 cyls. 350 h.p.
Motors: Two nose-suspended motors,
   single reduction gear drive.

15201	15202	15203

Total 3

0-6-0   Diesel Electric

Introduced 1949: English Electric and
   Bulleid design for S.R. (S.R. version
   of L.M.S.R. 12033 series, but designed
   for higher speeds).
Weight: 49 tons.
Driving Wheels: 4′ 6″.
T.E.: 24,000 lb.
Engine: English Electric 6 cyls. 350 h.p.
Motors: Two nose-suspended motors,
   double reduction gear drive

15211	15218	15225	15232
15212	15219	15226	15233
15213	15220	15227	15234
15214	15221	15228	15235
15215	15222	15229	15236
15216	15223	15230	
15217	15224	15231	

Total 26

AIA-AIA   Gas Turbine

Introduced 1949: Brown Boveri
   (Switzerland) design for G.W.R.
Weight: 115 tons.
Driving Wheels: 4′ 0½″.
T.E.: 31,500 lb. at 21 m.p.h.
Engine: 2,500 h.p. gas turbine.
Motors: Four independently mounted
   motors with spring drive.

18000   **Total 1**

Co-Co   Gas Turbine

Introduced 1951.
Metropolitan-Vickers and Hawksworth
design for G.W.R.
Weight: 129 tons 10 cwt.
Driving Wheels: 3′ 8″.

T.E.: maximum 60,000 lb. Continuous
rating : 30,000 lb

Motors: six nose-suspended motors
with single reduction gear drive

18100   Total 1

ELECTRIC LOCOMOTIVES

Co-Co   7P/5F   Class CC

*Introduced 1941: Raworth & Bulleid
design for S.R.
†Introduced 1948: Later design with
detail differences.
Weight: $\begin{cases} 99 \text{ tons } 14 \text{ cwt.*} \\ 104 \text{ tons } 14 \text{ cwt.†} \end{cases}$
Driving Wheels: 3′ 7″.
T.E.: $\begin{cases} 40,000 \text{ lb.*} \\ 45,000 \text{ lb.†} \end{cases}$
Voltage: 660 D.C.
Current Collection: Overhead and third
rail, with flywheel-driven generator
for gaps in third rail.

20001*   20002*   20003†
                              Total 3

Bo-Bo   Class EM1

*Introduced 1941: Metropolitan-Vickers
and Gresley design for L.N.E.R.
Remainder. Introduced 1950.
Production design with detail altera-
tions
Weight: 87 tons 18 cwt.
Driving Wheels: 4′ 2″.
T.E.: 45,000 lb.   Voltage: 1,500 D.C.
Current Collection: Overhead.

26000*	26010	26020	26030
26001	26011	26021	26031
26002	26012	26022	26032
26003	26013	26023	26033
26004	26014	26024	26034
26005	26015	26025	26035
26006	26016	26026	26036
26007	26017	26027	26037
26008	26018	26028	26038
26009	26019	26029	26039

26040	26045	26050	26055
26041	26046	26051	26056
26042	26047	26052	26057
26043	26048	26053	**Total**
26044	26049	26054	**58**

*26000 named Tommy

Bo-Bo   Class ES1

Built 1902: Brush & Thomson-Houston
shunting design for N.E.R.
Weight: 46 tons.
Voltage: 600 D.C.   T.E.: 25,000 lb.
Current collection : Overhead and
third rail.

26500   26501   Total 2

Bo-Bo   Class EB1

Introduced 1946 : L.N.E.R. rebuild
of N.E.R. Raven freight design
(introduced 1914) for banking work
on Manchester-Wath line.
Weight: 74 tons 8 cwt.
Driving Wheels: 4′ 0″.
T.E.: 37,600 lb.   Voltage: 1,500 D.C.
Current collection: Overhead.

26510   Total 1

Co-Co   Class EM2

Introduced 1954: Metropolitan-Vickers
and L.N.E.R. design, development
of EM1 with six axles and higher
speed range
Weight 102 tons.
Driving Wheels: 4′ 2″.
T.E.: 45,000 lb.   Voltage: 1,500 D.C.
Current Collection: Overhead.

27000	27002	27004	27006
27001	27003	27005	

                              Total 7

SUMMARY OF SOUTHERN REGION STEAM LOCOMOTIVE CLASSES
IN ALPHABETICAL ORDER
WITH HISTORICAL NOTES AND DIMENSIONS

Classes
0-6-0T   0P   A1 & A1X

*A1 Introduced 1872: Stroudley L.B.S.C. " Terrier," later fitted with Marsh boiler, retaining original type smokebox.

†A1X Introduced 1911: Rebuild of A1 with Marsh boiler and extended smokebox.

‡A1X Loco. with increased cylinder diameter.

Weight: $\begin{cases} 27 \text{ tons } 10 \text{ cwt.*} \\ 28 \text{ tons } 6 \text{ cwt.}††‡ \end{cases}$

Pressure: 150 lb. Cyls. $\begin{cases} 12" \times 20".*† \\ 14\frac{3}{16}" \times 20".‡ \end{cases}$

Driving Wheels: 4′ 0″.

T.E.: $\begin{cases} 7,650 \text{ lb.*†} \\ 10,695 \text{ lb.‡} \end{cases}$

*DS680
†DS377 DS681, 32640/6/50/5/61 /2/70/7/8.
‡32636

Total: A1   1
        A1X 12

0-4-0T   1F   Class B4

*Introduced 1891: Adams L.S.W. design for dock shunting.
†Introduced 1908: Drummond K14 locos., with smaller boiler and detail alterations.
‡Adams loco. fitted with Drummond boiler.
§Drummond loco. fitted with Adams boiler.

Weight: $\begin{cases} 33 \text{ tons } 9 \text{ cwt.*‡} \\ 32 \text{ tons } 18 \text{ cwt.†§} \end{cases}$

Pressure: 140 lb. Cyls. (O): 16″ × 22″.
Driving Wheels: 3′ 9¾″.
T.E.: 14,650 lb.

*30086/7/9/93/6, 30102.
†30082/3   ‡30088   §30034

Total 10

0-6-0   2F   Class C

Introduced 1900: Wainwright S.E.C. design.
Weight: Loco. 43 tons 16 cwt.
Pressure: 160 lb. Cyls.: 18½″ × 26″.
Driving Wheels: 5′ 2″.
T.E.: 19,520 lb.

31004/18/33/7/54/9 / 61 /8/71/ 86, 31102/12/3/50/91, 31218/9 /21/3/7 / 9/42–5/52/3 / 5 /6/ 67 /8/70–2/80/ 7 / 93 / 7/8, 31317, 31461/80/1/95/8, 31508/10/73/5 /6/8/9/81–5/8–90/2/3, 31681–4/ 6/8–95, 31714–7/9–25.

Total 86

0-6-0   2F   Class C2X

Introduced 1908: Marsh rebuild of R. J. Billinton L.B.S.C. C2 with larger C3-type boiler, extended smokebox, etc.
Weight: Loco. 45 tons 5 cwt.
Pressure: 170 lb.
Cyls.: 17½″ × 26″.
Driving Wheels: 5′ 0″.
T.E.: 19,175 lb.

32437/8/40–51,   32521–9/32/4–41/3–54.

Total 44

0-4-0T   0P   Class C14

Introduced 1923: Urie rebuild as shunting locos. of Drummond L.S.W. motor-train 2-2-0T (originally introduced 1906).
Weight: 25 tons 15 cwt.
Pressure: 150 lb.
Cyls.: (O) 14″ × 14″.
Driving Wheels: 3′ 0″.
T.E.: 9,720 lb.
Walschaerts valve gear.

DS77, 30588/9.   Total 3

Class DI-E3

4-4-0   3P   Class DI

Introduced 1921 : Maunsell rebuild of Wainwright D, with larger super-heated boiler, Belpaire firebox and long-travel piston valves.

Weight: Loco. 52 tons 4 cwt.
Pressure: 180 lb. Su.
Cyls.: 19″ × 26″.
Driving Wheels: 6′ 8″.
T.E.: 17,950 lb.

31145, 31246/7, 31470/87/9/ 92/4, 31505/9/45. 31727/35/9/ 41/3/9.

Total 17

4-4-0   3P   Class EI

Introduced 1919 : Maunsell rebuild of Wainwright E. with larger super-heated boiler, Belpaire firebox and long-travel piston valves.

Weight: Loco. 53 tons 9 cwt.
Pressure: 180 lb.
Cyls.: 19″ × 26″.
Driving Wheels: 6′ 6″.
T.E.: 18,410 lb.

31019/67, 31165, 31497, 31504/6/7.

Total 7

0-6-0T   2F   Class EI

Introduced 1874: Stroudley L.B.S.C design, reboilered by Marsh.
Weight: 44 tons 3 cwt.
Pressure: 170 lb. Cyls.: 17″ × 24″.
Driving Wheels: 4′ 6″.
T.E.: 18,560 lb.

32113 39/51, 32689/94. (W) 3/4.

Total 7

0-6-2T   IP2F   Class EI/R

Introduced 1927: Maunsell rebuild of Stroudley EI, with radial trailing axle and larger bunker for passenger service in West of England.

Weight: 50 tons 5 cwt.
Pressure: 170 lb. Cyls.: 17″ × 24″.
Driving Wheels: 4′ 6″.
T.E.: 18,560 lb.

32124/35, 32608/97

Total 4

0-6-0T   3F   Class E2

*Introduced 1913: L. B. Billinton L.B.S.C. design.
†Introduced 1915: Later locos. with tanks extended further forward.

Weight: $\begin{cases} 52 \text{ tons } 15 \text{ cwt.*} \\ 53 \text{ tons } 10 \text{ cwt.†} \end{cases}$
Pressure: 170 lb. Cyls.: 17½″ × 26″.
Driving Wheels: 4′ 6″.
T.E : 21,305 lb.

*32100–4.
†32105–9.

Total 10

0-6-2T   2F   Class E3

Introduced 1894: R. J. Billinton L.B.S.C. design, development of Stroudley " West Brighton " (introduced 1891), reboilered and fitted with extended smokebox, 1918 onwards; cylinder diameter reduced from 18″ by S.R.

Weight: 56 tons 10 cwt.
Pressure: 170 lb
Cyls.: 17¾″ × 26″.
Driving Wheels: 4′ 6″.
T.E.: 21,305 lb.

32165/6/70. 32454–6/62.

Total 7

Classes E4 & E4X

0-6-2T 2P2F

*E4 introduced 1897: R. J. Billinton L.B.S.C. design, development of E3 with larger wheels, reboilered with Marsh boiler and extended smokebox, cylinder diameter reduced from 18" by S.R.

†E4X introduced 1909: E4 reboilered with larger I2 4-4-2T type boiler.

Weight: $\begin{cases} 57 \text{ tons } 10 \text{ cwt.*} \\ 59 \text{ tons } 5 \text{ cwt.†} \end{cases}$

Pressure: 170 lb. Cyls.: 17½" × 26".
Driving Wheels: 5' 0".
T.E.: 19,175 lb.

*32463/7–76/9–81/4–8/91–5/7–9, 32500/2–10/2/5/7/9/56/7/9/60/2–6/77–81.

†32466/77

Total: E4 55
E4X 2

Classes E6 & E6X

0-6-2T 3F

*‡E6 introduced 1904: R. J. Billinton L.B.S.C. design, development of E5 with smaller wheels, some with higher pressure.

†E6X introduced 1911: E6 reboilered with larger C3-type boiler.

Weight: $\begin{cases} 61 \text{ tons.*‡} \\ 63 \text{ tons.†} \end{cases}$

Pressure: $\begin{cases} 160 \text{ lb.*} \\ 175 \text{ lb.‡} \\ 170 \text{ lb.†} \end{cases}$

Cyls. 18" × 26".
Driving Wheels: 4' 6".

T.E.: $\begin{cases} 21,215 \text{ lb.*} \\ 23,205 \text{ lb.‡} \\ 22,540 \text{ lb.†} \end{cases}$

*‡32408–10/2–3   †32407/11

Total: E6 10
E6X 2

Class G6

0-6-0T 2F

*Introduced 1894: Adams L.S.W. design, later additions by Drummond, but with Adams type boiler.
†Introduced 1925: Fitted with Drummond type boiler.
Weight: 47 tons 13 cwt.
Pressure: 160 lb. Cyls.: 17½" × 24".
Driving Wheels: 4' 10".
T.E.: 17,235 lb.

*30162, 30238/58/60/6/70/7, 30349, DS3152

†30160, 30274

Total 11

Class G16

4-8-0T 8F

Introduced 1921: Urie L.S.W. "Hump" loco.
Weight: 95 tons 2 cwt.
Pressure: 180 lb. Su.
Cyls. (O): 22" × 23".
Driving Wheels: 5' 1".
T.E. 33,990 lb.
Walschaerts valve gear. P.V.

30492–5   **Total 4**

Class H

0-4-4T 1P

Introduced 1904: Wainwright S.E.C. design.
*Introduced 1949: Fitted for push-and-pull working.
Weight: 54 tons 8 cwt.
Pressure: 160 lb. Cyls. 18" × 26".
Driving Wheels: 5' 6".
T.E.: 17,360 lb.

31005,   31259/61/3/5/6, 31305–7/21/4/6/8, 31500/3/33/40/2/50–3

*31161/2/4/77/84/93, 31239/69/74/6/8/9/95, 31308/10/9/22/7/9, 31512/7–23/30/43/4/8/54

Total 54

15

4-4-2   4P   Class H2

Introduced 1911: Marsh L.B.S.C.
design, superheated development of
H1 with larger cylinders.
Weight: Loco. 68 tons 5 cwt.
Pressure: 200 lb. Su.
Cyls.: (O) 21″ × 26″.
Driving Wheels: 6′ 7½″.
T.E.: 24,520 lb.
P.V.

32424   **Total 1**

4-6-0   4P5F   Class H15

*Introduced 1914: Urie L.S.W. design.
fitted with " Maunsell " superheater
from 1927. replacing earlier types.

†Introduced 1915: Urie rebuild with
two outside cylinders of Drummond
E14, 4 cyl. 4-6-0 introduced 1907, retaining original boiler retubed and
fitted with superheater

‡Introduced 1924: Maunsell locos
with N15 type boiler and smaller
tender.

§Introduced 1924: Maunsell rebuild of
Drummond F13 4-cyl. 4-6-0 introduced 1905, with detail differences
from rebuild of E14.

¶Introduced 1927: Urie loco. (built
1914 saturated) rebuilt with later
N15 type boiler. with smaller
firebox.

Weight: Loco. { 81 tons 5 cwt.*
{ 82 tons 1 cwt.†
{ 79 tons 19 cwt.‡¶
{ 80 tons 11 cwt.§
Pressure: { 180 lb. Su.*‡¶
{ 175 lb. Su.†§
Cyls.: (O) 21″ × 28″.
Driving Wheels: 6′0″.
T.E.: { 26,240 lb.*‡¶
{ 25 510 lb.†§
Walschaerts valve gear. P.V.

*30482-4/6-9
†30335
‡30473-8, 30521-4
§30330/1/3/4
¶30491   **Total 23**

4-6-2T   6F   Class H16

Introduced 1921: Urie L.S.W design
for heavy freight traffic.
Weight: 96 tons 8 cwt.
Pressure: 180 lb. Su.
Cyls.: (O) 21″ × 28″.
Driving Wheels: 5′ 7″.
T.E.: 28,200 lb.
Walschaerts valve gear. P.V.

30516-20   **Total 5**

2-6-0   4P5F   Class K

Introduced 1913 L. B. Billinton
L.B.S.C. design.
Weight: Loco. 63 tons 15 cwt.
Pressure: 180 lb. Su.
Cyls.: (O) 21″ × 26″.
Driving Wheels: 5′ 6″.
T.E.: 26,580 lb.
P.V.

32337-53   **Total 17**

4-4-0   3P   Class L

Introduced 1914 Wainwright S.E.C.
design, with detail alterations by
Maunsell.
Weight: Loco. 57 tons 9 cwt.
Pressure: 160 lb. Su.
Cyls.: 20½″ × 26″.
Driving Wheels: 6′ 3″.
T.E.: 18,575 lb.
P.V.

31760/2-8/70-81   **Total 21**

4-4-0   3P   Class L1

Introduced 1926: Post-grouping devel-
opment of L, with long-travel valves,
side window cab and detail alterations.
Weight: Loco. 57 tons 16 cwt.
Pressure: 180 lb. Su.
Cyls: 19½″ × 26″.
Driving Wheels: 6′ 3″.
T.E.: 18,910 lb.
P.V.

31753-9/82-9   **Total 15**

Class G6 0-6-0T No. 30162

[D. Marriott

Class O2 0-4-4T No. 30179

[R. A. Panting

Class M7 0-4-4T No. 30479

[G. Wheeler

Class H 0-4-4T No. 31522 [L. Marshall

Class P 0-6-0T No. 31178 [R. K. Evans

Class R1 0-6-0T No. 31147 [R. K. Evans

Top : Class B4 0-4-0T
No. 30096
[D. Marriott

Centre : Class 0298
2-4-0WT No. 30587
[D. Marriott

Right : Class C14
0-4-0T No. 30589
[G. Wheeler

Class 0415 4-4-2T No. 30584   *[A. W. Martin*

Class T9 4-4-0 No. 30283   *[Brian E. Morrison*

Class T9 4-4-0 No. 30300 (with wider cab and splashers and six-wheel tender)
G. Clarke

Class D1 4-4-0 No. 31727   [R. K. Evans

Class L 4-4-0 No. 31773   [F. J. Saunders

Class L1 4-4-0 No. 31788   [R. A. Panting

Class K 2-6-0 No. 32344

[*R. K. Evans*

Class N 2-6-0 No. 31407

[*R. M. Casserley*

Class N 2-6-0 No. 31848 (with modified front-end and without smoke deflectors)

[*P. Ransome-Wallis*

Class U 2-6-0 No. 31625   [T. K. Widd

Class U 2-6-0 No. 31807 (rebuilt from S.E.C. " River " Class 2-6-4T)   [G. Wheeler

Class U1 2-6-0 No. 31901   [R. K. Evans

Class MN 4-6-2 No. 35001 *Channel Packet* [P. H. Groom

Rebuilt Class MN 4-6-2 No. 35013 *Blue Funnel* [G. Wheeler

Class WC 4-6-2 No. 34013 *Okehampton* [John Robertson

4-6-0   7P   **Class LN**

*Introduced 1926: Maunsell design, cylinders and tender modified by Bulleid from 1938, and fitted with multiple-jet blastpipe and large chimney.

†Introduced 1929: Loco. fitted experimentally with smaller driving wheels.

‡Introduced 1929: Loco. fitted experimentally with longer boiler.

Weight: Loco. $\begin{cases} 83 \text{ tons } 10 \text{ cwt.}^{*}\dagger \\ 84 \text{ tons } 16 \text{ cwt.}\ddagger \end{cases}$

Pressure: 220 lb. Su.

Cyls.: (4) $16\frac{1}{2}'' \times 26''$.

Driving Wheels: $\begin{cases} 6' \ 7''. \ ^{*\ddagger} \\ 6' \ 3''. \ \dagger \end{cases}$

T.E.: $\begin{cases} 33,510 \text{ lb.}^{*}\ddagger \\ 35,300 \text{ lb.}\dagger \end{cases}$

Walschaerts valve gear. **P.V.**

*30850–8/61–5
†30859   ‡30860

Total 16

0-4-4T   2P   **Class M7**

*Introduced 1897: Drummond L.S.W. M7 design.

†Introduced 1903: Drummond X14 design, with increased front overhang, steam reverser and detail alterations, now classified M7 (30254 originally M7).

‡Introduced 1925: X14 design fitted for push-and-pull working.

Weight: $\begin{cases} 60 \text{ tons } 4 \text{ cwt.}^{*} \\ 60 \text{ tons } 3 \text{ cwt.}\dagger \\ 62 \text{ tons } 0 \text{ cwt.}\ddagger \end{cases}$

Pressure: 175 lb.

Cyls.: $18\frac{1}{2}'' \times 26''$.

Driving Wheels: 5' 7".

T.E.: 19,755 lb.

*30022–6/31–44, 30112, 30241–53/5/6, 30318–24/56/7, 30667–71/3–6

†30030, 30123/4/7/30/2/3, 30254, 30374–8, 30479

‡30021/7/8/9/45–60,30104–11/25/8/9/31, 30328/79, 30480/1

Total 103

4-6-2   8P   **Class MN**

*Introduced 1941 : Bulleid design originally with 280 lb. pressure, multiple-jet blastpipe and Bulleid valve gear.

†Introduced 1956 : Rebuilt with Walschaerts valve gear, modified details and air-smoothed casing removed.

Weight : Loco. $\begin{cases} 94 \text{ tons } 15 \text{ cwt.}^{*} \\ 97 \text{ tons } 18 \text{ cwt.}\dagger \end{cases}$

Pressure : 250 lb.

Cyls. : (3) $18'' \times 24''$.

Driving Wheels : 6' 2".

T.E. : 33,495 lb. **P.V.**

*35001–8/11/5/9/21/4/8–30
†35009/10/2–4/6–8/20/2/3/5–7

Total 30

2-6-0   4P5F   **Classes N & NI**

*N Introduced 1917: Maunsell S.E.C. mixed traffic design.

†NI Introduced 1922: 3-cylinder development of N.

Weight: Loco. $\begin{cases} 61 \text{ tons } 4 \text{ cwt.}^{*} \\ 64 \text{ tons } 5 \text{ cwt.}\dagger \end{cases}$

Pressure: 200 lb. Su.

Cyls.: $\begin{cases} (O) \ 19'' \times 28''.^{*} \\ (3) \ 16'' \times 28''.\dagger \end{cases}$

Driving Wheels: 5'6".

T.E.: $\begin{cases} 26,035 \text{ lb.}^{*} \\ 27,695 \text{ lb.}\dagger \end{cases}$

Walschaerts valve gear. **P.V.**

*31400–14, 31810–21/3–75
†31822/76–80

Total: Class N 80

Class NI 6

25

Classes N15–P

4-6-0   5P   **Class N15**

*Introduced 1918: Urie L.S.W. design.

†Introduced 1928: Urie Locos. modified with cylinders of reduced diameter.

‡Introduced 1925: Maunsell Locos. with long-travel valves, increased boiler pressure, smaller fireboxes, and tenders from Drummond G14 4-6-0's.

§Introduced 1925: Later locos. with detail alterations and increased weight.

‖Introduced 1925: Locos. with modified cabs to suit Eastern Section, and new bogie tenders

¶Introduced 1926: Locos. with detail alterations and six-wheeled tenders for Central Section.

Weight Loco. $\begin{cases} 80 \text{ tons } 7 \text{ cwt.}^{*\dagger} \\ 79 \text{ tons } 18 \text{ cwt.}^{\ddagger} \\ 80 \text{ tons } 19 \text{ cwt.}^{\S\parallel} \\ 81 \text{ tons } 17 \text{ cwt.}^{\P} \end{cases}$

Pressure: $\begin{cases} 180 \text{ lb. Su.}^{*\dagger} \\ 200 \text{ lb. Su.}^{\ddagger\S\parallel\P} \end{cases}$

Cyls.: $\begin{cases} (O) 22'' \times 28''.* \\ (O) 21'' \times 28''.† \\ (O) 20\frac{1}{2}'' \times 28''.‡§\parallel¶ \end{cases}$

Driving Wheels: 6' 7".

T.E.: $\begin{cases} 26,245 \text{ lb.}* \\ 23,915 \text{ lb.}† \\ 25,320 \text{ b.}‡§\parallel¶ \end{cases}$

Walschaerts valve gear. P.V.

NOTE: Nos. 30736 55 are fitted with multiple jet blastpipe and large diameter chimney

*30755   †30738/9/48-51
‡30453-7   §30448-52
‖30763-92   ¶30793-30806

Total 61

4-6-0   4P   **Class N15X**

Introduced 1934: Maunsell rebuild of L. B. Billinton L.B.S.C. Class L 4-6-4T (introduced 1914).
Weight: Loco 73 tons 2 cwt.
Pressure: 180 lb. Su.
Cyls.: (O) 21" × 28".
Driving Wheels: 6' 9".
T.E.: 23,325 lb.
Walschaerts valve gear. P.V.

32331   **Total 1**

0-6-0   2F   **Class O1**

*Introduced 1903: Wainwright rebuild with domed boiler and new cab of Stirling S.E. Class O 0-6-0 (introduced 1878).

†Introduced 1903: Loco. with smaller driving wheels.

Weight: Loco. 41 tons 1 cwt.
Pressure: 150 lb. Cyls.: 18" × 26".

Driving Wheels: $\begin{cases} 5' 2''.* \\ 5' 1''.† \end{cases}$

T.E.: $\begin{cases} 17,325 \text{ b.}* \\ 17,610 \text{ lb.}† \end{cases}$

*31064/5,   31258,   31370,
31425/30/4
†31048

Total 8

0-4-4T   0P   **Class O2**

*Introduced 1889: Adams L.S.W design.

†Introduced 1923: Fitted with Westinghouse brake for I.O.W bunkers enlarged from 1932.

‡Fitted with Drummond-type boiler.

§Fitted for push-and-pull working.

Weight: $\begin{cases} 46 \text{ tons } 18 \text{ cwt.}^{*\ddagger} \\ 48 \text{ tons } 8 \text{ cwt.}† \end{cases}$

Pressure: 160 lb. Cyls.: 17½" × 24".
Driving Wheels: 4' 10".
T.E.: 17,235 lb.

*30177/9/92/3/9   30200/12/6/
24/5/9/32/6
†(W)14/6-8/20-2/4-33
†§(W)35/6
‡30223/33
‡§30182/3, 30207

Total 37

0-6-0T   Unclass   **Class P**

Introduced 1909: Wainwright S.E.C. design for push-and-pull work, now used for shunting.
Weight: 28 tons 10 cwt.
Pressure: 160 lb. Cyls.: 12" × 18".
Driving Wheels: 3' 9⅝".
T.E.: 7,810 b.

31027, 31178, 31323/5, 31556-8

Total 7

0-6-0   4F   Class Q

Introduced 1938: Maunsell design, later
    fitted with multiple-jet blastpipe and
    large diameter chimney.
Weight: Loco. 49 tons 10 cwt.
Pressure: 200 lb. Su.
Cyls.: 19″ × 26″.
Driving Wheels: 5′ 1″.
T.E.: 26,160 lb.
P.V.

30530–49   **Total 20**

0-6-0   5F   Class Q1

Introduced 1942: Bulleid " Austerity "
    design.
Weight: Loco. 51 tons 5 cwt.
Pressure: 230 lb. Su.
Cyls.: 19″ × 26″.
Driving Wheels: 5′ 1″.
T.E.: 30,080 lb.
P.V.

33001–40   **Total 40**

0-6-0T   2F   Class R1

*Introduced 1888: Stirling S.E. design
    later rebuilt with domed boiler.
†Introduced 1938: Fitted with Urie
    type short chimney for Whitstable
    branch, and fitted with or retaining
    original Stirling-type cab.
‡ Introduced 1952. Rebuilt with
    domed boiler but retaining Stirling
    cab.
Weight: $\begin{cases} \text{46 tons 15 cwt.*} \\ \text{46 tons 8 cwt.†‡} \end{cases}$
Pressure: 160 lb. **Cyls.:** 18″ × 26″.
Driving Wheels: $\begin{cases} \text{5′ 2″.*} \\ \text{5′ 1″.†‡} \end{cases}$
T.E.: $\begin{cases} \text{18,480 lb.*} \\ \text{18,780 lb.†‡} \end{cases}$

*31047, 31107/28/74,
   31337/40
†31010, 31147, 31339
‡31069

            Total 10

4-6-0   6F   Class S15

*Introduced 1920: Urie L.S.W. design,
    development of N15 for mixed traffic
    work.
†Introduced 1927: Maunsell design,
    with higher pressure, smaller grate,
    modified footplating and other detail
    differences. 30833-7 with 6-wheel
    tenders for Central Section.
‡Introduced 1936: Later locos. with
    detail differences and reduced weight.
Weight: Loco $\begin{cases} \text{79 tons 16 cwt.*} \\ \text{80 tons 14 cwt.†} \\ \text{79 tons 5 cwt.‡} \end{cases}$
Pressure: $\begin{cases} \text{180 lb. Su.*} \\ \text{200 lb. Su.†‡} \end{cases}$
Cyls.: $\begin{cases} \text{(O) 21″ × 28″.*} \\ \text{(O) 20}\tfrac{1}{2}\text{″ × 28″.†‡} \end{cases}$
Driving Wheels: 5′ 7″.
T.E.: $\begin{cases} \text{28,200 lb.*} \\ \text{29,855 lb.†‡} \end{cases}$

Walschaerts valve gear. **P.V.**

*30496–30515   †30823–37
‡30838–47

            Total 45

4-4-0   3P   Class T9

*Introduced 1899: Drummond L.S.W.
    design, fitted with superheater and
    larger cylinders by Urie from 1922.
†Introduced 1899: Locos. with detail
    differences (originally fitted with fire-
    box watertubes).
‡Introduced 1900: Locos. with wider
    cab and splashers, without coup-
    ling rod splashers and originally
    fitted with firebox watertubes.
Weight: Loco. $\begin{cases} \text{51 tons 18 cwt.*} \\ \text{51 tons 16 cwt.†} \\ \text{51 tons 7 cwt.‡} \end{cases}$
Pressure: 175 lb. Su.
Cyls.: 19″ × 26″.
Driving Wheels: 6′ 7″.
T.E.: 17,675 lb.

*30117/20, 30283–5/7–9
†30702/5–12/5/7–9/21/4/6/7/9/
   30/2
‡30300/1/4/10/3/37/8

            Total 35

Classes U & UI

2-6-0   4P3F

*U Introduced 1928: Rebuild of Maunsell S.E.C. Class K (" River ") 2-6-4T (introduced 1917).
†U Introduced 1928: Locos. built as Class U, with smaller splashers and detail alterations.
‡UI Introduced 1928: 3-cylinder development of Class U (prototype 31890, rebuilt from 2-6-4T, originally built 1925).
Weight: Loco. {
63 tons.*
62 tons 6 cwt.†
65 tons 6 cwt.‡
}
Pressure: 200 lb. Su.
Cyls.: {
(O) 19″ × 28″.*†
(3) 16″ × 28″.‡
}
Driving Wheels: 6′ 0″.
T.E.: {
23,865 lb.*†
25,385 lb.‡
}
Walschaerts valve gear. P.V.

*31790–31809   †31610–39
‡31890–31910

Total: Class U 50
Class UI 21

0-6-0T   3F   Class USA

Introduced 1942: U.S. Army Transportation Corps design, purchased by S.R. 1946, and fitted with modified cab and bunker and other detail alterations.
Weight: 46 tons 10 cwt.
Pressure: 210 lb.
Cyls.: (O) 16½″ × 24″.
Driving Wheels: 4′ 6″.
T.E.: 21,600 lb.
Walschaerts valve gear. P.V.

30061–74   Total 14

4-4-0   5P   Class V

*Introduced 1930: Maunsell design.
†Introduced 1938: Fitted with multiple jet blastpipe and large diameter chimney by Bulleid.
Weight: Loco. 67 tons 2 cwt.
Pressure: 220 lb. Su.
Cyls.: (3) 16½″ × 26″.
Driving Wheels: 6′ 7″.
T.E.: 25,135 lb.
Walschaerts valve gear. P.V.

*30902–6/8/10–2/6/22/3/5–8/32/5/6
†30900/1/7/9/13–5/7–21/4/29–31/3/4/7–9

Total 40

2-6-4T   6F   Class W

Introduced 1931: Maunsell design, developed from Class NI 2-6-0.
Weight: 90 tons 14 cwt.
Pressure: 200 lb. Su.
Cyls.: (3) 16½″ × 28″.
Driving Wheels: 5′ 6″.
T.E.: 29,450 lb.
Walschaerts valve gear. P.V.

31911–25   Total 15

4-6-2   7P5F   Classes WC & BB

*Introduced 1945: Bulleid " West Country " Class.
†Introduced 1946: Bulleid " Battle of Britain " Class.
‡Introduced 1948: Locos. with larger tenders.
Weight: Loco. 86 tons 0 cwt.
Pressure: 250 lb. Su.
Cyls.: (3) 16⅜″ × 24″.
Driving Wheels: 6′ 2″.
T.E.: 27,715 lb.
Bulleid valve gear. P.V.

*34001–48   †34049–70
†‡34071–90, 34109/10
*‡34091–34108   Total 110

0-8-0T   6F   Class Z

Introduced 1929: Maunsell design for heavy shunting.
Weight: 71 tons 12 cwt.
Pressure: 180 lb. Cyls.: (3) 16″ × 28′.
Driving Wheels: 4′ 8″
T.E.: 29,375 lb.
Walschaerts valve gear. P.V.

30950–/   Total 8

0-6-0   3F   Class 700

Introduced 1897: Drummond L.S W.
design, superheated from 1921.
Weight: Loco. 46 tons 14 cwt.
Pressure: 180 lb. Su.
Cyls.: 19″ × 26″.
Driving Wheels: 5′ 1″.
T.E.: 23,540 lb.

30306/8/9/15–7/25–7/39/46/50/2/
5/68, 30687–30701

Total 30

0-6-2T   1P2F   Class 757

Introduced 1907: Hawthorn Leslie
design for P.D.S.W.J.
Weight: 49 tons 19 cwt.
Pressure: 170 lb.
Cyls.: (O) 16″ × 24″.
Driving Wheels: 4′ 0″.
T.E.: 18,495 lb.

30757

Total 1

2-4-0WT   0P   Class 0298

Introduced 1874: Beattie L.S.W.
design, rebuilt by Adams (1884-92),
Urie (1921-2) and Maunsell (1931-5)
Weight: 37 tons 16 cwt.
Pressure: 160 lb.
Cyls.: (O) 16½″ × 20″.
Driving Wheels: 5′ 7″.
T.E.: 11,050 lb.

30585–7

Total 3

0-6-0   2F   Class 0395

*Introduced 1881 Adams L.S.W.
design.
†Introduced 1885: Adams " 496 "
class with longer front overhang.
‡Introduced 1928: Reboilered with
ex-L.C. & D. Class M3 4–4–0 boiler.
Weight: Loco. $\begin{cases} 37 \text{ tons } 12 \text{ cwt.}*‡ \\ 38 \text{ tons } 14 \text{ cwt.}†‡ \end{cases}$
Pressure: $\begin{cases} 140 \text{ lb.}*† \\ 150 \text{ lb.}‡ \end{cases}$
Driving Wheels: 5′ 1″.
T.E.: $\begin{cases} 15,535 \text{ lb.}*† \\ 16,645 \text{ lb.}‡ \end{cases}$

*30568/75/8
†30566   *‡30567
†‡30564/80

Tota. 7

4-4-2T   1P   Class 0415

Introduced 1882: Adams L.S.W.
design, later reboilered.
Weight: 55 tons 2 cwt.
Pressure: 160 lb.
Cyls.: (O) 17½″ × 24″.
Driving Wheels: 5′ 7″.
T.E.: 14,920 lb.

30582–4

Total 3

SOUTHERN REGION SERVICE LOCOMOTIVES

No.	Old No.	Class	Station
*DS 74	—	Bo-Bo	{ Durnsford Road { Power Station
*DS 75	—	Bo	Waterloo & City
DS 77	0745	C14	{ Redbridge { Sleeper Depot
†DS 377	2635	A1X	Brighton Works
DS 600	—	0–4–0 Diesel	{ Eastleigh { Carriage Works
DS 680	{ L.B.S.C. 654 } { S.E.C. 751 }	A1	{ Lancing { Carriage Works
DS 681	L.B.S.C. 659	A1X	{ Lancing { Carriage Works
DS 1173	2217	0–6–0 Diesel	Engineer's Department
DS 3152	30272	G6	Meldon Quarry

* Electric   † Repainted 1947 in Stroudley livery

BRITISH RAILWAYS LOCOMOTIVES

Nos. 30021-35030, W3-36

Named Engines are indicated by an asterisk (*)

No.	Class	No.	Class	No.	Class	No.	Class
30021	M7	30056	M7	30110	M7	30238	G6
30022	M7	30057	M7	30111	M7	30241	M7
30023	M7	30058	M7	30112	M7	30242	M7
30024	M7	30059	M7	30117	T9	30243	M7
30025	M7	30060	M7	30120	T9	30244	M7
30026	M7	30061	U.S.A.	30123	M7	30245	M7
30027	M7	30062	U.S.A.	30124	M7	30246	M7
30028	M7	30063	U.S.A.	30125	M7	30247	M7
30029	M7	30064	U.S.A.	30127	M7	30248	M7
30030	M7	30065	U.S.A.	30128	M7	30249	M7
30031	M7	30066	U.S.A.	30129	M7	30250	M7
30032	M7	30067	U.S.A.	30130	M7	30251	M7
30033	M7	30068	U.S.A.	30131	M7	30252	M7
30034	M7	30069	U.S.A.	30132	M7	30253	M7
30035	M7	30070	U.S.A.	30133	M7	30254	M7
30036	M7	30071	U.S.A.	30160	G6	30255	M7
30037	M7	30072	U.S.A.	30162	G6	30256	M7
30038	M7	30073	U.S.A.	30177	O2	30258	G6
30039	M7	30074	U.S.A.	30179	O2	30260	G6
30040	M7	30082	B4	30182	O2	30266	G6
30041	M7	30083	B4	30183	O2	30270	G6
30042	M7	30084	B4	30192	O2	30274	G6
30043	M7	30086	B4	30193	O2	30277	G6
30044	M7	30087	B4	30199	O2	30283	T9
30045	M7	30088	B4	30200	O2	30284	T9
30046	M7	30089	B4	30207	O2	30285	T9
30047	M7	30093	B4	30212	O2	30287	T9
30048	M7	30096	B4	30216	O2	30288	T9
30049	M7	30102	B4	30223	O2	30289	T9
30050	M7	30104	M7	30224	O2	30300	T9
30051	M7	30105	M7	30225	O2	30301	T9
30052	M7	30106	M7	30229	O2	30304	T9
30053	M7	30107	M7	30232	O2	30306	700
30054	M7	30108	M7	30233	O2	30308	700
30055	M7	30109	M7	30236	O2	30309	700

No.	Class	No.	Class	No.	Class	No.	Class
30310	T9	30453*	N15	30513	S15	30586	0298
30313	T9	30454*	N15	30514	S15	30587	0298
30315	700	30455*	N15	30515	S15	30588	C14
30316	700	30456*	N15	30516	H16	30589	C14
30317	700	30457*	N15	30517	H16	30667	M7
30318	M7	30473	H15	30518	H16	30668	M7
30319	M7	30474	H15	30519	H16	30669	M7
30320	M7	30475	H15	30520	H16	30670	M7
30321	M7	30476	H15	30521	H15	30671	M7
30322	M7	30477	H15	30522	H15	30673	M7
30323	M7	30478	H15	30523	H15	30674	M7
30324	M7	30479	M7	30524	H15	30675	M7
30325	700	30480	M7	30530	Q	30676	M7
30326	700	30481	M7	30531	Q	30687	700
30327	700	30482	H15	30532	Q	30688	700
30328	M7	30483	H15	30533	Q	30689	700
30330	H15	30484	H15	30534	Q	30690	700
30331	H15	30486	H15	30535	Q	30691	700
30333	H15	30487	H15	30536	Q	30692	700
30334	H15	30488	H15	30537	Q	30693	700
30335	H15	30489	H15	30538	Q	30694	700
30337	T9	30491	H15	30539	Q	30695	700
30338	T9	30492	G16	30540	Q	30696	700
30339	700	30493	G16	30541	Q	30697	700
30346	700	30494	G16	30542	Q	30698	700
30349	G6	30495	G16	30543	Q	30699	700
30350	700	30496	S15	30544	Q	30700	700
30352	700	30497	S15	30545	Q	30701	700
30355	700	30498	S15	30546	Q	30702	T9
30356	M7	30499	S15	30547	Q	30705	T9
30357	M7	30500	S15	30548	Q	30706	T9
30368	700	30501	S15	30549	Q	30707	T9
30374	M7	30502	S15	30564	0395	30708	T9
30375	M7	30503	S15	30566	0395	30709	T9
30376	M7	30504	S15	30567	0395	30710	T9
30377	M7	30505	S15	30568	0395	30711	T9
30378	M7	30506	S15	30575	0395	30712	T9
30379	M7	30507	S15	30578	0395	30715	T9
30448*	N15	30508	S15	30580	0395	30717	T9
30449*	N15	30509	S15	30582	0415	30718	T9
30450*	N15	30510	S15	30583	0415	30719	T9
30451*	N15	30511	S15	30584	0415	30721	T9
30452*	N15	30512	S15	30585	0298	30724	T9

No.	Class	No.	Class	No.	Class	No.	Class
30726	T9	30793*	N15	30854*	LN	30931*	V
30727	T9	30794*	N15	30855*	LN	30932*	V
30729	T9	30795*	N15	30856*	LN	30933*	V
30730	T9	30796*	N15	30857*	LN	30934*	V
30732	T9	30797*	N15	30858*	LN	30935*	V
30738*	N15	30798*	N15	30859*	LN	30936*	V
30739*	N15	30799*	N15	30860*	LN	30937*	V
30748*	N15	30800*	N15	30861*	LN	30938*	V
30749*	N15	30801*	N15	30862*	LN	30939*	V
30750*	N15	30802*	N15	30863*	LN	30950	Z
30751*	N15	30803*	N15	30864*	LN	30951	Z
30755*	N15	30804*	N15	30865*	LN	30952	Z
30757*	757	30805*	N15	30900*	V	30953	Z
30763*	N15	30806*	N15	30901*	V	30954	Z
30764*	N15	30823	S15	30902*	V	30955	Z
30765*	N15	30824	S15	30903*	V	30956	Z
30766*	N15	30825	S15	30904*	V	30957	Z
30767*	N15	30826	S15	30905*	V	31004	C
30768*	N15	30827	S15	30906*	V	31005	H
30769*	N15	30828	S15	30907*	V	31010	R1
30770*	N15	30829	S15	30908*	V	31018	C
30771*	N15	30830	S15	30909*	V	31019	E1
30772*	N15	30831	S15	30910*	V	31027	P
30773*	N15	30832	S15	30911*	V	31033	C
30774*	N15	30833	S15	30912*	V	31037	C
30775*	N15	30834	S15	30913*	V	31047	R1
30776*	N15	30835	S15	30914*	V	31043	O1
30777*	N15	30836	S15	30915*	V	31054	C
30778*	N15	30837	S15	30916*	V	31059	C
30779*	N15	30838	S15	30917*	V	31061	C
30780*	N15	30839	S15	30918*	V	31064	O1
30781*	N15	30840	S15	30919*	V	31065	O1
30782*	N15	30841	S15	30920*	V	31067	E1
30783*	N15	30842	S15	30921*	V	31068	C
30784*	N15	30843	S15	30922*	V	31069	R1
30785*	N15	30844	S15	30923*	V	31071	C
30786*	N15	30845	S15	30924*	V	31086	C
30787*	N15	30846	S15	30925*	V	31102	C
30788*	N15	30847	S15	30926*	V	31107	R1
30789*	N15	30850*	LN	30927*	V	31112	C
30790*	N15	30851*	LN	30928*	V	31113	C
30791*	N15	30852*	LN	30929*	V	31128	R1
30792*	N15	30853*	LN	30930*	V	31145	D1

No.	Class	No.	Class	No.	Class	No.	Class
31147	R1	31278	H	31425	O1	31554	H
31150	C	31279	H	31430	O1	31556	P
31161	H	31280	C	31434	O1	31557	P
31162	H	31287	C	31461	C	31558	P
31164	H	31293	C	31470	D1	31573	C
31165	E1	31295	H	31480	C	31575	C
31174	R1	31297	C	31481	C	31576	C
31177	H	31298	C	31487	D1	31578	C
31178	P	31305	H	31489	D1	31579	C
31184	H	31306	H	31492	D1	31581	C
31191	C	31307	H	31494	D1	31582	C
31193	H	31308	H	31495	C	31583	C
31218	C	31310	H	31497	E1	31584	C
31219	C	31317	C	31498	C	31585	C
31221	C	31319	H	31500	H	31588	C
31223	C	31321	H	31503	H	31589	C
31227	C	31322	H	31504	E1	31590	C
31229	C	31323	P	31505	D1	31592	C
31239	H	31324	H	31506	E1	31593	C
31242	C	31325	P	31507	E1	31610	U
31243	C	31326	H	31508	C	31611	U
31244	C	31327	H	31509	D1	31612	U
31245	C	31328	H	31510	C	31613	U
31246	D1	31329	H	31512	H	31614	U
31247	D1	31337	R1	31517	H	31615	U
31252	C	31339	R1	31518	H	31616	U
31253	C	31340	R1	31519	H	31617	U
31255	C	31370	O1	31520	H	31618	U
31256	C	31400	N	31521	H	31619	U
31258	O1	31401	N	31522	H	31620	U
31259	H	31402	N	31523	H	31621	U
31261	H	31403	N	31530	H	31622	U
31263	H	31404	N	31533	H	31623	U
31265	H	31405	N	31540	H	31624	U
31266	H	31406	N	31542	H	31625	U
31267	C	31407	N	31543	H	31626	U
31268	C	31408	N	31544	H	31627	U
31269	H	31409	N	31545	D1	31628	U
31270	C	31410	N	31543	H	31629	U
31271	C	31411	N	31550	N	31630	U
31272	C	31412	N	31551	H	31631	U
31274	H	31413	N	31552	H	31632	U
31276	H	31414	N	31553	H	31633	U

No.	Class	No.	Class	No.	Class	No.	Class
31634	U	31760	L	31805	U	31848	N
31635	U	31762	L	31806	U	31849	N
31636	U	31763	L	31807	U	31850	N
31637	U	31764	L	31808	U	31851	N
31638	U	31765	L	31809	U	31852	N
31639	U	31766	L	31810	N	31853	N
31681	C	31767	L	31811	N	31854	N
31682	C	31768	L	31812	N	31855	N
31683	C	31770	L	31813	N	31856	N
31684	C	31771	L	31814	N	31857	N
31686	C	31772	L	31815	N	31858	N
31688	C	31773	L	31816	N	31859	N
31689	C	31774	L	31817	N	31860	N
31690	C	31775	L	31818	N	31861	N
31691	C	31776	L	31819	N	31862	N
31692	C	31777	L	31820	N	31863	N
31693	C	31778	L	31821	N	31864	N
31694	C	31779	L	31822	NI	31865	N
31695	C	31780	L	31823	N	31866	N
31714	C	31781	L	31824	N	31867	N
31715	C	31782	LI	31825	N	31868	N
31716	C	31783	LI	31826	N	31869	N
31717	C	31784	LI	31827	N	31870	N
31719	C	31785	LI	31828	N	31871	N
31720	C	31786	LI	31829	N	31872	N
31721	C	31787	LI	31830	N	31873	N
31722	C	31788	LI	31831	N	31874	N
31723	C	31789	LI	31832	N	31875	N
31724	C	31790	U	31833	N	31876	NI
31725	C	31791	U	31834	N	31877	NI
31727	DI	31792	U	31835	N	31878	NI
31735	DI	31793	U	31836	N	31879	NI
31739	DI	31794	U	31837	N	31880	NI
31741	DI	31795	U	31838	N	31890	UI
31743	DI	31796	U	31839	N	31891	UI
31749	DI	31797	U	31840	N	31892	UI
31753	LI	31798	U	31841	N	31893	UI
31754	LI	31799	U	31842	N	31894	UI
31755	LI	31800	U	31843	N	31895	UI
31756	LI	31801	U	31844	N	31896	UI
31757	LI	31802	U	31845	N	31897	UI
31758	LI	31803	U	31846	N	31898	UI
31759	LI	31804	U	31847	N	31899	UI

No.	Class	No.	Class	No.	Class	No.	Class
31900	UI	32170	E3	32449	C2X	32508	E4
31901	UI	32331*	N15X	32450	C2X	32509	E4
31902	UI	32337	K	32451	C2X	32510	E4
31903	UI	32338	K	32454	E3	32512	E4
31904	UI	32339	K	32455	E3	32515	E4
31905	UI	32340	K	32456	E3	32517	E4
31906	UI	32341	K	32462	E3	32519	E4
31907	UI	32342	K	32463	E4	32521	C2X
31908	UI	32343	K	32466	E4X	32522	C2X
31909	UI	32344	K	32467	E4	32523	C2X
31910	UI	32345	K	32468	E4	32524	C2X
31911	W	32346	K	32469	E4	32525	C2X
31912	W	32347	K	32470	E4	32526	C2X
31913	W	32348	K	32471	E4	32527	C2X
31914	W	32349	K	32472	E4	32528	C2X
31915	W	32350	K	32473	E4	32529	C2X
31916	W	32351	K	32474	E4	32532	C2X
31917	W	32352	K	32475	E4	32534	C2X
31918	W	32353	K	32476	E4	32535	C2X
31919	W	32407	E6X	32477	E4X	32536	C2X
31920	W	32408	E6	32479	E4	32537	C2X
31921	W	32409	E6	32480	E4	32538	C2X
31922	W	32410	E6	32481	E4	32539	C2X
31923	W	32411	E6X	32484	E4	32540	C2X
31924	W	32412	E6	32485	E4	32541	C2X
31925	W	32413	E6	32486	E4	32543	C2X
32100	E2	32414	E6	32487	E4	32544	C2X
32101	E2	32415	E6	32488	E4	32545	C2X
32102	E2	32416	E6	32491	E4	32546	C2X
32103	E2	32417	E6	32492	E4	32547	C2X
32104	E2	32418	E6	32493	E4	32548	C2X
32105	E2	32424*	H2	32494	E4	32549	C2X
32106	E2	32437	C2X	32495	E4	32550	C2X
32107	E2	32438	C2X	32497	E4	32551	C2X
32108	E2	32440	C2X	32498	E4	32552	C2X
32109	E2	32441	C2X	32499	E4	32553	C2X
32113	EI	32442	C2X	32500	E4	32554	C2X
32124	EI/R	32443	C2X	32502	E4	32556	E4
32135	EI/R	32444	C2X	32503	E4	32557	E4
32139	EI	32445	C2X	32504	E4	32559	E4
32151	EI	32446	C2X	32505	E4	32560	E4
32165	E3	32447	C2X	32506	E4	32562	E4
32166	E3	32448	C2X	32507	E4	32563	E4

No.	Class	No.	Class	No.	Class	No.	Class
32564	E4	33022	Q1	34025*	WC	34068*	BB
32565	E4	33023	Q1	34026*	WC	34069*	BB
32566	E4	33024	Q1	34027*	WC	34070*	BB
32577	E4	33025	Q1	34028*	WC	34071*	BB
32578	E4	33026	Q1	34029*	WC	34072*	BB
32579	E4	33027	Q1	34030*	WC	34073*	BB
32580	E4	33028	Q1	34031*	WC	34074*	BB
32581	E4	33029	Q1	34032*	WC	34075*	BB
32608	E1/R	33030	Q1	34033*	WC	34076*	BB
32636	A1X	33031	Q1	34034*	WC	34077*	BB
32640	A1X	33032	Q1	34035*	WC	34078*	BB
32646	A1X	33033	Q1	34036*	WC	34079*	BB
32650	A1X	33034	Q1	34037*	WC	34080*	BB
32655	A1X	33035	Q1	34038*	WC	34081*	BB
32661	A1X	33036	Q1	34039*	WC	34082*	BB
32662	A1X	33037	Q1	34040*	WC	34083*	BB
32670	A1X	33038	Q1	34041*	WC	34084*	BB
32677	A1X	33039	Q1	34042*	WC	34085*	BB
32678	A1X	33040	Q1	34043*	WC	34086*	BB
32689	E1	34001*	WC	34044*	WC	34087*	BB
32694	E1	34002*	WC	34045*	WC	34088*	BB
32697	E1/R	34003*	WC	34046*	WC	34089*	BB
33001	Q1	34004*	WC	34047*	WC	34090*	BB
33002	Q1	34005*	WC	34048*	WC	34091*	WC
33003	Q1	34006*	WC	34049*	BB	34092*	WC
33004	Q1	34007*	WC	34050*	BB	34093*	WC
33005	Q1	34008*	WC	34051*	BB	34094*	WC
33006	Q1	34009*	WC	34052*	BB	34095*	WC
33007	Q1	34010*	WC	34053*	BB	34096*	WC
33008	Q1	34011*	WC	34054*	BB	34097*	WC
33009	Q1	34012*	WC	34055*	BB	34098*	WC
33010	Q1	34013*	WC	34056*	BB	34099*	WC
33011	Q1	34014*	WC	34057*	BB	34100*	WC
33012	Q1	34015*	WC	34058*	BB	34101*	WC
33013	Q1	34016*	WC	34059*	BB	34102*	WC
33014	Q1	34017*	WC	34060*	BB	34103*	WC
33015	Q1	34018*	WC	34061*	BB	34104*	WC
33016	Q1	34019*	WC	34062*	BB	34105*	WC
33017	Q1	34020*	WC	34063*	BB	34106*	WC
33018	Q1	34021*	WC	34064*	BB	34107*	WC
33019	Q1	34022*	WC	34065*	BB	34108*	WC
33020	Q1	34023*	WC	34066*	BB	34109*	BB
33021	Q1	34024*	WC	34067*	BB	34110*	BB

No.	Class	No.	Class	No.	Class	No.	Class
35001*	MN	35015*	MN	35029*	MN	W21*	O2
35002*	MN	35016*	MN	35030*	MN	W22*	O2
35003*	MN	35017*	MN			W24*	O2
35004*	MN	35018*	MN			W25*	O2
35005*	MN	35019*	MN	**Isle of Wight**		W26*	O2
35006*	MN	35020*	MN	**Locomotives**		W27*	O2
35007*	MN	35021*	MN	W1*	E1	W28*	O2
35008*	MN	35022*	MN	W3*	E1	W29*	O2
35009*	MN	35023*	MN	W4*	E1	W30*	O2
35010*	MN	35024*	MN	W14*	O2	W31*	O2
35011*	MN	35025*	MN	W16*	O2	W32*	O2
35012*	MN	35026*	MN	W17*	O2	W33*	O2
35013*	MN	35027*	MN	W18*	O2	W35*	O2
35014*	MN	35028*	MN	W20*	O2	W36*	O2

BRITISH RAILWAYS LOCOMOTIVES
Nos. 26000-35030 and W3-W36

NAMED LOCOMOTIVES

CLASS EM1 BO-BO ELECTRIC

26000 Tommy

CLASS N15 " KING ARTHUR " 4-6-0

30448	Sir Tristram	30453	King Arthur
30449	Sir Torre	30454	Queen Guinevere
30450	Sir Kay	30455	Sir Launcelot
30451	Sir Lamorak	30456	Sir Galahad
30452	Sir Meliagrance	30457	Sir Bedivere

CLASS N15 " KING ARTHUR " 4-6-0

30738	King Pellinore	30750	Morgan le Fay
30739	King Leodegrance	30751	Etarre
30748	Vivien	30755	The Red Knight
30749	Iseult		

CLASS 757 0-6-2T

30757 Earl of Mount Edgcumbe

CLASS N15 " KING ARTHUR " 4-6-0

30763 Sir Bors de Ganis	30785 Sir Mador de la Porte
30764 Sir Gawain	30786 Sir Lionel
30765 Sir Gareth	30787 Sir Menadeuke
30766 Sir Geraint	30788 Sir Urre of the Mount
30767 Sir Valence	30789 Sir Guy
30768 Sir Balin	30790 Sir Villiars
30769 Sir Balan	30791 Sir Uwaine
30770 Sir Prianius	30792 Sir Hervis de Revel
30771 Sir Sagramore	30793 Sir Ontzlake
30772 Sir Percivale	30794 Sir Ector de Maris
30773 Sir Lavaine	30795 Sir Dinadan
30774 Sir Gaheris	30796 Sir Dodinas le Savage
30775 Sir Agravaine	30797 Sir Blamor de Ganis
30776 Sir Galagars	30798 Sir Hectimere
30777 Sir Lamiel	30799 Sir Ironside
30778 Sir Pelleas	30800 Sir Meleaus de Lile
30779 Sir Colgrevance	30801 Sir Meliot de Logres
30780 Sir Persant	30802 Sir Durnore
30781 Sir Aglovale	30803 Sir Harry le Fise Lake
30782 Sir Brian	30804 Sir Cador of Cornwall
30783 Sir Gillemere	30805 Sir Constantine
30784 Sir Nerovens	30806 Sir Galleron

CLASS LN " LORD NELSON " 4-6-0

30850 Lord Nelson	30858 Lord Duncan
30851 Sir Francis Drake	30859 Lord Hood
30852 Sir Walter Raleigh	30860 Lord Hawke
30853 Sir Richard Grenville	30861 Lord Anson
30854 Howard of Effingham	30862 Lord Collingwood
30855 Robert Blake	30863 Lord Rodney
30856 Lord St. Vincent	30864 Sir Martin Frobisher
30857 Lord Howe	30865 Sir John Hawkins

CLASS V " SCHOOLS " 4-4-0

30900 Eton	30904 Lancing
30901 Winchester	30905 Tonbridge
30902 Wellington	30906 Sherborne
30903 Charterhouse	30907 Dulwich

30908	Westminster	30924	Haileybury
30909	St. Paul's	30925	Cheltenham
30910	Merchant Taylors	30926	Repton
30911	Dover	30927	Clifton
30912	Downside	30928	Stowe
30913	Christ's Hospital	30929	Malvern
30914	Eastbourne	30930	Radley
30915	Brighton	30931	King's Wimbledon
30916	Whitgift	30932	Blundells
30917	Ardingly	30933	King's Canterbury
30918	Hurstpierpoint	30934	St. Lawrence
30919	Harrow	30935	Sevenoaks
30920	Rugby	30936	Cranleigh
30921	Shrewsbury	30937	Epsom
30922	Marlborough	30938	St. Olave's
30923	Bradfield	30939	Leatherhead

CLASS N15X " REMEMBRANCE " 4—6—0

32331　Beattie

CLASS H2 4—4—2

32424　Beachy Head

CLASSES WC & BB 4—6—2
" WEST COUNTRY " and " BATTLE OF BRITAIN "

34001	Exeter	34019	Bideford
34002	Salisbury	34020	Seaton
34003	Plymouth	34021	Dartmoor
34004	Yeovil	34022	Exmoor
34005	Barnstaple	34023	Blackmore Vale
34006	Bude	34024	Tamar Valley
34007	Wadebridge	34025	Whimple
34008	Padstow	34026	Yes Tor
34009	Lyme Regis	34027	Taw Valley
34010	Sidmouth	34028	Eddystone
34011	Tavistock	34029	Lundy
34012	Launceston	34030	Watersmeet
34013	Okehampton	34031	Torrington
34014	Budleigh Salterton	34032	Camelford
34015	Exmouth	34033	Chard
34016	Bodmin	34034	Honiton
34017	Ilfracombe	34035	Shaftesbury
34018	Axminster	34036	Westward Ho

34037	Clovelly	34075	264 Squadron
34038	Lynton	34076	41 Squadron
34039	Boscastle	34077	603 Squadron
34040	Crewkerne	34078	222 Squadron
34041	Wilton	34079	141 Squadron
34042	Dorchester	34080	74 Squadron
34043	Combe Martin	34081	92 Squadron
34044	Woolacombe	34082	615 Squadron
34045	Ottery St. Mary	34083	605 Squadron
34046	Braunton	34084	253 Squadron
34047	Callington	34085	501 Squadron
34048	Crediton	34086	219 Squadron
34049	Anti-Aircraft Command	34087	145 Squadron
34050	Royal Observer Corps	34088	213 Squadron
34051	Winston Churchill	34089	602 Squadron
34052	Lord Dowding	34090	Sir Eustace Missenden, Southern Railway
34053	Sir Keith Park		
34054	Lord Beaverbrook	34091	Weymouth
34055	Fighter Pilot	34092	City of Wells
34056	Croydon	34093	Saunton
34057	Biggin Hill	34094	Mortehoe
34058	Sir Frederick Pile	34095	Brentor
34059	Sir Archibald Sinclair	34096	Trevone
34060	25 Squadron	34097	Holsworthy
34061	73 Squadron	34098	Templecombe
34062	17 Squadron	34099	Lynmouth
34063	229 Squadron	34100	Appledore
34064	Fighter Command	34101	Hartland
34065	Hurricane	34102	Lapford
34066	Spitfire	34103	Calstock
34067	Tangmere	34104	Bere Alston
34068	Kenley	34105	Swanage
34069	Hawkinge	34106	Lydford
34070	Manston	34107	Blandford Forum
34071	601 Squadron	34108	Wincanton
34072	257 Squadron	34109	Sir Trafford Leigh-Mallory
34073	249 Squadron		
34074	46 Squadron	34110	66 Squadron

CLASS MN " MERCHANT NAVY " 4-6-2

35001	Channel Packet	35006	Peninsular & Oriental S.N. Co.
35002	Union Castle		
35003	Royal Mail	35007	Aberdeen Commonwealth
35004	Cunard White Star		
35005	Canadian Pacific	35008	Orient Line

40

Class LN 4-6-0 No. 30851 *Sir Francis Drake*   [*C. P. Boocock*

Class V 4-4-0 No. 30905 *Tonbridge*   [*R. Russell*

Class S15 (Urie) 4-6-0 No. 30498   [*M. J. Ecclestone*

Class H15 (Urie) 4-6-0 No. 30487 [R. K. Evans

Class H15 4-6-0 No. 30491 (Urie loco. with Maunsell taper boiler)
[S. M. Watkins

Class H15 (Maunsell) 4-6-0 No. 30524 [R. J. Buckley

Class S15 (Maunsell) 4-6-0 No. 30829   [J. A. Young

Class N15 (Urie) 4-6-0 No. 30748 *Vivien*   [L. Elsey

Class N15 (Maunsell) 4-6-0 No. 30770 *Sir Prianius*   [D. Marriott

Class Q1 0-6-0 No. 33025

[R. C. Riley

Class Q 0-6-0 No. 30534

[A. J. Temple

Class 0395 0-6-0 No. 30567

[Brian E. Morrison

Class C2X 0-6-0 No. 32446

[R. K. Evans

Class H16 4-6-2T No. 30518

[R. K. Evans

Class Z 0-8-0T No. 30956

[R. A. Panting

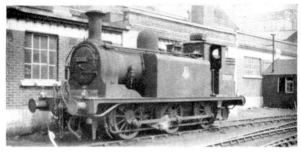

Class E1 0-6-0T No. 32689   [A. A. Cameron

Class E1/R 0-6-2T No. 32124   [K. R. Pirt

Class E2 0-6-0T No. 32106   [A. R. Carpenter

Class E4 0-6-2T No. 32581   [F. J. Saunders

Class E4X 0-6-2T No. 32478 (since withdrawn)   [R. K. Evans

Class E6 0-6-2T No. 32414   [D. Marriott

Class E6X 0-6-2T No. 32407   [D. Marriott

Class A1X 0-6-0T No. 32662   [W. M. J. Jackson

Class 4 2-6-0 No. 76059   [R. C. Rile

35009	Shaw Savill
35010	Blue Star
35011	General Steam Navigation
35012	United States Line
35013	Blue Funnel
35014	Nederland Line
35015	Rotterdam Lloyd
35016	Elders Fyffes
35017	Belgian Marine
35018	British India Line
35019	French Line CGT
35020	Bibby Line
35021	New Zealand Line
35022	Holland-America Line
35023	Holland-Afrika Line
35024	East Asiatic Company
35025	Brocklebank Line
35026	Lamport & Holt Line
35027	Port Line
35028	Clan Line
35029	Ellerman Lines
35030	Elder Dempster Lines

CLASS EI 0–6–0T

W 3	Ryde
W 4	Wroxall

CLASS O2 0–4–4T

W14	Fishbourne
W16	Ventnor
W17	Seaview
W18	Ningwood
W20	Shanklin
W21	Sandown
W22	Brading
W24	Calbourne
W25	Godshill
W26	Whitwell
W27	Merstone
W28	Ashey
W29	Alverstone
W30	Shorwell
W31	Chale
W32	Bonchurch
W33	Bembridge
W35	Freshwater
W36	Carisbrooke

BRITISH RAILWAYS STANDARD LOCOMOTIVES

Chief Officer (Mechanical Engineering) :
R. C. BOND

4-6-2　　　　　　　**7P6F**

Introduced 1951. Designed at Derby.
Weight: Loco. 94 tons 0 cwt.
　　　　Tender (see page 57).
Pressure: 250 lb.　　Su.
Cyls.: (O) 20″ × 28″.
Driving Wheels: 6′ 2″. T.E.: 32,150 lb.
Walschaerts valve gear. P.V.

70000	Britannia
70001	Lord Hurcomb
70002	Geoffrey Chaucer

70003	John Bunyan
70004	William Shakespeare
70005	John Milton
70006	Robert Burns
70007	Coeur-de-Lion
70008	Black Prince
70009	Alfred the Great
70010	Owen Glendower
70011	Hotspur
70012	John of Gaunt

70013	Oliver Cromwell
70014	Iron Duke
70015	Apollo
70016	Ariel
70017	Arrow
70018	Flying Dutchman
70019	Lightning
70020	Mercury
70021	Morning Star
70022	Tornado
70023	Venus
70024	Vulcan
70025	Western Star
70026	Polar Star
70027	Rising Star
70028	Royal Star
70029	Shooting Star
70030	William Wordsworth
70031	Byron
70032	Tennyson
70033	Charles Dickens
70034	Thomas Hardy
70035	Rudyard Kipling
70036	Boadicea
70037	Hereward the Wake
70038	Robin Hood
70039	Sir Christopher Wren
70040	Clive of India
70041	Sir John Moore
70042	Lord Roberts
70043	
70044	Earl Haig
70045	
70046	
70047	
70048	
70049	
70050	Firth of Clyde
70051	Firth of Forth
70052	Firth of Tay
70053	Moray Firth
70054	Dornoch Firth

Total 55

4-6-2   8P

Introduced 1954. Designed at Derby.
Weight: Loco. 101 tons 5 cwt.
      Tender (see page 57).
Pressure: 250 lb.   Su.
Cyls.: (3) 18″ × 28″.
Driving Wheels: 6′ 2″. T.E.: 39,080 lb.
Caprotti valve gear.

71000	Duke of Gloucester

Total 1

4-6-2   6P5F

Introduced 1952. Designed at Derby.
Weight: Loco. 86 tons 19 cwt.
      Tender (see page 57).
Pressure: 225 lb.   Su.
Cyls.: (O) 19½ × 28″.
Driving Wheels: 6′ 2″. T.E.: 27,520 lb.
Walschaerts valve gear. P.V.

72000	Clan Buchanan
72001	Clan Cameron
72002	Clan Campbell
72003	Clan Fraser
72004	Clan Macdonald
72005	Clan Macgregor
72006	Clan Mackenzie
72007	Clan Mackintosh
72008	Clan Macleod
72009	Clan Stewart

Total 10

4-6-0   5

Introduced 1951. Designed at Don-
     caster.
*Introduced 1956. Fitted with Caprotti
     valve gear.
Weight: Loco. 76 tons 4 cwt.
      Tender (see page 57).
Pressure: 225 lb.   Su.
Cyls.: (O) 19″ × 28″.
Driving Wheels : 6′ 2″. T.E.: 26,120 lb′
Walschaerts valve gear. P.V.

73000	73007	73014	73021
73001	73008	73015	73022
73002	73009	73016	73023
73003	73010	73017	73024
73004	73011	73018	73025
73005	73012	73019	73026
73006	73013	73020	73027

73028	73064	73100	73136*
73029	73065	73101	73137*
73030	73066	73102	73138*
73031	73067	73103	73139*
73032	73068	73104	73140*
73033	73069	73105	73141*
73034	73070	73106	73142*
73035	73071	73107	73143*
73036	73072	73108	73144*
73037	73073	73109	73145*
73038	73074	73110	73146*
73039	73075	73111	73147*
73040	73076	73112	73148*
73041	73077	73113	73149*
73042	73078	73114	73150*
73043	73079	73115	73151*
73044	73080	73116	73152*
73045	73081	73117	73153*
73046	73082	73118	73154*
73047	73083	73119	73155
73048	73084	73120	73156
73049	73085	73121	73157
73050	73086	73122	73158
73051	73087	73123	73159
73052	73088	73124	73160
73053	73089	73125*	73161
73054	73090	73126*	73162
73055	73091	73127*	73163
73056	73092	73128*	73164
73057	73093	73129*	73165
73058	73094	73130*	73166
73059	73095	73131*	73167
73060	73096	73132*	73168
73061	73097	73133*	73169
73062	73098	73134*	73170
73063	73099	73135*	73171

Engines of this class are still being delivered.

4-6-0 4

Introduced 1951. Designed at Brighton.
Weight: Loco. 69 tons 0 cwt.
　　　　Tender (see page 57).
Pressure: 225 lb.　Su.
Cyls.: (O) 18″ × 28″.

Driving Wheels: 5′ 8″. T.E.: 25,100 lb.
Walschaerts valve gear.　P V.

75000	75020	75040	75060
75001	75021	75041	75061
75002	75022	75042	75062
75003	75023	75043	75063
75004	75024	75044	75064
75005	75025	75045	75065
75006	75026	75046	75066
75007	75027	75047	75067
75008	75028	75048	75068
75009	75029	75049	75069
75010	75030	75050	75070
75011	75031	75051	75071
75012	75032	75052	75072
75013	75033	75053	75073
75014	75034	75054	75074
75015	75035	75055	75075
75016	75036	75056	75076
75017	75037	75057	75077
75018	75038	75058	75078
75019	75039	75059	75079

Total 80

2-6-0 4

Introduced 1953. Designed at Doncaster.
Weight: Loco. 59 tons 2 cwt.
　　　　Tender (see page 57).
Pressure: 225 lb.　Su.
Cyls.: (O) 17½″ × 26″.
Driving Wheels: 5′ 3″. T.E.: 24,170 lb.
Walschaerts valve gear.　P.V.

76000	76013	76026	76039
76001	76014	76027	76040
76002	76015	76028	76041
76003	76016	76029	76042
76004	76017	76030	76043
76005	76018	76031	76044
76006	76019	76032	76045
76007	76020	76033	76046
76008	76021	76034	76047
76009	76022	76035	76048
76010	76023	76036	76049
76011	76024	76037	76050
76012	76025	76038	76051

76052	76068	76084	76100
76053	76069	76085	76101
76054	76070	76086	76102
76055	76071	76087	76103
76056	76072	76088	76104
76057	76073	76089	76105
76058	76074	76090	76106
76059	76075	76091	76107
76060	76076	76092	76108
76061	76077	76093	76109
76062	76078	76094	76110
76063	76079	76095	76111
76064	76080	76096	76112
76065	76081	76097	76113
76066	76082	76098	76114
76067	76083	76099	

Engines of this class are still being delivered.

2-6-0 3

Introduced 1954. Designed at Swindon.
Weight: Loco. 57 tons 9 cwt.
Tender (see page 57).
Pressure: 200 lb.   Su.
Cyls.: (O) 17½″ × 26″.
Driving Wheels: 5′ 3″ T.E.: 21,490 lb.
Walschaerts valve gear. P.V.

77000	77005	77010	77015
77001	77006	77011	77016
77002	77007	77012	77017
77003	77008	77013	77018
77004	77009	77014	77019

Total 20

2-6-0 2

Introduced 1953. Designed at Derby.
Weight: Loco. 49 tons 5 cwt.
Tender (see page 57).
Pressure: 200 lb.   Su.
Cyls.: (O) 16½″ × 24″.
Driving Wheels: 5′ 0″ T.E.: 18,515 lb.
Walschaerts valve gear. P.V.

78000	78005	78010	78015
78001	78006	78011	78016
78002	78007	78012	78017
78003	78008	78013	78018
78004	78009	78014	78019

78020	78032	78044	78056
78021	78033	78045	78057
78022	78034	78046	78058
78023	78035	78047	78059
78024	78036	78048	78060
78025	78037	78049	78061
78026	78038	78050	78062
78027	78039	78051	78063
78028	78040	78052	78064
78029	78041	78053	
78030	78042	78054	
78031	78043	78055	

Total 65

2-6-4T 4

Introduced 1951. Designed at Brighton.
Weight: 88 tons 10 cwt.
Pressure: 225 lb.   Su.
Cyls.: (O) 18″ × 28″.
Driving Wheels: 5′ 8″. T.E.: 25,100 lb.
Walschaerts valve gear. P.V.

80000	80024	80048	80072
80001	80025	80049	80073
80002	80026	80050	80074
80003	80027	80051	80075
80004	80028	80052	80076
80005	80029	80053	80077
80006	80030	80054	80078
80007	80031	80055	80079
80008	80032	80056	80080
80009	80033	80057	80081
80010	80034	80058	80082
80011	80035	80059	80083
80012	80036	80060	80084
80013	80037	80061	80085
80014	80038	80062	80086
80015	80039	80063	80087
80016	80040	80064	80088
80017	80041	80065	80089
80018	80042	80066	80090
80019	80043	80067	80091
80020	80044	80068	80092
80021	80045	80069	80093
80022	80046	80070	80094
80023	80047	80071	80095

80096	80111	80126	80141
80097	80112	80127	80142
80098	80113	80128	80143
80099	80114	80129	80144
80100	80115	80130	80145
80101	80116	80131	80146
80102	80117	80132	80147
80103	80118	80133	80148
80104	80119	80134	80149
80105	80120	80135	80150
80106	80121	80136	80151
80107	80122	80137	80152
80108	80123	80138	80153
80109	80124	80139	80154
80110	80125	80140	

Total 155

2-6-2T 3

Introduced 1952. Designed at Swindon.
Weight: 73 tons 10 cwt.
Pressure: 200 lb. Su.
Cyls.: (O) 17½″ × 26″.
Driving Wheels: 5′ 3″. T.E.: 21,490 lb.
Walschaerts valve gear. P.V.

82000	82012	82024	82036
82001	82013	82025	82037
82002	82014	82026	82038
82003	82015	82027	82039
82004	82016	82028	82040
82005	82017	82029	82041
82006	82018	82030	82042
82007	82019	82031	82043
82008	82020	82032	82044
82009	82021	82033	
82010	82022	82034	
82011	82023	82035	

Total 45

2-6-2T 2

Introduced 1953. Designed at Derby.
Weight: 63 tons 5 cwt.
Pressure: 200 lb. Su.
Cyls.: (O) 16½″ × 24″.
Driving Wheels: 5′ 0″. T.E.: 18,515 lb.
Walschaerts valve gear. P.V.

84000	84008	84016	84024
84001	84009	84017	84025
84002	84010	84018	84026
84003	84011	84019	84027
84004	84012	84020	84028
84005	84013	84021	84029
84006	84014	84022	
84007	84015	84023	

Engines of this class are still being delivered.

2-8-0 8F WD

Ministry of Supply " Austerity " 2-8-0 locomotives purchased by British Railways, 1948.
Introduced 1943. Riddles M.o.S. design
Weight: Loco. 70 tons 5 cwt.
Tender 55 tons 10 cwt.
Pressure:225 lb. Su. Cyls.: (O) 19″ ×28″
Driving Wheels: 4′ 8½″. T.E.: 34,215 lb.
Walschaerts valve gear. P.V.

90000	90024	90048	90072
90001	90025	90049	90073
90002	90026	90050	90074
90003	90027	90051	90075
90004	90028	90052	90076
90005	90029	90053	90077
90006	90030	90054	90078
90007	90031	90055	90079
90008	90032	90056	90080
90009	90033	90057	90081
90010	90034	90058	90082
90011	90035	90059	90083
90012	90036	90060	90084
90013	90037	90061	90085
90014	90038	90062	90086
90015	90039	90063	90087
90016	90040	90064	90088
90017	90041	90065	90089
90018	90042	90066	90090
90019	90043	90067	90091
90020	90044	90068	90092
90021	90045	90069	90093
90022	90046	90070	90094
90023	90047	90071	90095

90096	90140	90184	90228	90272	90316	90360	90404
90097	90141	90185	90229	90273	90317	90361	90405
90098	90142	90186	90230	90274	90318	90362	90406
90099	90143	90187	90231	90275	90319	90363	90407
90100	90144	90188	90232	90276	90320	90364	90408
90101	90145	90189	90233	90277	90321	90365	90409
90102	90146	90190	90234	90278	90322	90366	90410
90103	90147	90191	90235	90279	90323	90367	90411
90104	90148	90192	90236	90280	90324	90368	90412
90105	90149	90193	90237	90281	90325	90369	90413
90106	90150	90194	90238	90282	90326	90370	90414
90107	90151	90195	90239	90283	90327	90371	90415
90108	90152	90196	90240	90284	90328	90372	90416
90109	90153	90197	90241	90285	90329	90373	90417
90110	90154	90198	90242	90286	90330	90374	90418
90111	90155	90199	90243	90287	90331	90375	90419
90112	90156	90200	90244	90288	90332	90376	90420
90113	90157	90201	90245	90289	90333	90377	90421
90114	90158	90202	90246	90290	90334	90378	90422
90115	90159	90203	90247	90291	90335	90379	90423
90116	90160	90204	90248	90292	90336	90380	90424
90117	90161	90205	90249	90293	90337	90381	90425
90118	90162	90206	90250	90294	90338	90382	90426
90119	90163	90207	90251	90295	90339	90383	90427
90120	90164	90208	90252	90296	90340	90384	90428
90121	90165	90209	90253	90297	90341	90385	90429
90122	90166	90210	90254	90298	90342	90386	90430
90123	90167	90211	90255	90299	90343	90387	90431
90124	90168	90212	90256	90300	90344	90388	90432
90125	90169	90213	90257	90301	90345	90389	90433
90126	90170	90214	90258	90302	90346	90390	90434
90127	90171	90215	90259	90303	90347	90391	90435
90128	90172	90216	90260	90304	90348	90392	90436
90129	90173	90217	90261	90305	90349	90393	90437
90130	90174	90218	90262	90306	90350	90394	90438
90131	90175	90219	90263	90307	90351	90395	90439
90132	90176	90220	90264	90308	90352	90396	90440
90133	90177	90221	90265	90309	90353	90397	90441
90134	90178	90222	90266	90310	90354	90398	90442
90135	90179	90223	90267	90311	90355	90399	90443
90136	90180	90224	90268	90312	90356	90400	90444
90137	90181	90225	90269	90313	90357	90401	90445
90138	90182	90226	90270	90314	90358	90402	90446
90139	90183	90227	90271	90315	90359	90403	90447

90448	90492	90536	90580	90624	90652	90680	90708
90449	90493	90537	90581	90625	90653	90681	90709
90450	90494	90538	90582	90626	90654	90682	90710
90451	90495	90539	90583	90627	90655	90683	90711
90452	90496	90540	90584	90628	90656	90684	90712
90453	90497	90541	90585	90629	90657	90685	90713
90454	90498	90542	90586	90630	90658	90686	90714
90455	90499	90543	90587	90631	90659	90687	90715
90456	90500	90544	90588	90632	90660	90688	90716
90457	90501	90545	90589	90633	90661	90689	90717
90458	90502	90546	90590	90634	90662	90690	90718
90459	90503	90547	90591	90635	90663	90691	90719
90460	90504	90548	90592	90636	90664	90692	90720
90461	90505	90549	90593	90637	90665	90693	90721
90462	90506	90550	90594	90638	90666	90694	90722
90463	90507	90551	90595	90639	90667	90695	90723
90464	90508	90552	90596	90640	90668	90696	90724
90465	90509	90553	90597	90641	90669	90697	90725
90466	90510	90554	90598	90642	90670	90698	90726
90467	90511	90555	90599	90643	90671	90699	90727
90468	90512	90556	90600	90644	90672	90700	90728
90469	90513	90557	90601	90645	90673	90701	90729
90470	90514	90558	90602	90646	90674	90702	90730
90471	90515	90559	90603	90647	90675	90703	90731
90472	90516	90560	90604	90648	90676	90704	90732
90473	90517	90561	90605	90649	90677	90705	Vulcan
90474	90518	90562	90606	90650	90678	90706	
90475	90519	90563	90607	90651	90679	90707	

Total 733

90476	90520	90564	90608
90477	90521	90565	90609
90478	90522	90566	90610
90479	90523	90567	90611
90480	90524	90568	90612
90481	90525	90569	90613
90482	90526	90570	90614
90483	90527	90571	90615
90484	90528	90572	90616
90485	90529	90573	90617
90486	90530	90574	90618
90487	90531	90575	90619
90488	90532	90576	90620
90489	90533	90577	90621
90490	90534	90578	90622
90491	90535	90579	90623

2-10-0   8F   WD

Ministry of Supply " Austerity " 2-10-0 locomotives purchased by British Railways, 1948.
Introduced 1943. Riddles M.o.S. design.
Weight: Loco. 78 tons 6 cwt.
       Tender 55 tons 10 cwt.
Pressure: 225 lb. Su. Cyls.: (O) 19″ × 28″.
Driving Wheels: 4′ 8½″. T.E. 34,215 lb.
Walschaerts valve gear. P.V.

90750	90754	90758	90762
90751	90755	90759	90763
90752	90756	90760	90764
90753	90757	90761	90765

90766	90769	90771	90773
90767	90770	90772	90774
90768			

Total 25

2-10-0   9F

Introduced 1954. Designed at Brighton.
*Introduced 1955. Fitted with Crosti
boiler.
Weight: Loco. {86 tons 14 cwt.
{90 tons 4 cwt.*
Tender (see page 57).
Pressure: 250 lb.   Su.
Cyls.: (O) 20″ × 28″.
Driving Wheels: 5′ 0:. T.E.: 39,670 lb.
Walschaerts valve gear. P.V.

92000	92029	92058	92087
92001	92030	92059	92088
92002	92031	92060	92089
92003	92032	92061	92090
92004	92033	92062	92091
92005	92034	92063	92092
92006	92035	92064	92093
92007	92036	92065	92094
92008	92037	92066	92095
92009	92038	92067	92096
92010	92039	92068	92097
92011	92040	92069	92098
92012	92041	92070	92099
92013	92042	92071	92100
92014	92043	92072	92101
92015	92044	92073	92102
92016	92045	92074	92103
92017	92046	92075	92104
92018	92047	92076	92105
92019	92048	92077	92106
92020*	92049	92078	92107
92021*	92050	92079	92108
92022*	92051	92080	92109
92023*	92052	92081	92110
92024*	92053	92082	92111
92025*	92054	92083	92112
92026*	92055	92084	92113
92027*	92056	92085	92114
92028*	92057	92086	92115

92116	92138	92160	92182
92117	92139	92161	92183
92118	92140	92162	92184
92119	92141	92163	92185
92120	92142	92164	92186
92121	92143	92165	92187
92122	92144	92166	92188
92123	92145	92167	92189
92124	92146	92168	92190
92125	92147	92169	92191
92126	92148	92170	92192
92127	92149	92171	92193
92128	92150	92172	92194
92129	92151	92173	92195
92130	92152	92174	92196
92131	92153	92175	92197
92132	92154	92176	92198
92133	92155	92177	92199
92134	92156	92178	92200
92135	92157	92179	92201
92136	92158	92180	92202
92137	92159	92181	

Engines of this class are still being delivered.

BRITISH RAILWAYS STANDARD TENDERS

N.B.—These pairings are not permanent and are liable to alteration with changed operating conditions

| Type | Capacity | | Weight in Full W.O. | | Locos. to which Allocated |
	Water galls.	Coal tons	tons	cwt.	
BRI ...	4,250	7	49	3	70000–24/30–44 72000–9 73000–49
BRIA ...	5,000	7	52	10	70025–9
BRIB ...	4,725	7	50	5	73080–9 73100–9/20–34/45–71 75065–79 76053–69 92020–9/60–6/97–9
BRIC ...	4,725	9	53	5	73065–79/90–9 73135–44 92015–9/45–59/77–86 92100–39/50–67
BRID ...	4,725	9	54	10	70045–54
BRIE ...	4,725	10	55	10	71000
BRIF ...	5,625	7	55	5	73110–9 92010–4/30–44/67–76 92087–96 92140–9/68–92202
BRIG ...	5,000	7	52	10	73050–2 92000–9
BRIH ...	4,250	7	49	3	73053–64
BR2 ...	3,500	6	42	3	75000–49 76000–44
BR2A ...	3,500	6	42	3	75050–64/80–9 76045–52/70–76114 77000–24
BR3 ...	3,000	4	36	17	78000–64

SOME S.R. LOCOMOTIVE HEADCODES

his list is not complete and gives only the principal one, two and three disc (or lamp) codes.

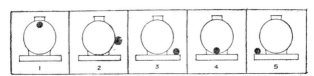

NO. 1

Victoria and Dover via Chatham
Victoria and Norwood Yard via Selhurst
Loughborough Sidings to Holborn
Ashford and Hastings
Reading and Margate via Redhill
Eastleigh and Bulford via Chandlers Ford and Andover
Southampton Terminus and Brockenhurst and Weymouth via Wimborne
Plymouth Friary and Tavistock
Woking and Reading via Virginia Water West Curve
Exeter Central and Ilfracombe
Bodmin and Wadebridge
Petersfield and Midhurst
Exeter Central and Exmouth

NO. 2

Victoria or Clapham Junction and Holborn (L.L.)
London Bridge or Bricklayers' Arms and Portsmouth via Quarry line and
    Horsham
Via Mid Kent Line and Beckenham Junction
Ashford and Eastbourne direct
Waterloo or Nine Elms and Southampton Terminus, direct (not boat trains)
Willesden and Feltham Yard via Gunnersbury
Waterloo or Nine Elms and Windsor via Twickenham
Southampton Central to Lymington
Yeovil Junction and Yeovil Town
Seaton Junction and Seaton
Barnstaple Junction and Torrington
Halwill and Bude

NO. 3

Victoria or Clapham Junction and Holborn
London Bridge or Bricklayers' Arms and Brighton via Quarry Line
Tonbridge and Brighton via Eridge
Hastings via Mid Kent Line, Oxted, Crowhurst Junction and Tonbridge
Dunton Green and Westerham
Ashford and Margate via Canterbury West
Lydd Branch
Folkestone Junction and Folkestone Harbour
Crowhurst and Bexhill West
Swanley Junction and Gravesend West
Sittingbourne and Sheerness
Deal and Kearsney
Gravesend Central and Allhallows-on-Sea or Port Victoria
All stations to Feltham (except via Mortlake)

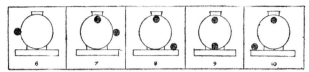

| 6 | 7 | 8 | 9 | 10 |

Weymouth and Portland and Easton (goods trains)
Bournemouth West and Brockenhurst via Wimborne

NO. 4

Victoria or Battersea Yard and Brighton via Redhill
Oxted and Eastbourne via Eridge
London Bridge and New Cross via Bricklayers' Arms Junction
Horsham and Brighton
Alton and Fareham
Bentley and Bordon
Salisbury and Bulford
Axminster and Lyme Regis
Tipton St. John's and Exmouth
Wareham and Swanage
Brockenhurst and Lymington Pier
Bere Alston and Callington

NO. 5

Victoria or Stewarts Lane and Clapham Junction
Oxted and Tunbridge Wells West via East Grinstead (H.L.)
Pulborough, Midhurst and Chichester
Havant and Hayling Island
London Bridge and Bricklayers' Arms
Tonbridge and Maidstone West
Ashford (Kent) and Dover via Minster and Deal
Stewarts Lane to Victoria
Southampton Docks and Nine Elms via main line (market goods, fruit or potato train)

NO. 6

London Bridge or Bricklayers' Arms and Dover or Ramsgate via East Croydon Oxted and Tonbridge
Tonbridge and Hawkhurst
Battersea Yard and Kensington
Waterloo or Nine Elms and Reading via Twickenham
Willesden and Feltham Yard via Kew East Junction
Exeter Central and Sidmouth
Plymouth Friary and Turnchapel
Eastleigh or Southampton and Fawley
Bournemouth Central and Brockenhurst via Wimborne
Torrington and Halwill

NO. 7

Victoria or Battersea Yard and Portsmouth via Quarry Line and Horsham
Via Maidstone East line to Victoria or Holborn
Waterloo or Nine Elms and Southampton Docks via Brentford, Chertsey and Woking

NO. 8

London Bridge or Bricklayers' Arms and Eastbourne or Hastings via Quarry line
Victoria or West London line and Ramsgate via Herne Hill or Catford Loop
London Bridge or Bricklayers' Arms and Hastings via Chislehurst and Tunbridge Wells Central

| 11 | 12 | 13 | 14 | 15 |

West London line to East Croydon via Crystal Palace (L.L.)
Special boat trains Waterloo and Southampton Docks via Northam
Special boat trains from Southampton Docks to Waterloo via Millbrook
Southampton and Andover via Redbridge

NO. 9

Victoria or Battersea Yard and Eastbourne or Hastings via Quarry line
London and Hither Green Sidings
Victoria and Folkestone Harbour or Dover Marine via Swanley, Otford and
 Tonbridge
Waterloo or Nine Elms and Plymouth
Bournemouth Central and Dorchester goods trains
Battersea Yard and Brent via New Kew Junction
Southampton Terminus and Portsmouth Harbour **via Netley**

NO. 10

London Bridge or Bricklayers' Arms and Portsmouth via Redhill and Horsham
Victoria or Battersea Yard and Norwood Yard via Crystal Palace (L.L.)
London Bridge and New Cross Gate to Eardley Sidings via Peckham Rye
Deptford Wharf and New Cross Gate
London Bridge or Bricklayers' Arms and Folkestone or Dover via Chislehurst
 Tonbridge and Ashford
Dover and Margate via Deal and Minster Loop
Special boat trains Waterloo to Southampton Docks via Millbrook
Feltham to Durnsford Road via Chertsey

NO. 11

Victoria or Battersea Yard and Portsmouth via Redhill and Horsham
Via Dartford Loop line
Victoria or Holborn and Hastings line via Orpington Loop and Tunbridge
 Wells Central
Bricklayers' Arms and Guildford via Leatherhead and Effingham Junction
Waterloo or Nine Elms and Southampton Terminus via Alton
Salisbury and Bournemouth West via Wimborne
Fareham and Gosport
Ballast trains to Meldon Quarry from Exeter Central and stations west thereof

NO. 12

Victoria or Battersea Yard and Portsmouth via Mitcham Junction
London Bridge or Bricklayers' Arms and Eastbourne or Hastings via Redhill
Victoria, Stewarts Lane or Holborn to North Kent line via Nunhead line
Nine Elms and Feltham via Mortlake
Exeter Central to Nine Elms (market goods and fish)
Down main line goods terminating at Woking
Southampton Docks and Salisbury via Eastleigh

NO. 13

London Bridge or Bricklayers' Arms and Brighton via Redhill
Oxted and Brighton via East Grinstead (L.L.) and Lewes
Three Bridges and Tunbridge Wells West
West London line to Norwood Yard via Thornton Heath
Victoria or Holborn to Dover via Nunhead line and Maidstone East
Parcels and empty trains Waterloo to Clapham Junction (Kensington sidings)

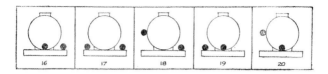

Feltham Yard and Neasden via Kew East Junction
Portsmouth Harbour or Portsmouth and Southsea to Fratton Loco. Depot
Exeter Central and Exmouth Junction
Bournemouth West to Dorchester
Southampton and Salisbury via Redbridge

NO. 14

London Bridge and Portsmouth via Mitcham Junction
London Bridge, Oxted and Tunbridge Wells West via Hever
Oxted and Lewes or Seaford or Eastbourne via Haywards Heath and Keymer
    Junction (change to No. 5 or No. 21 code at Lewes)
London Bridge or Bricklayers' Arms and Dover via Chislehurst Loop and
    Maidstone East
Waterloo or Nine Elms and Brockenhurst and Bournemouth West via Sway

NO. 15

Via Bexleyheath line
Victoria, Stewarts Lane or Holborn via Nunhead line and Bexleyheath
Oxted and Brighton via Haywards Heath
Waterloo or Nine Elms and Reading via Loop line
All trains terminating at Portsmouth and Southsea (trains from Salisbury to
    carry No. 17 to Eastleigh)
Exeter Central and Padstow
Light engines, Bournemouth Central or Bournemouth West to Bournemouth
    Central via triangle to turn
Light engines Eastleigh Loco. to Portsmouth and Southsea
Light engines to Guildford Loco. via Woking (except via Staines)

NO. 16

London Bridge or Bricklayers' Arms and Portsmouth via West Croydon
Victoria or Battersea Yard and Eastbourne or Hastings via Redhill
Oxted and Brighton via Eridge
London Bridge or Bricklayers' Arms and Ramsgate via Tonbridge and Canter-
    bury West
Waterloo or Nine Elms and Woking via Richmond and Chertsey
Milk and empty trains to Clapham Junction via Byfleet curve and Richmond

NO. 17

London Bridge or Bricklayers' Arms and Tonbridge or Reading via East Croydon
    and Redhill (also Tonbridge and Reading)
Brighton and Hove via Preston Park Spur
Three Bridges and Eridge
Victoria or Holborn and Folkestone or Dover via Orpington Loop, Tonbridge
    and Ashford
London Bridge or Bricklayers' Arms and Gillingham, Faversham, Ramsgate or
    Dover via Chislehurst Loop and Chatham
Waterloo or Nine Elms and Clapham Junction (empty trains and light engines)
Passenger trains Bournemouth Central and Weymouth

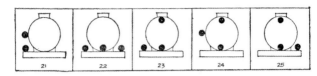

| 21 | 22 | 23 | 24 | 25 |

NO. 18

London Bridge or Bricklayers' Arms and Dover, Ramsgate or Hastings via Chislehurst, Swanley, Otford and Sevenoaks
Victoria, Oxted and Tunbridge Wells West via Hever
Holborn and Ramsgate via Herne Hill or Catford Loop
Light engines and trains requiring to run to up main loop, Clapham Junction, from stations westward
Southampton and Andover via Eastleigh
Light engines or engines with vehicles attached running round the triangle at Bournemouth West to turn

NO. 19

Victoria or Battersea Yard and Brighton via Quarry line
London Bridge or New Cross Gate and Norwood Yard
Tunbridge Wells West and Eastbourne
Victoria or Holborn and Ramsgate, Dover or Hastings via Nunhead line and Tonbridge
Horsham and Guildford
Waterloo or Nine Elms and Southampton Docks via East Putney
Salisbury and Portsmouth Harbour via Eastleigh
Portsmouth and Southsea to Salisbury via Eastleigh

NO. 20

Victoria, Stewarts Lane or Holborn to Ramsgate via Nunhead line, Chislehurst and Chatham
London Bridge or Bricklayers' Arms and North Kent line via Greenwich
Via Streatham Spur
Feltham Yard and Brent via Kew East Junction
Clapham Junction and Kensington
Portsmouth and Southsea to Salisbury via Redbridge
Salisbury and Portsmouth Harbour via Redbridge

NO. 21

Victoria and Newhaven Harbour
Victoria or Holborn to Ramsgate via Nunhead line and Maidstone East
Waterloo or Nine Elms and Portsmouth via Woking and Guildford
Light engines from all stations to Feltham Loco.
Light engines from all stations west of Basingstoke to Eastleigh Loco.

NO. 22

Waterloo and Portsmouth Harbour via Eastleigh
Feltham and Brent via Richmond
S.R. and W.R. trains Hither Green Sidings, Stewarts Lane or South Lambeth to Old Oak Common
L.M. (Western Division) trains between Willesden and Redhill via Clapham Junction
L.M. (Midland Division) and E.R. (G.N.) trains to or from Hither Green Sidings
W.R. trains, Norwood Yard to Old Oak Common
W.R. trains Cattewater Junction and Plymstock

| 26 | 27 | 28 | 29 | 30 |

NO. 23

Nine Elms and Willesden via New Kew Junction
Brighton and Salisbury via Southampton Central
Eastleigh and Micheldever or Basingstoke (light engines for testing)
Windsor and Hastings Excursion trains
Windsor and Margate or Dover Excursion trains or between Windsor and Redhill
W.R. trains to South Lambeth
E.R. trains to or from Lower Sydenham

NO. 24

Waterloo and Guildford via Leatherhead (except light engines Nine Elms to Raynes Park)
Southampton and Willesden via Richmond and Gunnersbury
Southampton or Salisbury and Willesden via Chertsey and Kew East Junction (or from Basingstoke)
Reading to Willesden via Feltham

NO. 25

Nine Elms and Brent via New Kew Junction
Kingston and Shepperton
Brighton and Salisbury through trains via Eastleigh
Windsor and Bognor Regis Excursion trains
To L.M.R. via West London line

NO. 26

Brighton and Bournemouth
Waterloo and Wimbledon Park Sidings via East Putney (empty trains and light engines)
Merstham and Staines Moor via Guildford, Byfleet Junction and Staines
Victoria (E. or C.), Stewarts Lane, Clapham Junction or Holborn and Eardley Sidings via Herne Hill

NO. 27

Hither Green Sidings and Feltham via Brentford
Feltham to Wimbledon West Yard
London Bridge or Bricklayers' Arms and Brighton via Oxted, Eridge and Lewes

NO. 28

Hither Green Sidings and Feltham via Richmond
London Bridge or Bricklayers' Arms and Brighton via Oxted, East Grinstead and Lewes

NO. 29

Plumstead and Feltham via Brentford
Victoria or Battersea Yard and Brighton via Oxted, Eridge and Lewes

NO. 30

Plumstead and Feltham via Richmond
Victoria or Battersea Yard and Brighton via Oxted, East Grinstead and Lewes

SOUTHERN RAILWAY LOCOMOTIVE SUPERINTENDENTS AND CHIEF MECHANICAL ENGINEERS OF CONSTITUENT COMPANIES

LONDON & SOUTH WESTERN RAILWAY

J. Woods	...	...	1835–1841
J. V. Gooch	...	...	1841–1850
J. Beattie	...	...	1850–1871
W. G. Beattie	...	...	1871–1878
W. Adams	...	...	1878–1895
D. Drummond	...	...	1895–1912
R. W. Urie	...	...	1912–1922

LONDON BRIGHTON AND SOUTH COAST RAILWAY

—. Statham	...	...	? –1845
J. Gray	...	...	1845–1847
S. Kirtley	...	...	1847
J. C. Craven	...	...	1847–1869
W. Stroudley	...	...	1870–1889
R. J. Billinton	...	...	1890–1904
D. Earle Marsh	...	...	1905–1911
L. B. Billinton	...	...	1911–1922

SOUTH EASTERN RAILWAY

B. Cubitt	...	...	? –1845
J. Cudworth	...	...	1845–1876
A. M. Watkin	...	...	1876
R. Mansell	...	...	1877–1878
J. Stirling	...	...	1878–1898

LONDON, CHATHAM AND DOVER RAILWAY

W. Cubitt	...	...	? –1860
W. Martley	...	...	1860–1874
W. Kirtley	...	...	1874–1898

SOUTH EASTERN AND CHATHAM RAILWAY

H. S. Wainwright	...		1899–1913
R. E. L. Maunsell	...	...	1913–1922

SOUTHERN RAILWAY

R. E. L. Maunsell	...	...	1923–1937
O. V. Bulleid	...	...	1937–1949

THE abc OF
BRITISH RAILWAYS
LOCOMOTIVES

PART 3—Nos. 40000-59999

and

70000-99999

SUMMER
1957
EDITION

LONDON

Ian Allan Ltd

FOREWORD

THIS booklet lists all British Railways locomotives numbered between 40000 and 59999 and 70000 and 99999. This series of numbers includes all London Midland Region and Scottish (ex-L.M.S.) Region steam locos.

For details of Diesel locomotives and trains, see A.B.C. BRITISH RAILWAYS DIESEL LOCOMOTIVES AND TRAINS.

For details of Multiple-unit electric trains see A.B.C. BRITISH ELECTRIC TRAINS.

1. At the head of each class will be found a list of any important sub-divisions of the class, usually in order of introduction. Each sub-division is given a reference mark. by which its relevant dimensions (if differing from those of other sub-divisions) and the locomotives it comprises (if known) may be identified.

2. The lists of dimensions at the head of each class show locomotives fitted with two inside cylinders unless otherwise stated, e.g. (O) = two outside cylinders.

3. Superheated classes are denoted by the letters " Su " after the boiler pressure. " SS " denotes that some locomotives of the class are superheated.

4. The date on which the first locomotive of a class was built or modified is denoted by " Introduced."

5. S denotes a Service (Departmental) locomotive. This reference letter is introduced only for the reader's guidance and is not borne by the locomotive concerned.

6. The numbers of locomotives in service have been checked to **February 23rd, 1957.**

BRITISH RAILWAYS LOCOMOTIVE SHEDS AND SHED CODES

THIS LIST INCLUDES ONLY THOSE DEPOTS WHICH HAVE ENGINES ALLOCATED TO THEM. IT DOES NOT INCLUDE OVERNIGHT STABLING OR SIGNING-ON POINTS.

ALL B.R. LOCOMOTIVES CARRY THE CODE OF THEIR HOME DEPOT ON A SMALL PLATE AFFIXED TO THE SMOKEBOX DOOR.

LONDON MIDLAND REGION

1A	**Willesden**	9A	**Longsight**	17E	Heaton Mersey
1B	Camden	9B	Stockport (Edgeley)	17F	Trafford Park
1C	Watford	9C	Macclesfield		
1D	Devons Road (Bow)	9D	Buxton	18A	**Toton**
1E	Bletchley	9G	Northwich	18B	Westhouses
	Leighton Buzzard			18C	Hasland
		10A	**Springs Branch**	18D	Staveley
2A	**Rugby**		**(Wigan)**		Sheepbridge
	Seaton	10B	Preston		
2B	Nuneaton	10C	Patricroft	19A	**Sheffield**
2C	Warwick	10D	Sutton Oak	19B	Millhouses
2D	Coventry			19C	Canklow
2E	Northampton	11A	**Carnforth**		
2F	Market	11B	Barrow	20F	Skipton
	Harborough		Coniston	20G	Hellifield
		11C	Oxenholme		
3A	**Bescot**	11D	Tebay	21A	**Saltley**
3B	Bushbury	11E	Lancaster	21B	Bournville
3C	Walsall			21C	Bromsgrove
3D	Aston	12A	**Carlisle(Upperby)**		
3E	Monument Lane	12B	Penrith	22A	**Bristol**
		12C	Workington	22B	Gloucester
5A	**Crewe North**				Dursley
	Whitchurch	14A	**Cricklewood**		Tewkesbury
5B	Crewe South	14B	Kentish Town		
5C	Stafford	14C	St. Albans	24A	**Accrington**
5D	Stoke			24B	Rose Grove
5E	Alsager	15A	**Wellingborough**	24C	Lostock Hall
5F	Uttoxeter	15B	Kettering	24D	Lower Darwen
		15C	Leicester	24E	Blackpool
6A	**Chester**	15D	Bedford		Blackpool North
6B	Mold Junction			24F	Fleetwood
6C	Birkenhead	16A	**Nottingham**		
6D	Chester(Northgate)	16B	Kirkby	26A	**Newton Heath**
6E	Wrexham	16C	Mansfield	26B	Agecroft
6F	Bidston			26C	Bolton
6G	Llandudno Junction	17A	**Derby**	26D	Bury
6H	Bangor	17B	Burton	26E	Lees
6J	Holyhead		Horninglow		
6K	Rhyl		Overseal	27A	**Bank Hall**
		17C	Coalville	27B	Aintree
8A	**Edge Hill**	17D	Rowsley	27C	Southport
8B	Warrington		Cromford	27D	Wigan (L. & Y.)
	Warrington		Middleton	27E	Walton
	(Arpley)		Sheep Pasture		
8C	Speke Junction				
8E	Brunswick (L'pool)				

3

EASTERN REGION

30A	**Stratford**	32A	**Norwich**	36A	**Doncaster**
	Brentwood		Cromer Beach	36B	Mexborough
	Chelmsford		Dereham		Wath
	Enfield Town		Swaffham	36C	Frodingham
	Epping		Wymondham	36D	Barnsley
	Ilford	32B	Ipswich	36E	Retford
	Wood St.		Felixstowe Town		Newark
	(Walthamstow)		Stowmarket		
30B	Hertford East	32C	Lowestoft		
	Buntingford	32D	Yarmouth	38A	**Colwick**
	Ware		(South Town)	38B	Annesley
		32E	Yarmouth(Vauxhall)	38C	Leicester (G.C.)
30C	Bishops Stortford	32F	Yarmouth Beach	38D	Staveley
30E	Colchester	32G	Melton Constable	38E	Woodford Halse
	Braintree		Norwich City		
	Clacton			39A	**Gorton**
	Maldon	33A	**Plaistow**		Dinting
	Walton-on-Naze	33B	Tilbury		Hayfield
30F	Parkeston	33C	Shoeburyness		
		34A	**Kings Cross**	40A	**Lincoln**
31A	**Cambridge**	34B	Hornsey		Lincoln
	Ely	34C	Hatfield		(St. Mark's)
	Huntingdon East	34D	Hitchin	40B	Immingham
	Saffron Walden	34E	Neasden		Grimsby
31B	March		Aylesbury		New Holland
	Wisbech		Chesham	40C	Louth
31C	Kings Lynn			40D	Tuxford
	Hunstanton	35A	**New England**	40E	Langwith Junction
			Spalding	40F	Boston
			Stamford		Sleaford
31D	South Lynn	35B	Grantham		
31E	Bury St. Edmunds	35C	Peterborough		
	Sudbury (Suffolk)		(Spital)	41A	**Sheffield (Darnal**

NORTH EASTERN REGION

50A	**York**	52A	**Gateshead**	54A	**Sunderland**
50B	Leeds (Neville Hill)		Bowes Bridge		Durham
50C	Selby	52B	Heaton	54B	Tyne Dock
50D	Starbeck	52C	Blaydon	54C	Borough Gardens
50E	Scarborough		Alston	54D	Consett
50F	Malton		Hexham		
	Pickering	52D	Tweedmouth	55A	**Leeds (Holbeck)**
50G	Whitby		Alnmouth	55B	Stourton
		52E	Percy Main	55C	Farnley Junction
51A	**Darlington**	52F	North Blyth	55D	Royston
51B	Newport (Yorks.)		South Blyth	55E	Normanton
51C	West Hartlepool			55F	Manningham
51D	Middlesbrough	53A	**Hull** (Dairycoates)	55G	Huddersfield
51E	Stockton	53B	Hull		
51F	West Auckland		(Botanic Gardens)	56A	**Wakefield**
51G	Haverton Hill	53C	Hull (Springhead)	56B	Ardsley
51H	Kirkby Stephen		Alexandra Dock	56C	Copley Hill
51J	Northallerton	53D	Bridlington	56D	Mirfield
51K	Saltburn	53E	Goole	56E	Sowerby Bridge
				56F	Low Moor
				56G	Bradford

SCOTTISH REGION

60A	**Inverness**	63A	**Perth** South	65D	Dawsholm
	Dingwall		Aberfeldy		Dumbarton
	Kyle of Lochaish		Crieff	65E	Kipps
60B	Aviemore	63B	Stirling South	65F	Grangemouth
	Boat of Garten		Killin	65G	Yoker
60C	Helmsdale		Stirling	65H	Helensburgh
	Dornoch		(Shore Road)	65I	Balloch
	Tain	63C	Forfar	65J	Fort William
60D	Wick	63D	Oban		Mallaig
	Thurso		Ballachulish		
60E	Forres			66A	**Polmadie**
					(Glasgow)
61A	**Kittybrewster**			66B	Motherwell
	Ballater	64A	**St. Margarets**	66C	Hamilton
	Fraserburgh		(Edinburgh)	66D	Greenock
	Inverurie		Dunbar		(Ladyburn)
	Peterhead		Galashiels		Greenock
61B	Aberdeen (Ferryhill)		Longniddry		(Princes Pier)
61C	Keith		North Berwick		
	Banff	64B	Haymarket	67A	**Corkerhill**
	Elgin	64C	Dalry Road		(Glasgow)
		64D	Carstairs	67B	Hurlford
62A	**Thornton**	64E	Polmont		Beith
	Anstruther	64F	Bathgate		Muirkirk
	Burntisland	64G	Hawick	67C	Ayr
	Ladybank		Riccarton	67D	Ardrossan
	Methil		St. Boswells		
62B	Dundee (Tay Bridge)			68A	**Carlisle**
	Arbroath				(Kingmoor)
	Dundee West	65A	**Eastfield**	68B	Dumfries
	Montrose		(Glasgow)	68C	Stranraer
	St. Andrews		Arrochar		Newton Stewart
62C	Dunfermline	65B	St. Rollox	68D	Beattock
	Alloa	65C	Parkhead	68E	Carlisle Canal

SOUTHERN REGION

70A	**Nine Elms**	71I	Southampton Docks	73C	Hither Green
70B	Feltham	71J	Highbridge	73D	Gillingham (Kent)
70C	Guildford			73E	Faversham
70D	Basingstoke	72A	**Exmouth Junction**		
70E	Reading		Bude		
70F	Fratton		Exmouth	74A	**Ashford (Kent)**
70G	Newport (I.O.W.)		Lyme Regis	74B	Ramsgate
70H	Ryde (I.O.W.)		Okehampton	74C	Dover
			Seaton		Folkestone
		72B	Salisbury	74D	Tonbridge
		72C	Yeovil	74E	St. Leonards
71A	**Eastleigh**	72D	Plymouth		
	Andover Junction		Callington	75A	**Brighton**
	Lymington	72E	Barnstaple Junction		Newhaven
	Winchester		Ilfracombe	75B	Redhill
71B	Bournemouth		Torrington	75C	Norwood Junction
	Branksome	72F	Wadebridge	75D	Horsham
71G	Bath (S. & D.)			75E	Three Bridges
	Radstock	73A	**Stewarts Lane**	75F	Tunbridge Wells
71H	Templecombe	73B	Bricklayers Arms		West

5

BRITISH RAILWAYS LOCOMOTIVES
Nos. 40000-59999

2-6-2T   3

Introduced 1930. Fowler L.M.S. design
with parallel boiler.
*Introduced 1930. Condensing locos.
for working to Moorgate, London
Weight: { 70 tons 10 cwt.
{ 71 tons 16 cwt.*
Pressure: 200 lb. Su.
Cyls : (O) 17½″ × 26″.
Dr. Wheels: 5′ 3″.   T.E.: 21,485 lb.
Walschaerts valve gear. P.V.

40001	40019	40037*	40054
40002	40020	40038*	40055
40003	40021	40039*	40056
40004	40022*	40040*	40057
40005	40023*	40041	40058
40006	40024*	40042	40059
40007	40025*	40043	40060
40008	40026*	40044	40061
40009	40027*	40045	40062
40010	40028*	40046	40063
40011	40029*	40047	40064
40012	40030*	40048	40065
40013	40031*	40049	40066
40014	40032*	40050	40067
40015	40033*	40051	40068
40016	40034*	40052	40069
40017	40035*	40053	40070
40018	40036*		Total 70

2-6-2T   3

Introduced 1935. Stanier L.M.S. taper
boiler development of Fowler design
(above).
*Introduced 1941. Rebuilt with larger
boiler.
Weight: { 71 tons 5 cwt.
{ 72 tons 10 cwt.*
Pressure: 200 lb. Su.
Cyls.: (O) 17½″ × 26″.
Dr. Wheels: 5′ 3″.   T.E.: 21,485 lb
Walschaerts valve gear. P.V.

40071	40075	40079	40083
40072	40076	40080	40084
40073	40077	40081	40085
40074	40078	40082	40086

40087	40118	40149	40180
40088	40119	40150	40181
40089	40120	40151	40182
40090	40121	40152	40183
40091	40122	40153	40184
40092	40123	40154	40185
40093	40124	40155	40186
40094	40125	40156	40187
40095	40126	40157	40188
40096	40127	40158	40189
40097	40128	40159	40190
40098	40129	40160	40191
40099	40130	40161	40192
40100	40131	40162	40193
40101	40132	40163*	40194
40102	40133	40164	40195
40103	40134	40165	40196
40104	40135	40166	40197
40105	40136	40167*	40198
40106	40137	40168	40199
40107	40138	40169*	40200
40108	40139	40170	40201
40109	40140	40171	40202
40110	40141	40172	40203*
40111	40142	40173	40204
40112	40143	40174	40205
40113	40144	40175	40206
40114	40145	40176	40207
40115	40146	40177	40208
40116	40147	40178	40209
40117	40148*	40179	

Total 139

4-4-0   2P

Introduced 1912. Fowler rebuild of
Johnson locos. with superheater and
piston valves.
Weight: Loco. 53 tons 7 cwt.
Pressure: 160 lb. Su.
Cyls.: 20½″ × 26″.   Dr. Wheels: 7′ 0½″.
T.E.: 17,585 lb.   P.V.

40332	40433	40493	40540
40337	40439	40495	40541
40356	40443	40501	40542
40396	40447	40502	40543
40402	40450	40504	40548
40404	40452	40509	40550
40407	40453	40511	40552
40409	40454	40513	40553
40411	40461	40519	40557
40412	40464	40520	40559
40413	40482	40525	
40416	40485	40534	
40420	40487	40536	
40421	40489	40537	
40426	40491	40538	

Total 55

40624	40644	40664	40683
40625	40645	40665	40684
40626	40646	40666	40685
40627	40647	40667	40686
40628	40648	40668	40687
40629	40649	40669	40688
40630	40650	40670	40689
40631	40651	40671	40690
40632	40652	40672	40691
40633*†	40653†	40673	40692
40634*	40654	40674	40693
40635*	40655	40675	40694
40636	40656	40676	40695
40637	40657	40677	40696
40638	40658	40678	40697
40640	40659	40679	40698
40641	40660	40680	40699
40642	40661	40681	40700
40643	40663	40682	

Total 135

4-4-0   2P

Introduced 1928. Post-Grouping development of Midland design, with modified dimensions and reduced boiler mountings.
*Introduced 1928. Locos. built for S. & D.J.R. (taken into L.M.S. stock, 1930).
†Fitted experimentally in 1933 with Dabeg feed-water heater.
Weight: Loco. 54 tons 1 cwt.
Pressure: 180 lb. Su.
Cyls.: 19" × 26".
Dr. Wheels: 6' 9".   T.E.: 17,730 lb.
P.V

40563	40578	40594	40609
40564	40579	40595	40610
40565	40580	40596	40611
40566	40581	40597	40612
40567	40582	40598	40613
40568	40583	40599	40614
40569	40584	40600	40615
40570	40585	40601	40616
40571	40586	40602	40617
40572	40587	40603	40618
40573	40588	40604	40619
40574	40589	40605	40620
40575	40590	40606	40621
40576	40592	40607	40622
40577	40593	40608	40623

4-4-0 (3-Cyl. Compd.)   4P

Introduced 1924. Post-Grouping development of Johnson Midland compound with modified dimensions and (with some exceptions) reduced boiler mountings.
Weight: Loco. 61 tons 14 cwt.
Pressure: 200 lb. Su.
Cyls.: L.P. (2) 21" × 26".
       H.P. (1) 19" × 26".
Dr. Wheels: 6' 9".
T.E. (of L.P. cyls. at 80% boiler pressure): 22,650 lb.

P.V. (H.P. cyl. only).

40904	40936	41075	41101
40907	40937	41077	41102
40920	41045	41078	41103
40925	41048	41083	41105
40926	41049	41086	41106
40927	41060	41089	41111
40928	41062	41090	41112
40930	41063	41093	41113
40931	41066	41094	41114
40933	41068	41095	41116
40934	41071	41098	41118
40935	41073	41100	41119

41120	41155	41168	41192
41121	41156	41172	41193
41122	41157	41173	41194
41123	41158	41179	41195
41140	41159	41180	41196
41143	41162	41181	41197
41144	41163	41185	41199
41150	41164	41186	
41152	41165	41189	
41153	41167	41190	

Total 85

2-6-2T 2

Introduced 1946. Ivatt L.M.S. taper boiler design.
Weight: 63 tons 5 cwt.
Pressure: 200 lb. Su.
Cyls.: $\begin{cases} \text{(O) } 16'' \times 24''. \\ \text{(O) } 16\frac{1}{2}'' \times 24''.* \end{cases}$

Dr. Wheels: 5' 0". T.E.: $\begin{cases} 17,410 \text{ lb.} \\ 18,510 \text{ lb.}* \end{cases}$

Walschaerts valve gear. P.V.

41200	41220	41240	41260
41201	41221	41241	41261
41202	41222	41242	41262
41203	41223	41243	41263
41204	41224	41244	41264
41205	41225	41245	41265
41206	41226	41246	41266
41207	41227	41247	41267
41208	41228	41248	41268
41209	41229	41249	41269
41210	41230	41250	41270
41211	41231	41251	41271
41212	41232	41252	41272
41213	41233	41253	41273
41214	41234	41254	41274
41215	41235	41255	41275
41216	41236	41256	41276
41217	41237	41257	41277
41218	41238	41258	41278
41219	41239	41259	41279

41280	41293*	41306*	41318*
41281	41294*	41307*	41319*
41282	41295*	41308*	41320*
41283	41296*	41309*	41321*
41284	41297*	41310*	41322*
41285	41298*	41311*	41323*
41286	41299*	41312*	41324*
41287	41300*	41313*	41325*
41288	41301*	41314*	41326*
41289	41302*	41315*	41327*
41290*	41303*	41316*	41328*
41291*	41304*	41317*	41329*
41292*	41305*		

Total 130

0-4-0ST 0F

Introduced 1897. Johnson Midland design.
Weight: 32 tons 3 cwt.
Pressure: 140 lb.
Cyls.: 15" × 20".
Dr. Wheels: 3' 10"
T.E.: 11,640 lb.

41518 **Total 1**

0-4-0T 0F

Introduced 1907. Deeley Midland design.
Weight: 32 tons 16 cwt.
Pressure: 160 lb.
Cyls.: (O) 15" × 22".
Dr. Wheels: 3' 9¾". T.E.: 14,635 lb.
Walschaerts Valve Gear.

41528	41531	41534	41536
41529	41532	41535	41537
41530	41533		

Total 10

0-6-0T 1F

Introduced 1878. Johnson Midland design.
*Rebuilt with Belpaire firebox.
Weight: 39 tons 11 cwt
Pressure: $\begin{cases} 150 \text{ lb.} \\ 140 \text{ lb.}* \end{cases}$
Cyls.: 17" × 24".
Dr. Wheels: 4' 7".
T.E.: $\begin{cases} 16,080 \text{ lb.} \\ 15,005 \text{ lb.}* \end{cases}$

41661*	41706*	41710*	41724*
41702*	41708*	41712*	41726*

8

41734*	41769*	41804*	41860*
41739*	41773*	41835	41875*
41748*	41779	41844*	41878*
41752*	41795*	41847*	41879*
41754*	41797*	41855*	
41763*	41803*	41857*	

Total 30

0-4-4T   2P

Introduced 1932. Stanier L.M.S. design.
Push-and-pull fitted.
Weight: 58 tons 1 cwt.
Pressure: 160 lb.
Cyls.: 18″ × 26″.
Dr. Wheels: 5′ 7″.   T.E.: 17,100 lb.

41900	41903	41906	41908
41901	41904	41907	41909
41902	41905		

Total 10

4-4-2T   3P

Introduced 1923. Midland and L.M.S.
development of Whitelegg L.T. &
S. " 79 " Class.
Weight: 71 tons 10 cwt.
Pressure: 170 lb.
Cyls.: (O) 19″ × 26″.
Dr. Wheels: 6′ 6″.   T.E.: 17,390 lb.

41928	41945	41949	41977
41936	41946	41950	41978
41939	41947	41969	
41941	41948	41975	

Total 14

0-6-2T   3F

Introduced 1903. Whitelegg L.T. & S.
' 69 " Class (Nos. 41990-3 built 1912
taken directly into M.R. stock).
Weight: 64 tons 13 cwt.
Pressure: 170 lb.
Cyls.: 18″ × 26″.
Dr. Wheels: 5′ 3″.   T.E.: 19,320 lb.

41980	41984	41988	41991
41981	41985	41989	41992
41982	41986	41990	41993
41983	41987		

Total 14

2-6-4T   4

*Introduced 1927. Fowler L.M.S. parallel
   boiler design.
†Introduced 1933. As earlier engines,
   but with side-window cab and doors.
‡Introduced 1934.   Stanier taper-
   boiler 3-cylinder design for L.T. & S.
§Introduced 1935.   Stanier taper
   boiler 2-cylinder design.
¶Introduced 1945.   Fairburn develop-
   ment of Stanier design with shorter
   wheelbase and detail alterations.
Weight. { 86 tons 5 cwt.*†
         { 92 tons 5 cwt.‡
         { 87 tons 17 cwt.§
         { 85 tons 5 cwt.¶
Pressure (all types): 200 lb. Su.
Cyls.: { (O) 19″ × 26″.*†
       { (3) 16″ × 26″.‡
       { (O) 19⅝″ × 26″.§¶
Dr. Wheels (all types): 5′ 9″
T.E.: { 23,125 lb.*†
      { 24,600 lb.‡
      { 24,670 lb.§¶
Walschaerts valve gear.   P.V.

¶**FAIRBURN LOCOS.**

42050	42074	42098	42122
42051	42075	42099	42123
42052	42076	42100	42124
42053	42077	42101	42125
42054	42078	42102	42126
42055	42079	42103	42127
42056	42080	42104	42128
42057	42081	42105	42129
42058	42082	42106	42130
42059	42083	42107	42131
42060	42084	42108	42132
42061	42085	42109	42133
42062	42086	42110	42134
42063	42087	42111	42135
42064	42088	42112	42136
42065	42089	42113	42137
42066	42090	42114	42138
42067	42091	42115	42139
42068	42092	42116	42140
42069	42093	42117	42141
42070	42094	42118	42142
42071	42095	42119	42143
42072	42096	42120	42144
42073	42097	42121	42145

42146	42185	42224	42263
42147	42186	42225	42264
42148	42187	42226	42265
42149	42188	42227	42266
42150	42189	42228	42267
42151	42190	42229	42268
42152	42191	42230	42269
42153	42192	42231	42270
42154	42193	42232	42271
42155	42194	42233	42272
42156	42195	42234	42273
42157	42196	42235	42274
42158	42197	42236	42275
42159	42198	42237	42276
42160	42199	42238	42277
42161	42200	42239	42278
42162	42201	42240	42279
42163	42202	42241	42280
42164	42203	42242	42281
42165	42204	42243	42282
42166	42205	42244	42283
42167	42206	42245	42284
42168	42207	42246	42285
42169	42208	42247	42286
42170	42209	42248	42287
42171	42210	42249	42288
42172	42211	42250	42289
42173	42212	42251	42290
42174	42213	42252	42291
42175	42214	42253	42292
42176	42215	42254	42293
42177	42216	42255	42294
42178	42217	42256	42295
42179	42218	42257	42296
42180	42219	42258	42297
42181	42220	42259	42298
42182	42221	42260	42299
42183	42222	42261	
42184	42223	42262	

*FOWLER LOCOS.

42300	42305	42310	42315
42301	42306	42311	42316
42302	42307	42312	42317
42303	42308	42313	42318
42304	42309	42314	42319

42320	42339	42358	42377
42321	42340	42359	42378
42322	42341	42360	42379
42323	42342	42361	42380
42324	42343	42362	42381
42325	42344	42363	42382
42326	42345	42364	42383
42327	42346	42365	42384
42328	42347	42366	42385
42329	42348	42367	42386
42330	42349	42368	42387
42331	42350	42369	42388
42332	42351	42370	42389
42333	42352	42371	42390
42334	42353	42372	42391
42335	42354	42373	42392
42336	42355	42374	42393
42337	42356	42375	42394
42338	42357	42376	

†FOWLER LOCOS. WITH SIDE-WINDOW CAB.

42395	42403	42411	42418
42396	42404	42412	42419
42397	42405	42413	42420
42398	42406	42414	42421
42399	42407	42415	42422
42400	42408	42416	42423
42401	42409	42417	42424
42402	42410		

§STANIER 2-CYL. LOCOS.

42425	42440	42455	42470
42426	42441	42456	42471
42427	42442	42457	42472
42428	42443	42458	42473
42429	42444	42459	42474
42430	42445	42460	42475
42431	42446	42461	42476
42432	42447	42462	42477
42433	42448	42463	42478
42434	42449	42464	42479
42435	42450	42465	42480
42436	42451	42466	42481
42437	42452	42467	42482
42438	42453	42468	42483
42439	42454	42469	42484

42485	42488	42491	42493
42486	42489	42492	42494
42487	42490		

‡STANIER 3-CYL. LOCOS.

42500	42510	42519	42528
42501	42511	42520	42529
42502	42512	42521	42530
42503	42513	42522	42531
42504	42514	42523	42532
42505	42515	42524	42533
42506	42516	42525	42534
42507	42517	42526	42535
42508	42518	42527	42536
42509			

§STANIER 2-CYL. LOCOS.

42537	42566	42595	42624
42538	42567	42596	42625
42539	42568	42597	42626
42540	42569	42598	42627
42541	42570	42599	42628
42542	42571	42600	42629
42543	42572	42601	42630
42544	42573	42602	42631
42545	42574	42603	42632
42546	42575	42604	42633
42547	42576	42605	42634
42548	42577	42606	42635
42549	42578	42607	42636
42550	42579	42608	42637
42551	42580	42609	42638
42552	42581	42610	42639
42553	42582	42611	42640
42554	42583	42612	42641
42555	42584	42613	42642
42556	42585	42614	42643
42557	42586	42615	42644
42558	42587	42616	42645
42559	42588	42617	42646
42560	42589	42618	42647
42561	42590	42619	42648
42562	42591	42620	42649
42563	42592	42621	42650
42564	42593	42622	42651
42565	42594	42623	42652

42653	42658	42663	42668
42654	42659	42664	42669
42655	42660	42665	42670
42656	42661	42666	42671
42657	42662	42667	42672

¶FAIRBURN LOCOS.

42673	42680	42687	42694
42674	42681	42688	42695
42675	42682	42689	42696
42676	42683	42690	42697
42677	42684	42691	42698
42678	42685	42692	42699
42679	42686	42693	

Total 645

2-6-0　　　　　　6P5F

Introduced 1926. Hughes L.M.S. design
built under Fowler's direction. Wal-
schaerts valve gear. P.V.
*Introduced 1953. Locos. rebuilt
experimentally with Lentz R.C.
poppet valves in 1931; rebuilt with
Reidinger rotary poppet valve gear
in 1953.
Weight: Loco. 66 tons 0 cwt.
Pressure: 180 lb. Su.
Cyls.: (O) 21″ × 26″.
Dr. Wheels: 5′ 6″.　　T.E.: 26,580 lb.

42700	42717	42734	42751
42701	42718	42735	42752
42702	42719	42736	42753
42703	42720	42737	42754
42704	42721	42738	42755
42705	42722	42739	42756
42706	42723	42740	42757
42707	42724	42741	42758
42708	42725	42742	42759
42709	42726	42743	42760
42710	42727	42744	42761
42711	42728	42745	42762
42712	42729	42746	42763
42713	42730	42747	42764
42714	42731	42748	42765
42715	42732	42749	42766
42716	42733	42750	42767

42768	42813	42857	42901
42769	42814	42858	42902
42770	42815	42859	42903
42771	42816	42860	42904
42772	42817	42861	42905
42773	42818*	42862	42906
42774	42819	42863	42907
42775	42820	42864	42908
42776	42821	42865	42909
42777	42822*	42866	42910
42778	42823	42867	42911
42779	42824*	42868	42912
42780	42825*	42869	42913
42781	42826	42870	42914
42782	42827	42871	42915
42783	42828	42872	42916
42784	42829*	42873	42917
42785	42830	42874	42918
42786	42831	42875	42919
42787	42832	42876	42920
42788	42833	42877	42921
42789	42834	42878	42922
42790	42835	42879	42923
42791	42836	42880	42924
42792	42837	42881	42925
42793	42838	42882	42926
42794	42839	42883	42927
42795	42840	42884	42928
42796	42841	42885	42929
42797	42842	42886	42930
42798	42843	42887	42931
42799	42844	42888	42932
42800	42845	42889	42933
42801	42846	42890	42934
42802	42847	42891	42935
42803	42848	42892	42936
42804	42849	42893	42937
42805	42850	42894	42938
42806	42851	42895	42939
42807	42852	42896	42940
42808	42853	42897	42941
42809	42854	42898	42942
42810	42855	42899	42943
42811	42856	42900	42944
42812			

Total 245

2-6-0   6P5F

Introduced 1933. Stanier L.M.S. taper boiler design, some with safety valves mounted on the top feed.
Weight: Loco. 69 tons 2 cwt.
Pressure: 225 lb. Su.
Cyls.: (O) 18″ × 28″.
Dr. Wheels: 5′ 6″.   T.E.: 26,290 lb.
Walschaerts valve gear   P.V.

42945	42955	42965	42975
42946	42956	42966	42976
42947	42957	42967	42977
42948	42958	42968	42978
42949	42959	42969	42979
42950	42960	42970	42980
42951	42961	42971	42981
42952	42962	42972	42982
42953	42963	42973	42983
42954	42964	42974	42984

Total 40

2-6-0   4

Introduced 1947. Ivatt L.M.S. taper boiler design with double chimney. Later engines introduced with single chimney, with which earlier engines are being rebuilt.
Weight: Loco. 59 tons 2 cwt.
Pressure: 225 lb. Su.
Cyls.: (O) 17½″ × 26″.
Dr. Wheels: 5′ 3″.   T.E.: 24,170 lb.
Walschaerts valve gear   P.V.

43000	43018	43036	43054
43001	43019	43037	43055
43002	43020	43038	43056
43003	43021	43039	43057
43004	43022	43040	43058
43005	43023	43041	43059
43006	43024	43042	43060
43007	43025	43043	43061
43008	43026	43044	43062
43009	43027	43045	43063
43010	43028	43046	43064
43011	43029	43047	43065
43012	43030	43048	43066
43013	43031	43049	43067
43014	43032	43050	43068
43015	43033	43051	43069
43016	43034	43052	43070
43017	43035	43053	43071

43072	43095	43118	43140
43073	43096	43119	43141
43074	43097	43120	43142
43075	43098	43121	43143
43076	43099	43122	43144
43077	43100	43123	43145
43078	43101	43124	43146
43079	43102	43125	43147
43080	43103	43126	43148
43081	43104	43127	43149
43082	43105	43128	43150
43083	43106	43129	43151
43084	43107	43130	43152
43085	43108	43131	43153
43086	43109	43132	43154
43087	43110	43133	43155
43088	43111	43134	43156
43089	43112	43135	43157
43090	43113	43136	43158
43091	43114	43137	43159
43092	43115	43138	43160
43093	43116	43139	43161
43094	43117		

Total 162

0-6-0   3F

Introduced 1885. Johnson Midland locos., rebuilt from 1916 by Fowler with Belpaire firebox.

*Introduced 1885. Johnson Midland locos.. rebuilt from 1920 by Fowler with Belpaire firebox.

†Introduced 1896. Locos. built for S. & D.J. (taken into L.M.S. stock 1930).

Weight: Loco. 43 tons 17 cwt.

Pressure: 175 lb.

Cyls.: 18″ × 26″.

Dr. Wheels: $\left\{ \begin{array}{l} 5'\ 3'' \\ 4'\ 11'' \end{array} \right.$ * T E.: $\left\{ \begin{array}{l} 19,890\ \text{lb} \\ 21,240\ \text{lb.*} \end{array} \right.$

43174*	43187*	43201†	43212
43178*	43188*	43203	43213
43180*	43189*	43205	43214
43181*	43192	43207	43216†
43183*	43193	43208	43218†
43185*	43194†	43210	43219
43186*	43200	43211†	43222

43223	43307	43396	43520
43224	43308	43398	43521
43225	43309	43399	43522
43231	43312	43400	43523
43233	43314	43401	43529
43234	43315	43402	43531
43235	43318	43405	43538
43237	43321	43406	43548
43239	43323	43410	43553
43240	43324	43411	43558
43241	43325	43419	43562
43242	43326	43427	43565
43243	43327	43428	43570
43244	43329	43429	43572
43245	43330	43431	43574
43247	43332	43433	43575
43248†	43333	43435	43578
43249	43335	43436	43579
43250	43337	43440	43580
43251	43339	43441	43583
43253	43340	43443	43584
43254	43341	43444	43585
43256	43342	43446	43586
43257	43344	43449	43587
43258	43355	43453	43593
43261	43356	43456	43594
43263	43357	43457	43595
43266	43359	43459	43596
43267	43361	43464	43599
43268	43367	43468	43605
43271	43368	43469	43608
43274	43369	43474	43612
43277	43370	43476	43615
43278	43371	43482	43618
43282	43373	43484	43619
43284	43374	43490	43620
43286	43378	43491	43621
43287	43379	43496	43622
43290	43381	43499	43623
43292	43386	43502	43624
43294	43387	43506	43627
43295	43388	43507	43629
43300	43389	43509	43630
43301	43392	43510	43631
43305	43394	43514	43634
43306	43395	43515	43637

43638	43674	43714	43753
43639	43675	43715	43754
43644	43678	43717	43756
43645	43679	43721	43757
43650	43680	43727	43759
43651	43681	43728	43760
43652	43682	43729	43762
43656	43684	43731	43763
43657	43687	43734	43766
43658	43690	43735	43771
43660	43693	43737	43773
43664	43705	43742	
43665	43709	43745	
43668	43710	43749	
43669	43711	43750*	
43673	43712	43751	

Total 271

0-6-0   3F

Introduced 1906. Deeley Midland design. Rebuilt by Fowler with Belpaire firebox.

Weight: Loco. 46 tons 3 cwt.

Pressure: 175 lb.

Cyls.: 18½″×26″.

Dr. Wheels: 5′ 3″.   T.E.: 21,010 lb.

43776	43793	43808	43823
43778	43795	43809	43825
43784	43798	43812	43826
43785	43799	43814	43828
43786	43800	43815	43829
43787	43806	43822	43832
43789			

Total 25

0-6-0   4F

Introduced 1911. Fowler superheated Midland design.

Weight: Loco. 48 tons 15 cwt.

Pressure: 175 lb. Su.

Cyls.: 20″×26″.

Dr. Wheels: 5′ 3″.   T.E.: 24,555 lb.

P.V.

43836	43877	43918	43957
43837	43878	43919	43958
43839	43879	43920	43960
43840	43880	43921	43961
43841	43881	43922	43962
43842	43882	43923	43963
43843	43883	43924	43964
43844	43884	43925	43965
43845	43885	43926	43966
43846	43886	43927	43967
43847	43887	43928	43968
43848	43888	43929	43969
43849	43889	43930	43970
43850	43890	43931	43971
43851	43892	43932	43972
43852	43893	43933	43973
43853	43896	43934	43975
43854	43897	43935	43976
43855	43898	43937	43977
43856	43899	43938	43978
43857	43900	43939	43979
43858	43901	43940	43980
43859	43902	43941	43981
43860	43903	43942	43982
43861	43904	43944	43983
43863	43905	43945	43984
43864	43906	43946	43985
43865	43907	43947	43986
43866	43908	43948	43987
43868	43910	43949	43988
43869	43911	43950	43989
43870	43913	43951	43990
43871	43914	43952	43991
43872	43915	43953	43993
43873	43916	43954	43994
43876	43917	43955	43995

43996	44004	44013	44021
43997	44005	44014	44022
43998	44007	44015	44023
43999	44008	44016	44025
44000	44009	44017	44026
44001	44010	44018	
44002	44011	44019	
44003	44012	44020	

Total 173

0-6-0   4F

Introduced 1924. Post-grouping development of Midland design with reduced boiler mountings.

*Introduced 1922. Locos. built for S. & D.J.R. to M.R. design taken into L.M.S. stock 1930).
Weight: Loco. 48 tons 15 cwt.
Pressure: 175 lb. Su.
Cyls.: 20″×26″.
Dr. Wheels: 5′ 3″.   T.E.: 24,555 lb.
P.V.

44027	44050	44073	44096
44028	44051	44074	44097
44029	44052	44075	44098
44030	44053	44076	44099
44031	44054	44077	44100
44032	44055	44078	44101
44033	44056	44079	44102
44034	44057	44080	44103
44035	44058	44081	44104
44036	44059	44082	44105
44037	44060	44083	44106
44038	44061	44084	44107
44039	44062	44085	44108
44040	44063	44086	44109
44041	44064	44087	44110
44042	44065	44088	44111
44043	44066	44089	44112
44044	44067	44090	44113
44045	44068	44091	44114
44046	44069	44092	44115
44047	44070	44093	44116
44048	44071	44094	44117
44049	44072	44095	44118

44119	44165	44211	44257
44120	44166	44212	44258
44121	44167	44213	44259
44122	44168	44214	44260
44123	44169	44215	44261
44124	44170	44216	44262
44125	44171	44217	44263
44126	44172	44218	44264
44127	44173	44219	44265
44128	44174	44220	44266
44129	44175	44221	44267
44130	44176	44222	44268
44131	44177	44223	44269
44132	44178	44224	44270
44133	44179	44225	44271
44134	44180	44226	44272
44135	44181	44227	44273
44136	44182	44228	44274
44137	44183	44229	44275
44138	44184	44230	44276
44139	44185	44231	44277
44140	44186	44232	44278
44141	44187	44233	44279
44142	44188	44234	44280
44143	44189	44235	44281
44144	44190	44236	44282
44145	44191	44237	44283
44146	44192	44238	44284
44147	44193	44239	44285
44148	44194	44240	44286
44149	44195	44241	44287
44150	44196	44242	44288
44151	44197	44243	44289
44152	44198	44244	44290
44153	44199	44245	44291
44154	44200	44246	44292
44155	44201	44247	44293
44156	44202	44248	44294
44157	44203	44249	44295
44158	44204	44250	44296
44159	44205	44251	44297
44160	44206	44252	44298
44161	44207	44253	44299
44162	44208	44254	44300
44163	44209	44255	44301
44164	44210	44256	44302

44303	44349	44395	44441	44487	44517	44547	44577
44304	44350	44396	44442	44488	44518	44548	44578
44305	44351	44397	44443	44489	44519	44549	44579
44306	44352	44398	44444	44490	44520	44550	44580
44307	44353	44399	44445	44491	44521	44551	44581
44308	44354	44400	44446	44492	44522	44552	44582
44309	44355	44401	44447	44493	44523	44553	44583
44310	44356	44402	44448	44494	44524	44554	44584
44311	44357	44403	44449	44495	44525	44555	44585
44312	44358	44404	44450	44496	44526	44556	44586
44313	44359	44405	44451	44497	44527	44557*	44587
44314	44360	44406	44452	44498	44528	44558*	44588
44315	44361	44407	44453	44499	44529	44559*	44589
44316	44362	44408	44454	44500	44530	44560*	44590
44317	44363	44409	44455	44501	44531	44561*	44591
44318	44364	44410	44456	44502	44532	44562	44592
44319	44365	44411	44457	44503	44533	44563	44593
44320	44366	44412	44458	44504	44534	44564	44594
44321	44367	44413	44459	44505	44535	44565	44595
44322	44368	44414	44460	44506	44536	44566	44596
44323	44369	44415	44461	44507	44537	44567	44597
44324	44370	44416	44462	44508	44538	44568	44598
44325	44371	44417	44463	44509	44539	44569	44599
44326	44372	44418	44464	44510	44540	44570	44600
44327	44373	44419	44465	44511	44541	44571	44601
44328	44374	44420	44466	44512	44542	44572	44602
44329	44375	44421	44467	44513	44543	44573	44603
44330	44376	44422	44468	44514	44544	44574	44604
44331	44377	44423	44469	44515	44545	44575	44605
44332	44378	44424	44470	44516	44546	44576	44606
44333	44379	44425	44471				
44334	44380	44426	44472				
44335	44381	44427	44473				
44336	44382	44428	44474				
44337	44383	44429	44475				
44338	44384	44430	44476				
44339	44385	44431	44477				
44340	44386	44432	44478				
44341	44387	44433	44479				
44342	44388	44434	44480				
44343	44389	44435	44481				
44344	44390	44436	44482				
44345	44391	44437	44483				
44346	44392	44438	44484				
44347	44393	44439	44485				
44348	44394	44440	44486				

Total 580

4-6-0   **5**

Introduced 1934. Stanier L.M.S. taper boiler design.

Experimental locomotives:—
1. Introduced 1947. Stephenson link motion (outside), Timken roller bearings.

2. Introduced 1948. Caprotti valve gear.

Class 3 (Stanier) 2-6-2T No. 40165

[R. J. Buckley

Class 3 (Stanier) 2-6-2T No. 40148 (with large boiler)

[R. J. Buckley

Class 4 (Fowler) 2-6-4T No. 42393

[J. E. Wilkinson

Class 4 (Stanier 3-cylinder) 2-6-4T No. 42525   [Brian E. Morrison

Class 2P (L.M.S.) 4-4-0 No. 40613   [I. S. Swanson

Class 4P 4-4-0 No. 41195   [D. Penney

Class 6P5F (Hughes-Fowler) 2-6-0 No. 42703 [C. G. Pearson

Class 6P5F (Stanier) 2-6-0 No. 42976 [C. G. Pearson

Class 5 4-6-0 No. 44757 (with Caprotti valve gear and double chimney) [Brian E. Morrison

Class 7F 0-8-0 No. 49268

[R. J. Buckley

Class 7F (Fowler) 0-8-0 No. 49547

[P. H. Groom

Class 7F 2-8-0 No. 53802

[T. K. Widd

Class 3F 0-6-0 No. 43453 [P. H. Groom

Class 4F (Midland) 0-6-0 No. 44013 [K. R. Pirt

Class 4F (L.M.S.) 0-6-0 No. 44328 (fitted with tender cab and tablet exchange apparatus)
[David A. Anderson

Class 2P 0-4-4T No. 41902   [B. R. Goodlad

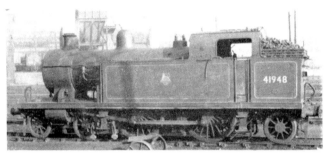

Class 3P 4-4-2T No. 41948 (fitted with sleet brushes for clearing snow from live rails of L.T.E. line to Upminster)   [A. A. Cameron

Class 3F 0-6-2T No. 41989   [R. E. Vincent

Class 0F 0-4-0ST No. 41518   [D. Marriott

Class 1F 0-6-0T No. 41875   [K. R. Pirt

Class 0F 0-4-0ST No. 47001   [J. A. Young

Class 6P5F 4-6-0 No. 45689 *Ajax*   [D. Marriott

Class 6P5F 4-6-0 No. 45547   [K. R. Pirt

Class 7P 4-6-0 No. 46163 *Civil Service Rifleman*   [Brian E. Morrison

3 Introduced 1948. Caprotti valve gear, Timken roller bearings.

4 Introduced 1948. Caprotti valve gear, Timken roller bearings. double chimney.

5. Introduced 1947 Timken roller bearings.

6. Introduced 1947. Timken roller bearings, double chimney.

7. Introduced 1949. Fitted with steel firebox.

8 Introduced 1950 Skefko roller bearings.

9. Introduced 1950. Timken roller bearings on driving coupled axle only

10. Introduced 1950. Skefko roller bearings on driving coupled axle only.

11. Introduced 1951 Caprotti valve gear, Skefko roller bearings

Weight: Loco { 72 tons 2 cwt. / 75 tons 6 cwt. (1, 5, 6, 8, 9, 10). / 74 tons 0 cwt. (2, 3, 4, 11). / 72 tons 2 cwt. (7).

Pressure: 225 lb. Sq.

Cyls.: (O) $18\frac{1}{2}'' \times 28''$

Dr. Wheels: 6' 0"   T.E.: 25,455 lb.

Walschaerts valve gear and P.V. except where otherwise shown

44658	44673[10]	44688[9]	44703
44659	44674[10]	44689[9]	44704
44660	44675[10]	44690[9]	44705
44661	44676[10]	44691[9]	44706
44662	44677[10]	44692[9]	44707
44663	44678[8]	44693[9]	44708
44664	44679[8]	44694[9]	44709
44665	44680[8]	44695[9]	44710
44666	44681[8]	44696[9]	44711
44667	44682[8]	44697[9]	44712
44668[10]	44683[8]	44698	44713
44669[10]	44684[8]	44699	44714
44670[10]	44685[8]	44700	44715
44671[10]	44686[11]	44701	44716
44672[10]	44687[11]	44702	44717

44718[7]	44764[6]	44810	44856
44719[7]	44765[6]	44811	44857
44720[7]	44766[6]	44812	44858
44721[7]	44767[1]	44813	44859
44722[7]	44768	44814	44860
44723[7]	44769	44815	44861
44724[7]	44770	44816	44862
44725[7]	44771	44817	44863
44726[7]	44772	44818	44864
44727[7]	44773	44819	44865
44728	44774	44820	44866
44729	44775	44821	44867
44730	44776	44822	44868
44731	44777	44823	44869
44732	44778	44824	44870
44733	44779	44825	44871
44734	44780	44826	44872
44735	44781	44827	44873
44736	44782	44828	44874
44737	44783	44829	44875
44738[2]	44784	44830	44876
44739[2]	44785	44831	44877
44740[2]	44786	44832	44878
44741[2]	44787	44833	44879
44742[2]	44788	44834	44880
44743[2]	44789	44835	44881
44744[2]	44790	44836	44882
44745[2]	44791	44837	44883
44746[2]	44792	44838	44884
44747[2]	44793	44839	44885
44748[3]	44794	44840	44886
44749[3]	44795	44841	44887
44750[3]	44796	44842	44888
44751[3]	44797	44843	44889
44752[3]	44798	44844	44890
44753[3]	44799	44845	44891
44754[3]	44800	44846	44892
44755[4]	44801	44847	44893
44756[4]	44802	44848	44894
44757[4]	44803	44849	44895
44758[5]	44804	44850	44896
44759[5]	44805	44851	44897
44760[5]	44806	44852	44898
44761[5]	44807	44853	44899
44762[5]	44808	44854	44900
44763[5]	44809	44855	44901

44902	44941	44980	45019	45058	45098	45138	45178
44903	44942	44981	45020	45059	45099	45139	45179
44904	44943	44982	45021	45060	45100	45140	45180
44905	44944	44983	45022	45061	45101	45141	45181
44906	44945	44984	45023	45062	45102	45142	45182
44907	44946	44985	45024	45063	45103	45143	45183
44908	44947	44986	45025	45064	45104	45144	45184
44909	44948	44987	45026	45065	45105	45145	45185
44910	44949	44988	45027	45066	45106	45146	45186
44911	44950	44989	45028	45067	45107	45147	45187
44912	44951	44990	45029	45068	45108	45148	45188
44913	44952	44991	45030	45069	45109	45149	45189
44914	44953	44992	45031	45070	45110	45150	45190
44915	44954	44993	45032	45071	45111	45151	45191
44916	44955	44994	45033	45072	45112	45152	45192
44917	44956	44995	45034	45073	45113	45153	45193
44918	44957	44996	45035	45074	45114	45154*	45194
44919	44958	44997	45036	45075	45115	45155	45195
44920	44959	44998	45037	45076	45116	45156*	45196
44921	44960	44999	45038	45077	45117	45157*	45197
44922	44961	45000	45039	45078	45118	45158*	45198
44923	44962	45001	45040	45079	45119	45159	45199
44924	44963	45002	45041	45080	45120	45160	45200
44925	44964	45003	45042	45081	45121	45161	45201
44926	44965	45004	45043	45082	45122	45162	45202
44927	44966	45005	45044	45083	45123	45163	45203
44928	44967	45006	45045	45084	45124	45164	45204
44929	44968	45007	45046	45085	45125	45165	45205
44930	44969	45008	45047	45086	45126	45166	45206
44931	44970	45009	45048	45087	45127	45167	45207
44932	44971	45010	45049	45088	45128	45168	45208
44933	44972	45011	45050	45089	45129	45169	45209
44934	44973	45012	45051	45090	45130	45170	45210
44935	44974	45013	45052	45091	45131	45171	45211
44936	44975	45014	45053	45092	45132	45172	45212
44937	44976	45015	45054	45093	45133	45173	45213
44938	44977	45016	45055	45094	45134	45174	45214
44939	44978	45017	45056	45095	45135	45175	45215
44940	44979	45018	45057	45096	45136	45176	45216
				45097	45137	45177	45217

NOTE

To understand the system of reference marks used in this book it is essential to read the notes on page 2.

* NAMES:

45154 Lanarkshire Yeomanry.
45156 Ayrshire Yeomanry.
45157 The Glasgow Highlander.
45158 Glasgow Yeomanry.

45218	45264	45310	45356	45402	45427	45452	45476
45219	45265	45311	45357	45403	45428	45453	45477
45220	45266	45312	45358	45404	45429	45454	45478
45221	45267	45313	45359	45405	45430	45455	45479
45222	45268	45314	45360	45406	45431	45456	45480
45223	45269	45315	45361	45407	45432	45457	45481
45224	45270	45316	45362	45408	45433	45458	45482
45225	45271	45317	45363	45409	45434	45459	45483
45226	45272	45318	45364	45410	45435	45460	45484
45227	45273	45319	45365	45411	45436	45461	45485
45228	45274	45320	45366	45412	45437	45462	45486
45229	45275	45321	45367	45413	45438	45463	45487
45230	45276	45322	45368	45414	45439	45464	45488
45231	45277	45323	45369	45415	45440	45465	45489
45232	45278	45324	45370	45416	45441	45466	45490
45233	45279	45325	45371	45417	45442	45467	45491
45234	45280	45326	45372	45418	45443	45468	45492
45235	45281	45327	45373	45419	45444	45469	45493
45236	45282	45328	45374	45420	45445	45470	45494
45237	45283	45329	45375	45421	45446	45471	45495
45238	45284	45330	45376	45422	45447	45472	45496
45239	45285	45331	45377	45423	45448	45473	45497
45240	45286	45332	45378	45424	45449	45474	45498
45241	45287	45333	45379	45425	45450	45475	45499
45242	45288	45334	45380	45426	45451		
45243	45289	45335	45381				
45244	45290	45336	45382				
45245	45291	45337	45383				
45246	45292	45338	45384				
45247	45293	45339	45385				
45248	45294	45340	45386				
45249	45295	45341	45387				
45250	45296	45342	45388				
45251	45297	45343	45389				
45252	45298	45344	45390				
45253	45299	45345	45391				
45254	45300	45346	45392				
45255	45301	45347	45393				
45256	45302	45348	45394				
45257	45303	45349	45395				
45258	45304	45350	45396				
45259	45305	45351	45397				
45260	45306	45352	45398				
45261	45307	45353	45399				
45262	45308	45354	45400				
45263	45309	45355	45401				

Total 842

"Patriot" Class
4-6-0   6P5F & 7P

*6P5F Introduced 1930. Fowler 3-cyl. rebuild of L.N.W. "Claughton" Class (introduced 1912), retaining original wheels and other details.

Remainder. Introduced 1933. New locos. to Fowler design (45502-41 were officially considered as rebuilds).

†7P Introduced 1946. Ivatt rebuild of Fowler locos. with large taper boiler, new cylinders and double chimney.

Weight: Loco. $\begin{cases} 80 \text{ tons } 15 \text{ cwt.} \\ 82 \text{ tons } 0 \text{ cwt.}† \end{cases}$

Pressure: $\begin{cases} 200 \text{ lb. Su.} \\ 250 \text{ lb. Su.}† \end{cases}$

Cyls.: $\begin{cases} (3) \ 18'' \times 26''. \\ (3) \ 17'' \times 26''.† \end{cases}$

Dr. Wheels: 6' 9".

T.E.: $\begin{cases} 26,520 \text{ lb.} \\ 29,570 \text{ lb.}† \end{cases}$

Walschaerts valve gear.   **P.V**

45500 *Patriot
45501 *St. Dunstan's
45502 Royal Naval Division
45503 The Royal Leicestershire
       Regiment
45504 Royal Signals
45505 The Royal Army
       Ordnance Corps
45506 The Royal Pioneer Corps
45507 Royal Tank Corps
45508
45509 The Derbyshire
       Yeomanry
45510
45511 Isle of Man
45512 †Bunsen
45513
45514 †Holyhead
45515 Caernarvon
45516 The Bedfordshire and
       Hertfordshire Regiment
45517
45518 Bradshaw
45519 Lady Godiva
45520 Llandudno
45521 †Rhyl
45522 †Prestatyn
45523 †Bangor
45524 Blackpool
45525 †Colwyn Bay
45526 †Morecambe and Heysham
45527 †Southport
45528 †
45529 †Stephenson
45530 †Sir Frank Ree
45531 †Sir Frederick Harrison
45532 †Illustrious
45533 Lord Rathmore
45534 †E. Tootal Broadhurst
45535 †Sir Herbert Walker.
       K.C.B.
45536 †Private W. Wood, V.C.
45537 Private E. Sykes, V.C.
45538 Giggleswick
45539 E. C. Trench
45540 †Sir Robert Turnbull

45541 Duke of Sutherland
45542
45543 Home Guard
45544
45545 †Planet
45546 Fleetwood
45547
45548 Lytham St. Annes
45549
45550
45551

Total 52

"Jubilee" Class

4-6-0   6P5F & 7P

6P5F Introduced 1934. Stanier L.M.S.
taper boiler development of the
"Patriot" class.
*7P Introduced 1942. Rebuilt with
larger boiler and double chimney.

Weight: Loco. $\begin{cases} 79 \text{ tons } 11 \text{ cwt.} \\ 82 \text{ tons } 0 \text{ cwt.*} \end{cases}$

Pressure: $\begin{cases} 225 \text{ lb. Su.} \\ 250 \text{ lb. Su.*} \end{cases}$

Cyls.: (3) 17" × 26".
Dr Wheels: 6' 9".

T.E.: $\begin{cases} 26,610 \text{ lb.} \\ 29,570 \text{ lb.*} \end{cases}$

Walschaerts valve gear. **P.V.**

45552 Silver Jubilee
45553 Canada
45554 Ontario
45555 Quebec
45556 Nova Scotia
45557 New Brunswick
45558 Manitoba
45559 British Columbia
45560 Prince Edward Island
45561 Saskatchewan
45562 Alberta
45563 Australia
45564 New South Wales
45565 Victoria

45566	Queensland	45612	Jamaica
45567	South Australia	45613	Kenya
45568	Western Australia	45614	Leeward Islands
45569	Tasmania	45615	Malay States
45570	New Zealand	45616	Malta G.C.
45571	South Africa	45617	Mauritius
45572	Eire	45618	New Hebrides
45573	Newfoundland	45619	Nigeria
45574	India	45620	North Borneo
45575	Madras	45621	Northern Rhodesia
45576	Bombay	45622	Nyasaland
45577	Bengal	45623	Palestine
45578	United Provinces	45624	St. Helena
45579	Punjab	45625	Sarawak
45580	Burma	45626	Seychelles
45581	Bihar and Orissa	45627	Sierra Leone
45582	Central Provinces	45628	Somaliland
45583	Assam	45629	Straits Settlements
45584	North West Frontier	45630	Swaziland
45585	Hyderabad	45631	Tanganyika
45586	Mysore	45632	Tonga
45587	Baroda	45633	Aden
45588	Kashmir	45634	Trinidad
45589	Gwalior	45635	Tobago
45590	Travancore	45636	Uganda
45591	Udaipur	45638	Zanzibar
45592	Indore	45639	Raleigh
45593	Kolhapur	45640	Frobisher
45594	Bhopal	45641	Sandwich
45595	Southern Rhodesia	45642	Boscawen
45596	Bahamas	45643	Rodney
45597	Barbados	45644	Howe
45598	Basutoland	45645	Collingwood
45599	Bechuanaland	45646	Napier
45600	Bermuda	45647	Sturdee
45601	British Guiana	45648	Wemyss
45602	British Honduras	45649	Hawkins
45603	Solomon Islands	45650	Blake
45604	Ceylon	45651	Shovell
45605	Cyprus	45652	Hawke
45606	Falkland Islands	45653	Barham
45607	Fiji	45654	Hood
45608	Gibraltar	45655	Keith
45609	Gilbert and Ellice Islands	45656	Cochrane
45610	Gold Coast	45657	Tyrwhitt
45611	Hong Kong	45658	Keyes

45659 Drake	45704 **Leviathan**
45660 Rooke	45705 Seahorse
45661 Vernon	45706 Express
45662 Kempenfelt	45707 Valiant
45663 Jervis	45708 Resolution
45664 Nelson	45709 Implacable
45665 Lord Rutherford of	45710 Irresistible
Nelson	45711 **Courageous**
45666 Cornwallis	45712 Victory
45667 Jellicoe	45713 Renown
45668 Madden	45714 Revenge
45669 Fisher	45715 Invincible
45670 Howard of Effingham	45716 Swiftsure
45671 Prince Rupert	45717 Dauntless
45672 Anson	45718 Dreadnought
45673 Keppel	45719 Glorious
45674 Duncan	45720 Indomitable
45675 Hardy	45721 Impregnable
45676 Codrington	45722 Defence
45677 Beatty	45723 Fearless
45678 De Robeck	45724 Warspite
45679 Armada	45725 Repulse
45680 Camperdown	45726 Vindictive
45681 Aboukir	45727 Inflexible
45682 Trafalgar	45728 Defiance
45683 Hogue	45729 Furious
45684 Jutland	45730 Ocean
45685 Barfleur	45731 Perseverance
45686 St. Vincent	45732 Sanspareil
45687 Neptune	45733 Novelty
45688 Polyphemus	45734 Meteor
45689 Ajax	45735*Comet
45690 Leander	45736*Phoenix
45691 Orion	45737 Atlas
45692 Cyclops	45738 Samson
45693 Agamemnon	45739 Ulster
45694 Bellerophon	45740 Munster
45695 Minotaur	45741 Leinster
45696 Arethusa	45742 Connaught
45697 Achilles	**Total 190**
45698 Mars	
45699 Galatea	
45700 Amethyst	
45701 Conqueror	
45702 Colossus	
45703 Thunderer	

For full details of
BRITISH RAILWAYS
DIESEL LOCOMOTIVES
see the
A.B.C. OF BRITISH RAILWAYS
LOCOMOTIVES PT. II.

"Royal Scot" Class

4-6-0   **7P**

Introduced 1943. Stanier rebuild of Fowler locos. (Introduced 1927) with taper boiler, new cylinders and double chimney.

*Introduced 1935. Stanier taper boiler rebuild with simple cyls. of experimental high pressure compound loco. No. 6399 *Fury*. (Introduced 1929.)

Weight: Loco. $\begin{cases} 83 \text{ tons.} \\ 84 \text{ tons I cwt.}^* \end{cases}$

Pressure: 250 lb. Su.

Cyls.: (3) 18″ × 26″.

Dr. Wheels: 6′ 9″.   T.E.: 33,150 lb.

Walschaerts valve gear. P.V.

46100 Royal Scot
46101 Royal Scots Grey
46102 Black Watch
46103 Royal Scots Fusilier
46104 Scottish Borderer
46105 Cameron Highlander
46106 Gordon Highlander
46107 Argyll and Sutherland Highlander
46108 Seaforth Highlander
46109 Royal Engineer
46110 Grenadier Guardsman
46111 Royal Fusilier
46112 Sherwood Forester
46113 Cameronian
46114 Coldstream Guardsman
46115 Scots Guardsman
46116 Irish Guardsman
46117 Welsh Guardsman
46118 Royal Welch Fusilier
46119 Lancashire Fusilier
46120 Royal Inniskilling Fusilier
46121 Highland Light Infantry, City of Glasgow Regiment

46122 Royal Ulster Rifleman
46123 Royal Irish Fusilier
46124 London Scottish
46125 3rd Carabinier
46126 Royal Army Service Corps
46127 Old Contemptibles
46128 The Lovat Scouts
46129 The Scottish Horse
46130 The West Yorkshire Regiment
46131 The Royal Warwickshire Regiment
46132 The King's Regiment Liverpool
46133 The Green Howards
46134 The Cheshire Regiment
46135 The East Lancashire Regiment
46136 The Border Regiment
46137 The Prince of Wales's Volunteers (South Lancashire)
46138 The London Irish Rifleman
46139 The Welch Regiment
46140 The King's Royal Rifle Corps
46141 The North Staffordshire Regiment
46142 The York & Lancaster Regiment
46143 The South Staffordshire Regiment
46144 Honourable Artillery Company
46145 The Duke of Wellington's Regt. (West Riding)
46146 The Rifle Brigade
46147 The Northamptonshire Regiment
46148 The Manchester Regiment
46149 The Middlesex Regiment
46150 The Life Guardsman
46151 The Royal Horse Guardsman
46152 The King's Dragoon Guardsman

46153 The Royal Dragoon
46154 The Hussar
46155 The Lancer
46156 The South Wales Borderer
46157 The Royal Artilleryman
46158 The Loyal Regiment
46159 The Royal Air Force
46160 Queen Victoria's Rifleman
46161 King's Own
46162 Queen's Westminster Rifleman
46163 Civil Service Rifleman
46164 The Artists' Rifleman
46165 The Ranger (12th London Regt.)
46166 London Rifle Brigade
46167 The Hertfordshire Regiment
46168 The Girl Guide
46169 The Boy Scout
46170*British Legion

Total 71

"Princess Royal" Class

4-6-2   8P

*Introduced 1933. Stanier L.M.S. taper boiler design.

Remainder. Introduced 1935. Development of original design with alterations to valve gear, boiler and other details.

Weight : Loco. 104 tons 10 cwt.

Pressure: 250 lb. Su.

Cyls.: (4) 16¼″ × 28″

Dr. Wheels: 6′ 6″   T.E.. 40,285 lb

Walschaerts valve gear (inside valves operated by rocking shafts on No. 46205 ; remainder have four sets of valve gear). P.V.

46200*The Princess Royal
46201*Princess Elizabeth
46203 Princess Margaret Rose
46204 Princess Louise
46205 Princess Victoria
46206 Princess Marie Louise
46207 Princess Arthur of Connaught
46208 Princess Helena Victoria
46209 Princess Beatrice
46210 Lady Patricia
46211 Queen Maud
46212 Duchess of Kent

Total 12

"Princess Coronation" Class

4-6-2   8P

Introduced 1937. Stanier L.M.S. enlargement of "Princess Royal" class. All except Nos. 46230–4/49–55 originally streamlined. (Streamlining removed from 1946).

*Introduced 1947. Ivatt development with roller bearings and detail alterations.

Weight: Loco. $\begin{cases} 105 \text{ tons } 5 \text{ cwt.} \\ 106 \text{ tons } 8 \text{ cwt.*} \end{cases}$

Pressure: 250 lb. Su.

Cyls.: (4) 16½″ × 28″.

Dr. Wheels: 6′ 9″.   T.E. 40,000 lb.

Walschaerts valve gear and rocking shafts. P.V.

46220 Coronation
46221 Queen Elizabeth
46222 Queen Mary
46223 Princess Alice
46224 Princess Alexandra
46225 Duchess of Gloucester
46226 Duchess of Norfolk
46227 Duchess of Devonshire
46228 Duchess of Rutland
46229 Duchess of Hamilton
46230 Duchess of Buccleuch

46231	Duchess of Atholl
46232	Duchess of Montrose
46233	Duchess of Sutherland
46234	Duchess of Abercorn
46235	City of Birmingham
46236	City of Bradford
46237	City of Bristol
46238	City of Carlisle
46239	City of Chester
46240	City of Coventry
46241	City of Edinburgh
46242	City of Glasgow
46243	City of Lancaster
46244	King George VI
46245	City of London
46246	City of Manchester
46247	City of Liverpool
46248	City of Leeds
46249	City of Sheffield
46250	City of Lichfield
46251	City of Nottingham
46252	City of Leicester
46253	City of St. Albans
46254	City of Stoke-on-Trent
46255	City of Hereford
46256*Sir William A. Stanier, F.R.S.
46257*City of Salford

Total 38

46420	46447	46474*	46501*
46421	46448	46475*	46502*
46422	46449	46476*	46503*
46423	46450	46477*	46504*
46424	46451	46478*	46505*
46425	46452	46479*	46506*
46426	46453	46480*	46507*
46427	46454	46481*	46508*
46428	46455	46482*	46509*
46429	46456	46483*	46510*
46430	46457	46484*	46511*
46431	46458	46485*	46512*
46432	46459	46486*	46513*
46433	46460	46487*	46514*
46434	46461	46488*	46515*
46435	46462	46489*	46516*
46436	46463	46490*	46517*
46437	46464	46491*	46518*
46438	46465*	46492*	46519*
46439	46466*	46493*	46520*
46440	46467*	46494*	46521*
46441	46468*	46495*	46522*
46442	46469*	46496*	46523*
46443	46470*	46497*	46524*
46444	46471*	46498*	46525*
46445	46472*	46499*	46526*
46446	46473*	46500*	46527*

Total 128

2-6-0   2

Introduced 1946   Ivatt L.M.S. taper boiler design.
Weight: Loco. 47 tons 2 cwt.
Pressure: 200 lb. Su.
Cyls.: $\begin{cases} (O) \ 16'' \times 24'' \\ (O) \ 16\frac{1}{2}'' \times 24''.* \end{cases}$
Dr. Wheels: 5' 0". T.E.: $\begin{cases} 17,410 \ \text{lb.} \\ 18,510 \ \text{lb.*} \end{cases}$
Walschaerts valve gear. P.V.

46400	46405	46410	46415
46401	46406	46411	46416
46402	46407	46412	46417
46403	46408	46413	46418
46404	46409	46414	46419

0-4-0ST   0F

Introduced 1932. Kitson design prepared to Stanier's requirements for L.M.S.
*Introduced 1953   Extended saddle tanks and coal space.
Weight: $\begin{cases} 33 \ \text{tons 0 cwt.} \\ 34 \ \text{tons 0 cwt.*} \end{cases}$
Pressure: 160 lb.
Cyls. :(O) $15\frac{1}{2}'' \times 30''$.
Dr. Wheels: 3' 10"   T.E.: 14,205 lb.

47000	47003	47006*	47008*
47001	47004	47007*	47009*
47002	47005*		

Total 10

0-6-0T 2F

Introduced 1928. Fowler L.M.S. short-wheelbase dock tanks.
Weight: 43 tons 12 cwt.
Pressure: 160 lb.
Cyls.: (O) 17″×22″.
Dr. Wheels: 3′ 11″.   T.E.: 18,400 lb.
Walschaerts valve gear.

47160	47163	47166	47168
47161	47164	47167	47169
47162	47165		

Total 10

0-4-0T Sentinel

Geared Sentinel locos.
Introduced 1929. Single-speed locos. for S. & D.J. (taken into L.M.S. stock 1930).
Weight: 27 tons 15 cwt.
Pressure: 275 lb Su.
Cyls.: (4) 6¾″×9″.
Dr. Wheels: 3′ 1¼″.
T.E.: 15,500 lb.
Poppet valves.

47190   47191

Total 2

0-6-0T 3F

Introduced 1899. Johnson large Midland design, rebuilt with Belpaire firebox from 1919; fitted with condensers for London area.
*Introduced 1899.   Non-Condensing locos.
Weight: 48 tons 15 cwt.
Pressure: 160 lb.
Cyls.: 18″×26″.
Dr. Wheels: 4′ 7″.   T.E.: 20,835 lb.

47200	47213	47228	47246*
47201*	47214	47229	47247
47202	47216	47230*	47248*
47203	47217	47231*	47249
47204	47218	47234*	47250*
47205	47219	47235*	47251
47206	47221	47236*	47254*
47207	47222	47238*	47255*
47208	47223	47239*	47257*
47209	47224	47240	47258*
47210	47225	47241	47259*
47211	47226	47242	
47212	47227	47243	

Total 50

0-6-0T 3F

Introduced 1924. Post-grouping development of Midland design with detail alterations.
*Introduced 1929.   Locos. built for S. & D.J. (taken into L.M.S. stock 1930).
†Push-and-pull fitted.
Weight: 49 tons 10 cwt.
Pressure: 160 lb.
Cyls.: 18″×26″.
Dr. Wheels: 4′ 7″.   T.E.: 20,835 lb.

47260	47270	47280	47290
47261	47271	47281	47291
47262	47272	47282	47292
47263	47273	47283	47293
47264	47274	47284	47294
47265	47275	47285	47295
47266	47276	47286	47296
47267	47277	47287	47297
47268	47278	47288	47298
47269	47279	47289	47299

47300	47346	47392	47438	47485	47531	47578	47626
47301	47347	47393	47439	47486	47532	47579	47627
47302	47348	47394	47440	47487	47533	47580	47628
47303	47349	47395	47441	47488	47534	47581	47629
47304	47350	47396	47442	47489	47535	47582	47630
47305	47351	47397	47443	47490	47536	47583	47631
47306	47352	47398	47444	47491	47537	47584	47632
47307	47353	47399	47445	47492	47538	47585	47633
47308	47354	47400	47446	47493	47539	47586	47634
47309	47355	47401	47447	47494	47540	47587	47635
47310*	47356	47402	47448	47495	47541	47588	47636
47311*	47357	47403	47449	47496	47542	47589	47637
47312*	47358	47404	47450	47497	47543	47590	47638
47313*	47359	47405	47451	47498	47544	47591	47639
47314*	47360	47406	47452	47499	47545	47592S	47640
47315*	47361	47407	47453	47500	47546	47593	47641
47316*	47362	47408	47454	47501	47547	47594	47642
47317	47363	47409	47455	47502	47548	47595	47643
47318	47364	47410	47457	47503	47549	47596	47644
47319	47365	47411	47458	47504	47550	47597	47645
47320	47366	47412	47459	47505	47551	47598	47646
47321	47367	47413	47460	47506	47552	47599	47647
47322	47368	47414	47461	47507	47554	47600	47648
47323	47369	47415	47462	47508	47555	47601	47649
47324	47370	47416	47463	47509	47556	47602	47650
47325	47371	47417	47464	47510	47557	47603	47651
47326	47372	47418	47465	47511	47558	47604	47652
47327	47373	47419	47466	47512	47559	47605	47653
47328	47374	47420	47467	47513	47560	47606	47654
47329	47375	47421	47468	47514	47561	47607	47655†
47330	47376	47422	47469	47515	47562	47608	47656
47331	47377	47423	47470	47516	47563	47609	47657
47332	47378	47424	47471	47517	47564	47610	47658
47333	47379	47425	47472	47518	47565	47611	47659
47334	47380	47426	47473	47519	47566	47612	47660
47335	47381	47427	47474	47520	47567	47614	47661
47336	47382	47428	47475	47521	47568	47615	47662
47337	47383	47429	47476	47522	47569	47616	47664
47338	47384	47430	47477†	47523	47570	47618	47665
47339	47385	47431	47478†	47524	47571	47619	47666
47340	47386	47432	47479†	47525	47572	47620	47667
47341	47387	47433	47480†	47526	47573	47621	47668
47342	47388	47434	47481†	47527	47574	47622	47669
47343	47389	47435	47482	47528	47575	47623	47670
47344	47390	47436	47483	47529	47576	47624	47671
47345	47391	47437	47484	47530	47577	47625	47672

47673	47676	47678	47680
47674	47677	47679	47681†
47675			**Total 417**

2-6-6-2T   Beyer-Garratt

Introduced 1930.   Development of Fowler & Beyer-Peacock, L.M.S., 1927 design, with detail alterations later fitted with revolving coal bunkers.

Weight: 155 tons 10 cwt.
Pressure: 190 lb. Su.
Cyls. (4) 18½″ × 26″.
Dr. Wheels: 5′ 3″.   T.E.: 45,620 lb.
Walschaerts valve gear. P.V.

47967	47972	47982	47994
47968	47973	47986	47995
47969	47978	47987	

Total 11

2-8-0   8F

Introduced 1935.   Stanier L.M.S. taper boiler design.
Weight: Loco. 72 tons 2 cwt.
Pressure: 225 lb. Su.
Cyls.: (O) 18½″ × 28″.
Dr. Wheels: 4′ 8½″.   T.E.: 32,440 lb.
Walschaerts valve gear. P.V.

48000	48017	48050	48070	48088	48135	48181	48247
48001	48018	48053	48073	48089	48136	48182	48248
48002	48020	48054	48074	48090	48137	48183	48249
48003	48024	48055	48075	48092	48138	48184	48250
48004	48026	48056	48076	48093	48139	48185	48251
48005	48027	48057	48077	48094	48140	48186	48252
48006	48029	48060	48078	48095	48141	48187	48253
48007	48033	48061	48079	48096	48142	48188	48254
48008	48035	48062	48080	48097	48143	48189	48255
48009	48036	48063	48081	48098	48144	48190	48256
48010	48037	48064	48082	48099	48145	48191	48257
48011	48039	48065	48083	48100	48146	48192	48258
48012	48045	48067	48084	48101	48147	48193	48259
48016	48046	48069	48085	48102	48148	48194	48260
				48103	48149	48195	48261
				48104	48150	48196	48262
				48105	48151	48197	48263
				48106	48152	48198	48264
				48107	48153	48199	48265
				48108	48154	48200	48266
				48109	48155	48201	48267
				48110	48156	48202	48268
				48111	48157	48203	48269
				48112	48158	48204	48270
				48113	48159	48205	48271
				48114	48160	48206	48272
				48115	48161	48207	48273
				48116	48162	48208	48274
				48117	48163	48209	48275
				48118	48164	48210	48276
				48119	48165	48211	48277
				48120	48166	48212	48278
				48121	48167	48213	48279
				48122	48168	48214	48280
				48123	48169	48215	48281
				48124	48170	48216	48282
				48125	48171	48217	48283
				48126	48172	48218	48284
				48127	48173	48219	48285
				48128	48174	48220	48286
				48129	48175	48221	48287
				48130	48176	48222	48288
				48131	48177	48223	48289
				48132	48178	48224	48290
				48133	48179	48225	48291
				48134	48180	48246	48292

48293	48342	48388	48434	48490	48540	48626	48672
48294	48343	48389	48435	48491	48541	48627	48673
48295	48344	48390	48436	48492	48542	48628	48674
48296	48345	48391	48437	48493	48543	48629	48675
48297	48346	48392	48438	48494	48544	48630	48676
48301	48347	48393	48439	48495	48545	48631	48677
48302	48348	48394	48440	48500	48546	48632	48678
48303	48349	48395	48441	48501	48547	48633	48679
48304	48350	48396	48442	48502	48548	48634	48680
48305	48351	48397	48443	48503	48549	48635	48681
48306	48352	48398	48444	48504	48550	48636	48682
48307	48353	48399	48445	48505	48551	48637	48683
48308	48354	48400	48446	48506	48552	48638	48684
48309	48355	48401	48447	48507	48553	48639	48685
48310	48356	48402	48448	48508	48554	48640	48686
48311	48357	48403	48449	48509	48555	48641	48687
48312	48358	48404	48450	48510	48556	48642	48688
48313	48359	48405	48451	48511	48557	48643	48689
48314	48360	48406	48452	48512	48558	48644	48690
48315	48361	48407	48453	48513	48559	48645	48691
48316	48362	48408	48454	48514	48600	48646	48692
48317	48363	48409	48455	48515	48601	48647	48693
48318	48364	48410	48456	48516	48602	48648	48694
48319	48365	48411	48457	48517	48603	48649	48695
48320	48366	48412	48458	48518	48604	48650	48696
48321	48367	48413	48459	48519	48605	48651	48697
48322	48368	48414	48460	48520	48606	48652	48698
48323	48369	48415	48461	48521	48607	48653	48699
48324	48370	48416	48462	48522	48608	48654	48700
48325	48371	48417	48463	48523	48609	48655	48701
48326	48372	48418	48464	48524	48610	48656	48702
48327	48373	48419	48465	48525	48611	48657	48703
48328	48374	48420	48466	48526	48612	48658	48704
48329	48375	48421	48467	48527	48613	48659	48705
48330	48376	48422	48468	48528	48614	48660	48706
48331	48377	48423	48469	48529	48615	48661	48707
48332	48378	48424	48470	48530	48616	48662	48708
48333	48379	48425	48471	48531	48617	48663	48709
48334	48380	48426	48472	48532	48618	48664	48710
48335	48381	48427	48473	48533	48619	48665	48711
48336	48382	48428	43474	48534	48620	48666	48712
48337	48383	48429	48475	48535	48621	48667	48713
48338	48384	48430	48476	48536	48622	48668	48714
48339	48385	48431	48477	48537	48623	48669	48715
48340	48386	48432	48478	48538	48624	48670	48716
48341	48387	48433	48479	48539	48625	48671	48717

48718	48732	48746	48760
48719	48733	48747	48761
48720	48734	48748	48762
48721	48735	48749	48763
48722	48736	48751	48764
48723	48737	48751	48765
48724	48738	48752	48766
48725	48739	48753	48767
48726	48740	48754	48768
48727	48741	48755	48769
48728	48742	48756	48770
48729	48743	48757	48771
48730	48744	48758	48772
48731	48745	48759	

Total 663

0-8-0   7F

Introduced 1936. L.N.W. G2a Class. Bowen-Cooke G1 superheated design of 1912, rebuilt with G2 boiler and Belpaire firebox.
Weight: Loco. 62 tons 0 cwt.
Pressure: 175 lb. Su.
Cyls.: 20½" × 24".
Dr. Wheels: 4' 5½".
T.E.: 28,045 lb.
Joy valve gear.   P.V.

48895	48952	49046	49099
48898	48953	49047	49104
48905	48964	49048	49105
48907	49002	49049	49106
48914	49005	49057	49108
48915	49007	49061	49109
48917	49008	49063	49112
48921	49009	49064	49113
48922	49010	49066	49114
48926	49018	49070	49115
48927	49020	49073	49116
48930	49021	49077	49117
48932	49023	49078	49119
48940	49025	49079	49120
48942	49027	49081	49121
48943	49033	49082	49122
48944	49034	49087	49125
48945	49037	49088	49126
48950	49044	49093	49129
48951	49045	49094	49130

49132	49191	49268	49343
49134	49196	49270	49344
49137	49198	49271	49345
49139	49199	49275	49348
49141	49200	49276	49350
49142	49202	49277	49352
49143	49203	49278	49355
49144	49209	49281	49357
49145	49210	49287	49358
49146	49214	49288	49361
49147	49216	49289	49366
49148	49223	49293	49367
49149	49224	49301	49368
49150	49226	49304	49373
49153	49228	49306	49375
49154	49229	49308	49376
49155	49230	49310	49377
49157	49234	49311	49378
49158	49239	49313	49381
49160	49240	49314	49382
49161	49243	49315	49385
49164	49245	49318	49386
49167	49246	49321	49387
49168	49247	49323	49390
49172	49249	49327	49391
49173	49252	49328	49392
49174	49254	49330	49393
49177	49260	49335	49394
49180	49262	49340	
49181	49266	49341	
49186	49267	49342	

Total 201

0-8-0   7F

Introduced 1921. Development of L.N.W. G2 Class. Bowen-Cooke G1 superheated design of 1912 with higher pressure boiler. Many later rebuilt with Belpaire firebox.
Weight: Loco. 62 tons 0 cwt.
Pressure: 175 lb. Su.
Cyls.: 20½" × 24".
Dr. Wheels: 4' 5½".
T.E.: 28,045 lb.
Joy valve gear.   P.V.

49395	49410	49425	49440
49396	49411	49426	49441
49397	49412	49427	49442
49398	49413	49428	49443
49399	49414	49429	49444
49400	49415	49430	49445
49401	49416	49431	49446
49402	49417	49432	49447
49403	49418	49433	49448
49404	49419	49434	49449
49405	49420	49435	49450
49406	49421	49436	49451
49407	49422	49437	49452
49408	49423	49438	49453
49409	49424	49439	49454

Total 60

0-8-0   7F

Introduced 1929. Fowler L.M.S. design,
developed from L.N.W. G2.
Weight: Loco. 60 tons 15 cwt.
Pressure: 200 lb. Su.
Cyls.: $19\frac{1}{2}'' \times 26''$.
Dr. Wheels: $4' 8\frac{1}{2}''$.   T.E.: 29,745 lb.
Walschaerts valve gear. P.V.

49505	49545	49592	49659
49508	49547	49598	49662
49509	49555	49618	49667
49511	49560	49624	49668
49515	49566	49627	49672
49536	49573	49637	49674
49538	49582	49640	
49544	49586	49648	

Total 30

2-4-2T   2P

Introduced 1889.   Aspinall L. & Y.
Class 5 with 2 tons coal capacity.
*Introduced 1890. Locos. built or
rebuilt with smaller cylinders.
†Introduced 1893. Locos. with longer
tanks and 4 tons coal capacity.

‡Introduced 1905.   Hughes loco. built
with Belpaire firebox and extended
smokebox.
¶Introduced 1910. Locos. rebuilt with
belpaire firebox and extended smoke-
box.
Weight: $\begin{cases} 55 \text{ tons } 19 \text{ cwt.} \\ 55 \text{ tons } 19 \text{ cwt.}^* \\ 59 \text{ tons } 3 \text{ cwt.}†‡¶ \end{cases}$
Pressure: 180 lb.
Cyls.: $\begin{cases} 17\frac{1}{2}'' \times 26''.^* \\ 18'' \times 26''. \end{cases}$ T.E.: $\begin{cases} 18,360 \text{ lb.}^* \\ 18,955 \text{ lb.} \end{cases}$
Dr. Wheels: $5' 8''$.   Joy valve gear.

50636	50705	50757	50831†
50643*	50712	50777¶	50850†¶
50644	50721	50781	50855*†
50646	50725	50795*	50865*†
50647	50746	50818	50887‡†
50660	50752*	50829†¶	

Total 23

0-4-0ST   0F

Introduced 1891.   Aspinall L. & Y.
Class 21.
Weight: 21 tons 5 cwt.
Pressure: 160 lb.
Cyls.: (O) $13'' \times 18''$.
Dr. Wheels: $3' 0\frac{3}{8}''$.   T.E.: 11,335 lb.

51202	51218	51231	51241
51204	51221	51232	51244
51206	51222	51234	51246
51207	51227	51235	51253
51212	51229	51237	
51217	51230	51240	

Total 22

0-6-0ST   2F

Introduced 1891.   Aspinall rebuild of
L. & Y. Barton Wright Class 23 0-6-0.
Originally introduced 1877.
Weight: 43 tons 17 cwt.
Pressure: 140 lb.   Cyls.: $17\frac{1}{2}'' \times 26''$.
Dr. Wheels: $4' 6''$.   T.E.: 17,545 lb.

51304S	51324S	51368S	51408
51305S	51336	51371	51412S
51307	51338	51381	51413
51316	51343	51394S	51415
51319	51353	51397	51419
51321	51358	51404	51423

51424	51453	51491	51512
51429S	51457	51496	51524
51432	51458	51497	51526
51441	51474	51498	
51444S	51481	51499	
51445	51484	51503	
51446S	51486	51506	

Total 48

Dr. Wheels: $\begin{cases} 5' \ 1''. \\ 5' \ 1''.\bullet \\ 4' \ 7\frac{1}{2}''.\dagger \end{cases}$

T.E. $\begin{cases} 21,130 \ lb. \\ 21,130 \ lb.* \\ 23,225 \ lb.\dagger \end{cases}$

Joy valve gear.

0-6-0T   1F

Introduced 1897. Aspinall L & Y.
Class 24 dock tanks.
Weight: 50 tons 0 cwt.
Pressure: 140 lb.
Cyls.: (O) 17" × 24".
Dr. Wheels: 4' 0".   T.E. : 15,285 lb.
Allan straight link valve gear.

51537	51544	51546

Total 3

0-6-0   2F

Introduced 1887. Barton Wright
L. & Y. Class 25.
Weight: Loco. 39 tons 1 cwt.
Pressure: 140 lb.
Cyls.: 17½" × 26".
Dr. Wheels: 4' 6".   T.E.: 17,545 lb.

51044

Total 1

0-6-0   3F

Introduced 1889. Aspinall L. & Y Class
27. Nos. 52515-29 built superheated
with roundtop firebox and extended
smokebox, later rebuilt with
saturated boiler and short smokebox.
*Introduced 1911. Rebuilt with Bel-
paire firebox and extended smokebox.
†Furness 0-6-0 rebuilt with ex-L. & Y.
boiler.

Weight: Loco. $\begin{cases} 42 \ tons \ 3 \ cwt. \\ 43 \ tons \ 11 \ cwt.* \\ 42 \ tons \ 3 \ cwt.\dagger \end{cases}$

Pressure: 180 lb.
Cyls.: 18" × 26"

52089	52182	52305	52413*
52093S	52183	52311	52415
52094*	52186	52312*S	52427
52095	52201*	52319*	52429
52108	52203	52322	52431*
52119	52207S	52328	52432
52120	52212S	52336	52438*
52121	52216	52338	52441S
52123	52217	52341	52443
52125	52218S	52345S	52445*
52129	52225	52348	52449
52132*	52230	52350	52452
52133	52232	52351	52455
52135*	52235	52355	52456
52136	52236	52356	52458
52139	52237	52360	52459S
52140*	52240	52366	52461
52141	52244	52368	52464S
52143	52248	52376	52466
52154*	52252	52378	52501†
52159	52260	52379*	52510†
52160	52268	52387	52515
52161*	52269	52388	52517S
52162*	52270	52389	52521
52163	52271	52393	52523
52165	52275	52399	52526
52171	52278	52400*	52527
52172	52289	52410	52529
52175	52290	52411	
52179	52293	52412	

Total: L. & Y. 116, F.R. 2

Class 8P 4-6-2 No. 46229 *Duchess of Hamilton* [G. Wheeler

Class 8P 4-6-2 No. 46212 *Duchess of Kent* [T. B. Paisley

Class 6P5F 4-6-2 No. 72002 *Clan Campbell* [David A. Anderson

Class 2F (Midland) 0-6-0 No. 58246 (the last engine of this class to retain a round-top firebox) [A. W. Martin

Class 2F (Midland) 0-6-0 No. 58198 (with Belpaire firebox) [D. Marriott

Class 2F (L & Y) 0-6-0 No. 52044 (last engine of the class) [D. Marriott

Class 3F (L & Y) 0-6-0 No. 52201 (with extended smokebox and Belpaire firebox)
[S. D. Wainwright

Class 3F (L & Y) 0-6-0 No. 52455
[P. Ransome-Wallis

Class 3F (Furness) 0-6-0 No. 52509 (rebuilt with L & Y boiler ; since withdrawn)
[B. R. Goodlad

Top: Class 2P 2-4-2T
No. 50818
[*P. H. Wells*

Centre: Class 2P
2-4-2T No. 50831
(with larger tanks
and bunker)

Left: Class 2P 2-4-2T
No. 50777 (with
extended smokebox
and Belpaire firebox)
[*P. H. Wells*

Class 1P 0-4-4T No. 58065   [R. J. Buckley

Class 2F 0-6-0T No. 47161   [R. J. Buckley

Class 3F (Midland) 0-6-0T No. 47216   [R. A. Panting

Class 2F 0-6-0ST No. C.D.8 *Earlestown* [*P. B. Whitehouse*

Class 2F 0-6-0ST No. 51404 [*P. Ransome-Wallis*

Class 0F 0-4-0ST No. 51217 [*R. J. Buckley*

Class 3P 4-4-0 No. 54503   [I. S. Swanson

Class 2F 0-6-0 No. 57386   [C. Lawson Kerr

Class 3F 0-6-0 No. 57632   [David A. Anderson

Class 2P 0-4-4T No. 55261   [David A. Anderson

Class 3F 0-6-0T No. 56376   [H. Trickett

Class 2F 0-6-0T No. 56164   [A. W. Martin

0-6-0   3F

Introduced 1912. Hughes L. & Y. Class 28, superheated development of Class 27.
Weight: Loco. 46 tons 10 cwt.
Pressure: 180 lb. Su.
Cyls.: 20½″ × 26″.
Dr. Wheels: 5′ 1″.   T.E.: 27,405 lb.
Joy valve gear. P.V.

52551

Total 1

2-8-0   7F

Introduced 1914. Fowler design for S. & D.J.
(All taken into L.M.S. stock, 1930.)
Weight: Loco. 64 tons 15 cwt.
Pressure: 190 lb. Su.
Cyls.: (O) 21″ × 28″.
Dr. Wheels: 4′ 8½″.   T.E.: 35,295 lb.
Walschaerts valve gear. P.V.

53800	53803	53806	53809
53801	53804	53807	53810
53802	53805	53808	

Total 11

4-4-0   3P

Introduced 1910. McIntosh Caledonian "Dunalastair IV Superheater" or "139" class.
*Introduced 1915. Superheated rebuild of McIntosh Caledonian "Dunalastair IV" or "140" class (originally introduced 1904).
Weight: Loco. 61 tons 5 cwt.
Pressure: 180 lb. Su.
Cyls.: 20½″ × 26″.
Dr. Wheels: 6′ 6″.   T.E.: 20,915 lb. P V.

54439*	54452	54453	54458
54441			

Total 5

4-4-0   3P

Introduced 1916. Pickersgill Caledonian "113" and "928" classes.
Weight: Loco. 61 tons 5 cwt.
Pressure: 180 lb. Su.   Cyls.: 20″ × 26″.
Dr. Wheels: 6′ 6″. T.E. 20,400 lb. P.V.

54461	54465	54469	54473
54462	54466	54470	54474
54463	54467	54471	54475
54464	54468	54472	54476

Total 16

4-4-0   3P

Introduced 1920. Pickersgill Caledonian "72" class.
Weight: Loco. 61 tons 5 cwt.
Pressure: 180 lb. Su. Cyls.: 20½″ × 26″
Dr. Wheels: 6′ 6″. T.E.: 21,435 lb. P.V.

54477	54486	54494	54502
54478	54487	54495	54503
54479	54488	54496	54504
54480	54489	54497	54505
54482	54490	54498	54506
54482	54491	54499	54507
54483	54492	54500	54508
54484	54493	54501	
54485			

Total 31

0-4-4T   2P

*Introduced 1895. McIntosh Caledonian "19" class, with railed coal bunker
Remainder. Introduced 1897. McIntosh "92" class, developed from "29" class with larger tanks and highsided coal bunker (both classes originally fitted for condensing on Glasgow Central Low Level lines).
Weight: $\begin{cases} 53 \text{ tons } 16 \text{ cwt.*} \\ 53 \text{ tons } 19 \text{ cwt.} \end{cases}$
Pressure: 180 lb.   Cyls.: 18″ × 26″.
Dr. Wheels: 5′ 9″.   T.E.: 18,680 lb.

55124*   55126   55141

Total 3

0-4-4T 2P

Introduced 1900. McIntosh Caledonian " 439 " or " Standard Passenger " class.
*Introduced 1915. Pickersgill locos. with detail alterations.
Weight: { 53 tons 19 cwt.
{ 57 tons 12 cwt.*
Pressure: 180 lb.
Cyls.: 18″ × 26″.
Dr. Wheels: 5′ 9″.　　T.E.: 18,680 lb.

55160	55198	55212	55225
55164	55199	55213	55226
55165	55200	55214	55227*
55167	55201	55215	55228*
55168	55202	55216	55229*
55169	55203	55217	55230*
55173	55204	55218	55231*
55176	55206	55219	55232*
55178	55207	55220	55233*
55182	55208	55221	55234*
55185	55209	55222	55235*
55189	55210	55223	55236*
55195	55211	55224	

Total 51

0-4-4T 2P

Introduced 1922. Pickersgill Caledonian " 431 ' class (developed from " 439 " class) with cast-iron front buffer beam for banking.
Weight: 57 tons 17 cwt.
Pressure: 180 lb.
Cyls.: 18¼″ × 26″.
Dr. Wheels: 5′ 9″.　　T.E.: 19,200 lb.

55237	55238	55239	55240

Total 4

0-4-4T 2P

Introduced 1925. Post-Grouping development of Caledonian " 439 " class.
Weight: 59 tons 12 cwt.
Pressure: 180 lb.
Cyls.: 18¼″ × 26″.
Dr. Wheels: 5′ 9″.　　T.E.: 19,200 lb.

55260	55263	55266	55268
55261	55264	55267	55269
55262	55265		

Total 10

0-4-0ST 0F

Introduced 1885. Drummond and McIntosh Caledonian " Pugs."
Weight: 27 tons 7 cwt.
Pressure: 160 lb.　Cyls.: (O) 14″ × 20″.
Dr. Wheels: 3′ 8″.　　T.E.: 12,115 lb.

56011	56028	56031	56038
56025S	56029	56032S	56039
56027	56030	56035	

Total 11

0-6-0T 2F

Introduced 1911. McIntosh Caledonian dock shunters, " 498 " class.
Weight: 47 tons 15 cwt.
Pressure: 160 lb.　Cyls.: (O) 17″ × 22″.
Dr. Wheels: 4′ 0″.　　T.E.: 18,015 lb.

56151	56157	56163	56169
56152	56158	56164	56170
56153	56159	56165	56171
56154	56160	56166	56172
56155	56161	56167	56173
56156	56162	56168	

Total 23

0-6-0T 3F

Introduced 1895. McIntosh Caledonian " 29 " and " 782 " classes (56232-9 originally condensing).
Weight: 47 tons 15 cwt.
Pressure: 160 lb.　Cyls.: 18″ × 26″.
Dr. Wheels: 4′ 6″.　　T.E.: 21,215 lb.

56232	56244	56256	56269
56234	56245	56257	56272
56235	56246	56259	56274
56236	56247	56260	56275
56238	56251	56262	56277
56239	56252	56264	56278
56240	56253	56265	56279
56241	56254	56266	56280
56242	56255	56267	56281

56282	56306	56331	56356	57273	57326	57365	57419
56283	56308	56332	56357	57274	57328	57366	57424
56284	56309	56333	56359	57275	57329	57367	57426
56285	56310	56334	56360	57276	57331	57368	57429
56286	56311	56335	56361	57278	57335	57369	57430
56287	56312	56336	56362	57279	57336	57370	57431
56288	56313	56337	56363	57284	57338	57373	57432
56289	56314	56338	56364	57285	57339	57375	57434
56290	56315	56340	56365	57287	57340	57377	57435
56291	56316	56341	56367	57288	57341	57378	57436
56292	56318	56342	56368	57291	57345	57383	57437
56293	56320	56343	56369	57292	57346	57384	57441
56294	56321	56344	56370	57295	57347	57385	57443
56295	56322	56345	56371	57296	57348	57386	57444
56296	56323	56346	56372	57299	57349	57389	57445
56297	56324	56347	56373	57300	57350	57392	57446
56298	56325	56348	56374	57302	57353	57396	57447
56300	56326	56349	56375	57303	57354	57398	57448
56301	56327	56350	56376	57307	57355	57404	57451
56302	56328	56352		57309	57356	57405	57461
56304	56329	56353		57311	57357	57407	57462
56305	56330	56354		57314	57359	57411	57463
				57317	57360	57413	57465
				57319	57361	57414	57470
				57321	57362	57416	57472
				57324	57363	57417	57473
				57325	57364	57418	

Total 121

0-6-0   2F

Introduced 1883. Drummond Caledonian "Standard Goods"; later additions by Lambie and McIntosh.

Some rebuilt with L.M.S. boiler.*

Weight: Loco. $\begin{cases} 41 \text{ tons } 6 \text{ cwt.} \\ 42 \text{ tons } 4 \text{ cwt.}^* \end{cases}$

Pressure: 180 lb.

Cyls.: 18″ × 26″.

Dr. Wheels: 5′ 0″.   T.E.: 21,480 lb.

57232	57242	57252	57263
57233	57243	57253	57264
57234	57244	57254	57265
57236	57245	57256	57266
57237	57246	57257	57267
57238	57247	57258	57268
57239	57249	57259	57269
57240	57250	57261	57270
57241	57251	57262	57271

Total 143

0-6-0   3F

Introduced 1899. McIntosh Caledonian "812" (Nos. 57550–57623) and "652" (remainder) classes.

Weight: Loco. 45 tons 14 cwt.

Pressure: 180 lb.

Cyls.: 18½″ × 26″.

Dr. Wheels: 5′ 0″.   T.E.: 22,690 lb.

57550	57558	57566	57575
57552	57559	57568	57576
57553	57560	57569	57577
57554	57562	57570	57579
57555	57563	57571	57580
57556	57564	57572	57581
57557	57565	57573	57582

57583	57599	57614	57630
57585	57600	57615	57631
57586	57601	57617	57632
57587	57602	57618	57633
57588	57603	57619	57634
57590	57604	57620	57635
57591	57605	57621	57637
57592	57607	57622	57638
57593	57608	57623	57640
57594	57609	57625	57642
57595	57611	57626	57643
57596	57612	57627	57644
57597	57613	57628	57645

Total 80

0-6-0   3F

Introduced 1918. Pickersgill Caledonian '294'' class (superheated)
and ''670'' classes.

Weight: Loco. 50 tons 13 cwt.

Pressure: 180 lb. Su.

Cyls.: 18½″×26″.

Dr. Wheels: 5′ 0″   T.E.: 22,690 lb.
P.V.

57650	57661	57670	57682
57651	57663	57671	57684
57652	57665	57672	57686
57653	57666	57673	57688
57654	57667	57674	57689
57655	57668	57679	57690
57658	57669	57681	57691
57659			

Total 29

0-4-4T   1P

*Introduced 1889, Johnson Midland
design of 1881 with larger cylinders
and higher boiler pressure. All
rebuilt with Belpaire firebox.

†Introduced 1895. Final Johnson
0-4-4T design, with higher-pitched
boiler and larger tanks, later rebuilt
with Belpaire firebox.

Push-and-Pull fitted.

Weight: 53 tons 4 cwt.

Pressure: 150 lb.

Cyls.: $\begin{cases} 18″×24″.* \\ 17″×24″.† \end{cases}$ T.E.: $\begin{cases} 18,225 \text{ lb.*} \\ 16,255 \text{ lb.†} \end{cases}$

Dr. Wheels: 5′ 4″.

58065*	58083†	58085†	58086†
58066*			

Total 5

0-6-0   2F

*Introduced 1875. Johnson Midland
4′ 11″ design with round top firebox.

†Introduced 1917. Johnson 4′ 11″ design
rebuilt with Belpaire firebox.

§Introduced 1917. Johnson Midland 5′ 3″
design rebuilt with Belpaire firebox.

Weight: Loco. Various.
37 tons 12 cwt. to 40 tons 3 cwt.

Pressure: 160 lb.

Dr. Wheels: $\begin{cases} 4′ 11″.* \\ 4′ 11″.† \\ 5′ 3″.§ \end{cases}$ T.E.: $\begin{cases} 19,420 \text{ lb.*} \\ 19,420 \text{ lb.†} \\ 18,185 \text{ lb.§} \end{cases}$

58114†	58153†	58187†	58225§
58115†	58156†	58188§	58228§
58116†	58157†	58189§	58238†
58118†	58158†	58190›	58246*
58119†	58160†	58191§	58247†
58120†	58163†	58192§	58260§
58121†	58165†	58196§	58261§
58122†	58166†	58197§	58271§
58123†	58167†	58198§	58279§
58124†	58168†	58199§	58281§
58128†	58169†	58203§	58283§
58130†	58170†	58204§	58287§
58131†	58171†	58206§	58288§
58132†	58173†	58209§	58291§
58135†	58174†	58213§	58293§
58136†	58175†	58214§	58295§
58137†	58177†	58215§	58298§
58138†	58178†	58216§	58305§
58140†	58181†	58217§	58308§
58143†	58182†	58218§	
58144†	58183†	58219§	
58146†	58185†	58220§	
58148†	58186†	58221§	

Total 88

0-6-0T   2F

Introduced 1879. Park North London design.
Weight: 45 tons 10 cwt.
Pressure: 160 lb.
Cyls. : (O) 17″ × 24″.
Dr. Wheels: 4′ 4″.   T.E.: 18,140 lb.

58850	58857	58859	58860
58856			

Total 5

0-6-2T   2F

Introduced 1882. Webb L.N.W. " Coal Tanks."
Weight: 43 tons 15 cwt.
Pressure: 150 lb.
Cyls.: 17″ × 24″
Dr. Wheels: 4′ 5½″.   T.E.: 16,530 lb.

58926

Total 1

SERVICE LOCOS.

0-4-0   Diesel

Introduced 1936. Messrs. Fowler diesel.
Weight: 21 tons 5 cwt.

E.D.1	E.D.4	E.D.6
E.D.2	E.D.5	E.D.7
E.D.3		

0-6-0ST   2F

Introduced 1870. Webb version of Ramsbottom " Special Tank."
Weight: 34 tons 10 cwt.
Pressure: 140 lb.
Cyls.: 17″ × 24″.
Dr. Wheels: 4′ 5½″.   T.E.: 17,005 lb.
C.D.3 Wolverton Carriage Works
C.D.6   ,,   ,,   ,,
C.D.7   ,,   ,,   ,,
C.D.8 *Earlestown,* Wolverton C.W.

HISTORIC LOCOMOTIVES PRESERVED IN STORE

Type	Originating Company	Pre-Grouping No.	L.M.S. No.	Name	Place of Preservation
4-2-2	M.R.	118	(673)	—	Derby
2-4-0	M.R.	158A	—	—	Derby
*4-4-0	M.R.	1000	(1000)	—	Crewe
4-4-2T	L.T. & S.	80	(2148)	Thundersley	Derby
2-2-2	L.N.W.	(49)	—	Columbine	York Museum
2-2-2	L.N.W.	3020	—	Cornwall	Crewe
2-4-0	L.N.W.	790	(5031)	Hardwicke	Crewe
0-4-0ST	L.N.W.	1439	—	—	Crewe
†0-4-0T	L.N.W.	—	—	Pet	Crewe
0-4-0	F.R.	3	—	Coppernob	Horwich
0-4-2	Liverpool & Manchester	—	—	Lion	Crewe
4-2-2	C.R.	123	(14010)	—	St. Rollox
4-6-0	H.R.	103	(17916)	—	St. Rollox

The unbracketed numbers are the ones at present carried by the locos.
*Present number 41000.
† 18 in. gauge works shunter.

4-6-2 **7P6F**

Introduced 1951. Designed at Derby.
Weight : Loco. 94 tons 0 cwt.
Tender (see page 61).
Pressure : 250 lb.   Su.
Cyls. : (O) 20″ × 28″.
Driving Wheels : 6′ 2″. T.E. : 32,150 lb.
Walschaerts valve gear. P.V.

70000	Britannia
70001	Lord Hurcomb
70002	Geoffrey Chaucer
70003	John Bunyan
70004	William Shakespeare
70005	John Milton
70006	Robert Burns
70007	Coeur-de-Lion
70008	Black Prince
70009	Alfred the Great
70010	Owen Glendower
70011	Hotspur
70012	John of Gaunt
70013	Oliver Cromwell
70014	Iron Duke
70015	Apollo
70016	Ariel
70017	Arrow
70018	Flying Dutchman
70019	Lightning
70020	Mercury
70021	Morning Star
70022	Tornado
70023	Venus
70024	Vulcan
70025	Western Star
70026	Polar Star
70027	Rising Star
70028	Royal Star
70029	Shooting Star
70030	William Wordsworth
70031	Byron
70032	Tennyson
70033	Charles Dickens

70034	Thomas Hardy
70035	Rudyard Kipling
70036	Boadicea
70037	Hereward the Wake
70038	Robin Hood
70039	Sir Christopher Wren
70040	Clive of India
70041	Sir John Moore
70042	Lord Roberts
70043	
70044	Earl Haig
70045	
70046	
70047	
70048	
70049	
70050	Firth of Clyde
70051	Firth of Forth
70052	Firth of Tay
70053	Moray Firth
70054	Dornoch Firth

Total 55

4-6-2 **8P**

Introduced 1954. Designed at Derby.
Weight : Loco. 101 tons 5 cwt.
Tender (see page 61).
Pressure : 250 lb.   Su.
Cyls. : (3) 18″ × 28″.
Driving Wheels : 6′ 2″. T.E.: 39,080 lb.
Caprotti valve gear.

71000	Duke of Gloucester

Total 1

4-6-2 **6P5F**

Introduced 1952. Designed at Derby.
Weight : Loco. 86 tons 19 cwt.
Tender (see page 61).
Pressure : 225 lb.   Su.
Cyls. : (O) 19½″ × 28″.
Driving Wheels : 6′ 2″. T.E. : 27,520 lb.
Walschaerts valve gear. P.V.

72000	Clan Buchanan
72001	Clan Cameron
72002	Clan Campbell
72003	Clan Fraser

72004	Clan Macdonald
72005	Clan Macgregor
72006	Clan Mackenzie
72007	Clan Mackintosh
72008	Clan Macleod
72009	Clan Stewart **Total 10**

4-6-0   5

Introduced 1951. Designed at Don-
caster.
*Introduced 1956. Fitted with Caprotti
valve gear.
Weight :   Loco.   76 tons 4 cwt.
          Tender (see page 61).
Pressure : 225 lb.   Su.
Cyls. : (O) 19″ × 28″.
Driving Wheels : 6′ 2″. T.E. : 26,120 lb.
Walschaerts valve gear. P.V.

73000	73030	73060	73090
73001	73031	73061	73091
73002	73032	73062	73092
73003	73033	73063	73093
73004	73034	73064	73094
73005	73035	73065	73095
73006	73036	73066	73096
73007	73037	73067	73097
73008	73038	73068	73098
73009	73039	73069	73099
73010	73040	73070	73100
73011	73041	73071	73101
73012	73042	73072	73102
73013	73043	73073	73103
73014	73044	73074	73104
73015	73045	73075	73105
73016	73046	73076	73106
73017	73047	73077	73107
73018	73048	73078	73108
73019	73049	73079	73109
73020	73050	73080	73110
73021	73051	73081	73111
73022	73052	73082	73112
73023	73053	73083	73113
73024	73054	73084	73114
73025	73055	73085	73115
73026	73056	73086	73116
73027	73057	73087	73117
73028	73058	73088	73118
73029	73059	73089	73119

73120	73133*	73146*	73159
73121	73134*	73147*	73160
73122	73135*	73148*	73161
73123	73136*	73149*	73162
73124	73137*	73150*	73163
73125*	73138*	73151*	73164
73126*	73139*	73152*	73165
73127*	73140*	73153*	73166
73128*	73141*	73154*	73167
73129*	73142*	73155	73168
73130*	73143*	73156	73169
73131*	73144*	73157	73170
73132*	73145*	73158	73171

Engines of this class are still being
delivered.

4-6-0   4

Introduced 1951. Designed at Brighton
Weight :   Loco.   69 tons 0 cwt.
          Tender (see page 61).
Pressure : 225 lb.   Su.
Cyls. : (O) 18″ × 28″.
Driving Wheels : 5′ 8″. T.E. : 25,100 lb.
Walschaerts valve gear. P.V.

75000	75023	75046	75069
75001	75024	75047	75070
75002	75025	75048	75071
75003	75026	75049	75072
75004	75027	75050	75073
75005	75028	75051	75074
75006	75029	75052	75075
75007	75030	75053	75076
75008	75031	75054	75077
75009	75032	75055	75078
75010	75033	75056	75079
75011	75034	75057	75080
75012	75035	75058	75081
75013	75036	75059	75082
75014	75037	75060	75083
75015	75038	75061	75084
75016	75039	75062	75085
75017	75040	75063	75086
75018	75041	75064	75087
75019	75042	75065	75088
75020	75043	75066	75089
75021	75044	75067	
75022	75045	75068	

Engines of this class are still being
delivered.

2-6-0   4

Introduced 1953. Designed at Don-caster.
Weight : Loco.   59 tons 2 cwt.
          Tender (see page 61).
Pressure : 225 lb.   Su.
Cyls. : (O) 17½″ × 26″.
Driving Wheels : 5′ 3″.   T.E. : 24,170 lb.
Walschaerts valve gear. P.V.

76000	76029	76058	76087
76001	76030	76059	76088
76002	76031	76060	76089
76003	76032	76061	76090
76004	76033	76062	76091
76005	76034	76063	76092
76006	76035	76064	76093
76007	76036	76065	76094
76008	76037	76066	76095
76009	76038	76067	76096
76010	76039	76068	76097
76011	76040	76069	76098
76012	76041	76070	76099
76013	76042	76071	76100
76014	76043	76072	76101
76015	76044	76073	76102
76016	76045	76074	76103
76017	76046	76075	76104
76018	76047	76076	76105
76019	76048	76077	76106
76020	76049	76078	76107
76021	76050	76079	76108
76022	76051	76080	76109
76023	76052	76081	76110
76024	76053	76082	76111
76025	76054	76083	76112
76026	76055	76084	76113
76027	76056	76085	76114
76028	76057	76086	

Engines of this class are still being delivered.

2-6-0   3

Introduced 1954. Designed at Swindon.
Weight : Loco. 57 tons 9 cwt.
          Tender (see page 61).
Pressure : 200 lb. Su.
Cyls. : (O) 17½″ × 26″.
Driving Wheels : 5′ 3″. T.E. : 21,490 lb.
Walschaerts valve gear. P.V.

77000	77007	77014	77021
77001	77008	77015	77022
77002	77009	77016	77023
77003	77010	77017	77024
77004	77011	77018	
77005	77012	77019	
77006	77013	77020	

Engines of this class are still being delivered.

2-6-0   2

Introduced 1953. Designed at Derby.
Weight : Loco.   49 tons 5 cwt.
          Tender (see page 61).
Pressure : 200 lb. Su.
Cyls. : (O) 16½″ × 24″.
Driving Wheels : 5′ 0″. T.E. : 18,515 lb.
Walschaerts valve gear. P.V.

78000	78017	78034	78051
78001	78018	78035	78052
78002	78019	78036	78053
78003	78020	78037	78054
78004	78021	78038	78055
78005	78022	78039	78056
78006	78023	78040	78057
78007	78024	78041	78058
78008	78025	78042	78059
78009	78026	78043	78060
78010	78027	78044	78061
78011	78028	78045	78062
78012	78029	78046	78063
78013	78030	78047	78064
78014	78031	78048	
78015	78032	78049	
78016	78033	78050	

Total 65

2-6-4T   4

Introduced 1951. Designed at Brighton.
Weight: 88 tons 10 cwt.
Pressure: 225 lb. Su.
Cyls.: (O) 18″ × 28″.
Driving Wheels: 5′ 8″. T.E. 25,100 lb.
Walschaerts valve gear. P.V.

80000	80005	80010	80015
80001	80006	80011	80016
80002	80007	80012	80017
80003	80008	80013	80018
80004	80009	80014	80019

80020	80054	80088	80122
80021	80055	80089	80123
80022	80056	80090	80124
80023	80057	80091	80125
80024	80058	80092	80126
80025	80059	80093	80127
80026	80060	80094	80128
80027	80061	80095	80129
80028	80062	80096	80130
80029	80063	80097	80131
80030	80064	80098	80132
80031	80065	80099	80133
80032	80066	80100	80134
80033	80067	80101	80135
80034	80068	80102	80136
80035	80069	80103	80137
80036	80070	80104	80138
80037	80071	80105	80139
80038	80072	80106	80140
80039	80073	80107	80141
80040	80074	80108	80142
80041	80075	80109	80143
80042	80076	80110	80144
80043	80077	80111	80145
80044	80078	80112	80146
80045	80079	80113	80147
80046	80080	80114	80148
80047	80081	80115	80149
80048	80082	80116	80150
80049	80083	80117	80151
80050	80084	80118	80152
80051	80085	80119	80153
80052	80086	80120	80154
80053	80087	80121	

Total 155

2-6-2T 3

Introduced 1952. Designed at Swindon.
Weight: 73 tons 10 cwt.
Pressure: 200 lb. Su.
Cyls.: (O) $17\frac{1}{2}'' \times 26''$.
Driving Wheels: 5' 3". T.E.: 21,490 lb.
Walschaerts valve gear. P.V.

82000	82002	82004	82006
82001	82003	82005	82007

82008	82018	82028	82038
82009	82019	82029	82039
82010	82020	82030	82040
82011	82021	82031	82041
82012	82022	82032	82042
82013	82023	82033	82043
82014	82024	82034	82044
82015	82025	82035	
82016	82026	82036	
82017	82027	82037	

Total 45

2-6-2T 2

Introduced 1953. Designed at Derby
Weight: 63 tons 5 cwt.
Pressure: 200 lb. Su.
Cyls.: (O) $16\frac{1}{2}'' \times 24''$.
Driving Wheels: 5' 0". T.E.: 18,515 lb.
Walschaerts valve gear. P.V.

84000	84008	84016	84024
84001	84009	84017	84025
84002	84010	84018	84026
84003	84011	84019	84027
84004	84012	84020	84028
84005	84013	84021	84029
84006	84014	84022	
84007	84015	84023	

Engines of this class are still being
delivered

2-8-0 8F WD

Ministry of Supply " Austerity " 2-8-0
locomotives purchased by British
Railways, 1948.
Introduced 1943. Riddles M.o.S. design
Weight: Loco. 70 tons 5 cwt.
Tender 55 tons 10 cwt.
Pressure: 225 lb. Su. Cyls.: (O) 19" × 28"
Driving Wheels: 4' 8½". T.E.: 34,215 lb.
Walschaerts valve gear. P.V.

90000	90009	90018	90027
90001	90010	90019	90028
90002	90011	90020	90029
90003	90012	90021	90030
90004	90013	90022	90031
90005	90014	90023	90032
90006	90015	90024	90033
90007	90016	90025	90034
90008	90017	90026	90035

90036	90082	90128	90174	90220	90266	90312	90358
90037	90083	90129	90175	90221	90267	90313	90359
90038	90084	90130	90176	90222	90268	90314	90360
90039	90085	90131	90177	90223	90269	90315	90361
90040	90086	90132	90178	90224	90270	90316	90362
90041	90087	90133	90179	90225	90271	90317	90363
90042	90088	90134	90180	90226	90272	90318	90364
90043	90089	90135	90181	90227	90273	90319	90365
90044	90090	90136	90182	90228	90274	90320	90366
90045	90091	90137	90183	90229	90275	90321	90367
90046	90092	90138	90184	90230	90276	90322	90368
90047	90093	90139	90185	90231	90277	90323	90369
90048	90094	90140	90186	90232	90278	90324	90370
90049	90095	90141	90187	90233	90279	90325	90371
90050	90096	90142	90188	90234	90280	90326	90372
90051	90097	90143	90189	90235	90281	90327	90373
90052	90098	90144	90190	90236	90282	90328	90374
90053	90099	90145	90191	90237	90283	90329	90375
90054	90100	90146	90192	90238	90284	90330	90376
90055	90101	90147	90193	90239	90285	90331	90377
90056	90102	90148	90194	90240	90286	90332	90378
90057	90103	90149	90195	90241	90287	90333	90379
90058	90104	90150	90196	90242	90288	90334	90380
90059	90105	90151	90197	90243	90289	90335	90381
90060	90106	90152	90198	90244	90290	90336	90382
90061	90107	90153	90199	90245	90291	90337	90383
90062	90108	90154	90200	90246	90292	90338	90384
90063	90109	90155	90201	90247	90293	90339	90385
90064	90110	90156	90202	90248	90294	90340	90386
90065	90111	90157	90203	90249	90295	90341	90387
90066	90112	90158	90204	90250	90296	90342	90388
90067	90113	90159	90205	90251	90297	90343	90389
90068	90114	90160	90206	90252	90298	90344	90390
90069	90115	90161	90207	90253	90299	90345	90391
90070	90116	90162	90208	90254	90300	90346	90392
90071	90117	90163	90209	90255	90301	90347	90393
90072	90118	90164	90210	90256	90302	90348	90394
90073	90119	90165	90211	90257	90303	90349	90395
90074	90120	90166	90212	90258	90304	90350	90396
90075	90121	90167	90213	90259	90305	90351	90397
90076	90122	90168	90214	90260	90306	90352	90398
90077	90123	90169	90215	90261	90307	90353	90399
90078	90124	90170	90216	90262	90308	90354	90400
90079	90125	90171	90217	90263	90309	90355	90401
90080	90126	90172	90218	90264	90310	90356	90402
90081	90127	90173	90219	90265	90311	90357	90403

90404	90450	90496	90542	90588	90625	90662	90699
90405	90451	90497	90543	90589	90626	90663	90700
90406	90452	90498	90544	90590	90627	90664	90701
90407	90453	90499	90545	90591	90628	90665	90702
90408	90454	90500	90546	90592	90629	90666	90703
90409	90455	90501	90547	90593	90630	90667	90704
90410	90456	90502	90548	90594	90631	90668	90705
90411	90457	90503	90549	90595	90632	90669	90706
90412	90458	90504	90550	90596	90633	90670	90707
90413	90459	90505	90551	90597	90634	90671	90708
90414	90460	90506	90552	90598	90635	90672	90709
90415	90461	90507	90553	90599	90636	90673	90710
90416	90462	90508	90554	90600	90637	90674	90711
90417	90463	90509	90555	90601	90638	90675	90712
90418	90464	90510	90556	90602	90639	90676	90713
90419	90465	90511	90557	90603	90640	90677	90714
90420	90466	90512	90558	90604	90641	90678	90715
90421	90467	90513	90559	90605	90642	90679	90716
90422	90468	90514	90560	90606	90643	90680	90717
90423	90469	90515	90561	90607	90644	90681	90718
90424	90470	90516	90562	90608	90645	90682	90719
90425	90471	90517	90563	90609	90646	90683	90720
90426	90472	90518	90564	90610	90647	90684	90721
90427	90473	90519	90565	90611	90648	90685	90722
90428	90474	90520	90566	90612	90649	90686	90723
90429	90475	90521	90567	90613	90650	90687	90724
90430	90476	90522	90568	90614	90651	90688	90725
90431	90477	90523	90569	90615	90652	90689	90726
90432	90478	90524	90570	90616	90653	90690	90727
90433	90479	90525	90571	90617	90654	90691	90728
90434	90480	90526	90572	90618	90655	90692	90729
90435	90481	90527	90573	90619	90656	90693	90730
90436	90482	90528	90574	90620	90657	90694	90731
90437	90483	90529	90575	90621	90658	90695	90732
90438	90484	90530	90576	90622	90659	90696	Vulcan
90439	90485	90531	90577	90623	90660	90697	
90440	90486	90532	90578	90624	90661	90698	
90441	90487	90533	90579				
90442	90488	90534	90580				
90443	90489	90535	90581				
90444	90490	90536	90582				
90445	90491	90537	90583				
90446	90492	90538	90584				
90447	90493	90539	90585				
90448	90494	90540	90586				
90449	90495	90541	90587				

Total 733

2-10-0   8F   **WD**

Ministry of Supply "Austerity" 2-10-0 locomotives purchased by British Railways, 1948.

Introduced 1943. Riddles M.o.S. design.

Weight : Loco. 78 tons 6 cwt.
Tender 55 tons 10 cwt.

Pressure: 225 lbs. Su. Cyls.:(O)19″×28″.
Driving Wheels: 4′ 8½″. T.E.: 34,215 lb.
Walschaerts valve gear. P.V.

90750	90757	90764	90771
90751	90758	90765	90772
90752	90759	90766	90773
90753	90760	90767	90774
90754	90761	90768	
90755	90762	90769	
90756	90763	90770	

Total 25

2-10-0   9F

Introduced 1954. Designed at Brighton.
*Introduced 1955. Fitted with Crosti boiler.
Weight : Loco. $\begin{cases} \text{86 tons 14 cwt.} \\ \text{90 tons 4 cwt.*} \end{cases}$
Tender (see page 61).
Pressure : 250 lb. Su.
Cyls. : (O) 20″ × 28″.
Driving Wheels : 5′ 0″. T.E. : 39,670 lb.
Walschaerts valve gear. P.V.

92000	92023*	92046	92069	92092	92120	92148	92176
92001	92024*	92047	92070	92093	92121	92149	92177
92002	92025*	92048	92071	92094	92122	92150	92178
92003	92026*	92049	92072	92095	92123	92151	92179
92004	92027*	92050	92073	92096	92124	92152	92180
92005	92028*	92051	92074	92097	92125	92153	92181
92006	92029*	92052	92075	92098	92126	92154	92182
92007	92030	92053	92076	92099	92127	92155	92183
92008	92031	92054	92077	92100	92128	92156	92184
92009	92032	92055	92078	92101	92129	92157	92185
92010	92033	92056	92079	92102	92130	92158	92186
92011	92034	92057	92080	92103	92131	92159	92187
92012	92035	92058	92081	92104	92132	92160	92188
92013	92036	92059	92082	92105	92133	92161	92189
92014	92037	92060	92083	92106	92134	92162	92190
92015	92038	92061	92084	92107	92135	92163	92191
92016	92039	92062	92085	92108	92136	92164	92192
92017	92040	92063	92086	92109	92137	92165	92193
92018	92041	92064	92087	92110	92138	92166	92194
92019	92042	92065	92088	92111	92139	92167	92195
92020*	92043	92066	92089	92112	92140	92168	92196
92021*	92044	92067	92090	92113	92141	92169	92197
92022*	92045	92068	92091	92114	92142	92170	92198
				92115	92143	92171	92199
				92116	92144	92172	92200
				92117	92145	92173	92201
				92118	92146	92174	92202
				92119	92147	92175	

Engines of this class are still being delivered.

BRITISH RAILWAYS STANDARD TENDERS

N.B.—*These pairings are not permanent and are liable to alteration with changed operating conditions.*

Type	Capacity		Weight in Full W.O.		Locos to which Allocated
	Water galls.	Coal tons	tons	cwt.	
BRI ...	4,250	7	49	3	70000–24/30–44 72000–9 73000–49
BRIA ...	5,000	7	52	10	70025–29
BRIB ...	4,725	7	50	5	92020–29/60–6 97–9 73080–89 73100–09/20–34/45–71 75065–79 76053–69
BRIC ...	4,725	9	53	5	92015–19/45–59/77–86 92100–39 50–67 73065–79 90–9 73135–44
BRID ...	4,725	9	54	10	70045–54
BRIE ...	4,725	10	55	10	71000
BRIF ...	5,625	7	55	5	92010–14 30–44/67–76 92087–96 92140–49 68–92202 73110–19
BRIG ...	5,000	7	52	10	92000–9 73050–52
BRIH ...	4,250	7	49	3	73053–64
BR2 ...	3,500	6	42	3	75000–49 76000–44
BR2A ...	3,500	6	42	3	75050–64 80–9 76045–52/70–76114 77000–24
BR3 ...	3,000	4	36	17	78000–64

CHIEF MECHANICAL ENGINEERS

BRITISH RAILWAYS (L.M. Region)

H. G. Ivatt ... 1948–1951

L.M.S.

George Hughes ...	...	1923–1925	Sir William Stanier	...	1932–1944
Sir Henry Fowler	...	1925–1931	Charles E. Fairburn	...	1944–1945
E. H. J. Lemon	...	1931–1932	H. G. Ivatt	...	1945–1947
(Sir Ernest Lemon)					

LOCOMOTIVE SUPERINTENDENTS AND C.M.E.'S—L.M.S. CONSTITUENT COMPANIES

CALEDONIAN RAILWAY

Robert Sinclair		
(First loco. engineer)*		1847–1856
Benjamin Connor	...	1856–1876
George Brittain	...	1876–1882
Dugald Drummond	...	1882–1890
Hugh Smellie	...	1890
J. Lambie ...	...	1890–1895
J. F. McIntosh	...	1895–1914
William Pickersgill	...	1914–1923

FURNESS RAILWAY

R. Mason ...	...	...	1890–1897
W. F. Pettigrew ...	...	1897–1918
D. J. Rutherford ...	...	1918–1923

GLASGOW AND SOUTH WESTERN RLY.

Patrick Stirling	...	1853–1866
James Stirling	...	1866–1878
Hugh Smellie	...	1878–1890
James Manson	...	1890–1912
Peter Drummond	...	1912–1918
R. H. Whitelegg ...	...	1918–1923

HIGHLAND RAILWAY

William Stroudley		
(First loco. engineer)...		1866–1869
David Jones	...	1869–1896
Peter Drummond	...	1896–1911
F. G. Smith	...	1912–1915
C. Cumming	...	1915–1923

L. & Y.R.

Sir John Hawkshaw (Consultant),*		
Hurst and Jenkins successively to 1868		
W Hurst ...	...	1868–1876
W. Barton Wright	...	1876–1886
John A. F. Aspinall	...	1886–1899
H. A. Hoy...	...	1899–1904
George Hughes ...	...	1904–1921
The L. & Y. amalgamated with L.N.W.R. as from Jan. 1st, 1922.		

L.N.W.R.

Francis Trevithick and J. E. McConnell, first loco. engineers, 1846, with Alexander Allan largely responsible for design at Crewe.*		
John Ramsbottom	...	1857–1871
Francis William Webb	...	1871–1903
George Whale	...	1903–1909
Charles John Bowen-Cooke ...	...	1909–1920
Capt. Hewitt Pearson Montague Beames	...	1920–1921
George Hughes ...	...	1922

LT. & S.R.

Thomas Whitelegg	...	1880–1910
Robert Harben Whitelegg	...	1910–1912
(L.T. & S.R. absorbed by M.R., control of locos. transferred to Derby as from Aug., 1912.)		

---

* Exclusive of previous service with constituent company.

LOCOMOTIVE SUPERINTENDENTS
AND C.M.E.'S (continued)

MARYPORT & CARLISLE

Hugh Smellie	... ...	1870–1878
J. Campbell	...	1878–
William Coulthard	... *	–1904
J. B. Adamson	... ...	1904–1923

MIDLAND RAILWAY

Matthew Kirtley ...		
(First loco. engineer) ...		1844–1873
Samuel Waite Johnson	...	1873–1903
Richard Mountford Deeley		1903–1909
Henry Fowler	... ...	1909–1923

SOMERSET AND DORSET JOINT RAILWAY

Until leased by Mid. and L. & S. W. (as from 1st Nov., 1875) locomotives were bought from outside builders, principally George England of Hatcham Iron Works, S.E. After the above date, Derby and its various Loco. Supts. and C.M.E.'s have acted for S. & D.J., aided by a resident Loco. Supt. stationed at Highbridge works.

NORTH STAFFORDSHIRE RAILWAY

L. Clare	... ...	1876–1882
L. Longbottom	... ...	1882–1902
J. H. Adams	... ...	1902–1915
J. A. Hookham	... ...	1915–1923

W. Angus was Loco. Supt. at Stoke prior to 1876. No earlier records can be traced.

WIRRAL

Eric G. Barker	... ...	1892–1902
T. B. Hunter	... ...	1903–1923

Barker of the Wirral Railway is noteworthy for originating the 4-4-4 tank type in this country (1896).

NORTH LONDON RAILWAY

(Worked by L. & N.W. by agreement dated Dec., 1908.)

William Adams	... ...	1853–1873
J. C. Park ...	... ...	1873–1893
Henry J. Pryce	... ...	1893–1908

---

* Date of actual entry into office not known.

NOW is the time to join the

Ian Allan LOCOSPOTTERS CLUB

FILL IN THIS APPLICATION FORM

and be sure to note your promise to obey the Club Rule

YOUR PROMISE...

I, the undersigned, do hereby make application to join the Ian Allan Locospotters Club, and undertake on my honour, if this application is accepted, to keep the rule of the Club ; I understand that if I break this rule in any way I cease to be a member and forfeit the right to wear the badge and take part in the Club's activities.

Date.............................195...   Signed.......................................

These details to be completed in BLOCK LETTERS :

SURNAME.............................. DATE OF BIRTH........................19......

CHRISTIAN NAMES..

ADDRESS ....

....

You can order any or all of the MEMBERSHIP BADGES listed below *when you apply to join.* Please mark your requirements and send the remittance to cover. Put a cross (X) against the region and type of badges you want, and write the amount due in the end columns.

	Standard (cellu-loid) type, 6d.	De luxe (chrome) type, 1/3.	s.	d.
Western Region Brown				
Southern Region .. .. .. Green				
London Midland Region .. .. Red				
Eastern Region .. Dark Blue				
North-Eastern Region .. Tangerine				
Scottish Region .. Light Blue				
MEMBERSHIP ENTRANCE FEE (not including Badge) : (which must be paid before any badge orders can be accepted). Postal order enclosed :				9

MINIMUM REMITTANCE FOR MEMBERSHIP AND DE-LUXE BADGE IS 2s. 0d.

DON'T FORGET YOU MUST SEND A 2½d. STAMPED ADDRESSED ENVELOPE !

THE abc OF
BRITISH RAILWAYS
LOCOMOTIVES

PART 4 - Nos. 60000-99999

EASTERN, NORTH EASTERN, SCOTTISH
REGION, EX-W.D. & B.R. STANDARD
STEAM LOCOMOTIVES

SUMMER
1957
EDITION

LONDON :

Ian Allan Ltd

FOREWORD

THIS booklet lists all British Railways locomotives numbered between 60000 and 99999. This series of numbers includes all Eastern, North Eastern and Scottish (ex-L.N.E.R.) Region steam locomotives of the former L.N.E.R., Class "W.D." and British Railways standard steam locomotives.

Details of the following will be found in the books named :—

● Electric, Diesel electric and Diesel mechanical locomotives in *ABC of British Railways Locomotives*, Part 2 (Nos. 10000-39999).

● Diesel train units in *ABC of British Railways Diesel Locomotives and Trains*.

● Electric train units in *ABC of British Electric Trains*.

―――――――

NOTES ON THE USE OF THIS BOOK

In the list of locomotives which follows :

1. Many of the classes listed are sub-divided, the sub-divisions being denoted in some cases by " Parts " shown thus : D16/3. At the head of each class will be found a list of such sub-divisions, if any, usually arranged in order of introduction. Each part is given there a reference mark by which its relevant dimensions, if differing from those of other parts, and the locos included in this part, may be identified. Any other differences between locomotives are also indicated, with reference marks, below the details of the class's introduction.

2. The lists of dimensions at the head of each class show locomotives fitted with two inside cylinders, Stephenson valve gear and slide valves, unless otherwise stated. e.g. (O) = two outside cylinders, P.V. = piston valves.

3. The following method is used to denote superheated locomotives, the letters being inserted, where applicable, after the boiler pressure details : Su = All engines superheated.
SS = Some engines superheated.

4. The date on which the first locomotive of a class was built or modified is denoted by " Introduced ".

5. The numbers of locomotives in service have been checked to March 16th, 1957.

6. S. denotes Service (Departmental) locomotive still carrying B.R. number (see page 45). This reference letter is introduced only for the reader's guidance and is not borne by the locomotive concerned.

BRITISH RAILWAYS
EASTERN & NORTH EASTERN REGIONS

Chief Mechanical Engineer
A. H. Peppercorn - - 1948-1949
(*post abolished*)

LOCOMOTIVE SUPERINTENDENTS AND CHIEF MECHANICAL ENGINEERS OF THE L.N.E.R.

Sir Nigel Gresley   1923—1941 | E. Thompson   ...   1941—1946
A. H. Peppercorn 1946—1947

Great Northern Railway

A. Sturrock	...	1850—1866
P. Stirling	...	1866—1895
H. A. Ivatt	...	1896—1911
H. N. Gresley	...	1911—1922

North Eastern Railway

E. Fletcher	...	1854—1883
A. McDonnell*	...	1883—1884
T. W. Worsdell		1885—1890
W. Worsdell	...	1890—1910
Sir Vincent Raven	1910—1922

Great Eastern Railway

R. Sinclair	...	1862—1866
S. W. Johnson	...	1866—1873
W. Adams	...	1873—1878
M. Bromley	...	1878—1881
T. W. Worsdell	...	1881—1885
J. Holden	...	1885—1907
S. D. Holden	...	1908—1912
A. J. Hill		1912—1922

Lancashire, Derbyshire and East Coast Railway

R. A. Thom	...	1902—1907

Manchester, Sheffield and Lincolnshire Railway

Richard Peacock		—1854
W. G. Craig	...	1854—1859

Charles Sacré	...	1859—1886
T. Parker	...	1886—1893
H. Pollitt	...	1893—1897

Great Central Railway

H. Pollitt	...	1897—1900
J. G. Robinson	...	1900—1922

Hull and Barnsley Railway

M. Stirling	...	1885—1922

Midland and Great Northern Joint Railway

W. Marriott	...	1884—1924

North British Railway

T. Wheatley†	...	1867—1874
D. Drummond	...	1875—1882
M. Holmes	...	1882—1903
W. P. Reid	...	1903—1919
W. Chalmers	...	1919—1922

Great North of Scotland Railway

D. K. Clark	...	1853—1855
J. F. Ruthven	...	1855—1857
W. Cowan	...	1857—1883
J. Manson	...	1883—1890
J. Johnson	...	1890—1894
W. Pickersgill	...	1894—1914
T. E. Heywood	...	1914—1922

* Between McDonnell and T. W. Worsdell there was an interval during which the office was covered by a Locomotive Committee.

† Previous to whom the records are indeterminate.

3

BRITISH RAILWAYS LOCOMOTIVE SHEDS AND SHED CODES

EASTERN REGION

30A **Stratford**	32A **Norwich**	36A **Doncaster**
Brentwood	Cromer Beach	36B Mexborough
Chelmsford	Dereham	Wath
Enfield Town	Swaffham	36C Frodingham
Epping	Wymondham	36D Barnsley
Ilford	32B Ipswich	36E Retford
Wood Street	Felixstowe Town	Newark
(Walthamstow)	Stowmarket	
30B Hertford East	32C Lowestoft	38A **Colwick**
Buntingford	32D Yarmouth (South	38B Annesley
Ware	Town)	38C Leicester (ex-G.C.)
30C Bishops Stortford	32E Yarmouth (Vauxhall)	38D Staveley
30E Colchester	32F Yarmouth Beach	38E Woodford Halse
Braintree	32G Melton Constable	
Clacton	Norwich City	39A **Gorton**
Maldon		Dinting
Walton-on-Naze	33A **Plaistow**	Hayfield
30F Parkeston	33B Tilbury	
	33C Shoeburyness	40A **Lincoln**
		Lincoln (St. Mark's)
	34A **Kings Cross**	40B Immingham
31A **Cambridge**	34B Hornsey	Grimsby
Ely	34C Hatfield	New Holland
Huntingdon East	34D Hitchin	40D Tuxford
Saffron Walden	34E Neasden	40E Langwith Junction
31B March	Aylesbury	40F Boston
Wisbech	Chesham	Sleaford
31C Kings Lynn	35A **New England**	
Hunstanton	Spalding	
31D South Lynn	Stamford	
31E Bury St. Edmunds	35B Grantham	
Sudbury (Suffolk)	35C Peterborough (Spital)	41A **Sheffield (Darnall)**

NORTH EASTERN REGION

50A **York**	52A **Gateshead**	54B Tyne Dock
50B Leeds (Neville Hill)	Bowes Bridge	54C Borough Gardens
50C Selby	52B Heaton	54D Consett
50D Starbeck	52C Blaydon	
50E Scarborough	Alston	
50F Malton	Hexham	55A **Leeds (Holbeck)**
Pickering	52D Tweedmouth	55B Stourton
50G Whitby	Alnmouth	55C Farnley Junction
	52E Percy Main	55D Royston
	52F North Blyth	55E Normanton
	South Blyth	55F Manningham
51A **Darlington**		55G Huddersfield
Middleton-in-		
Teesdale	53A **Hull (Dairycoates)**	
51B Newport (Yorks.)	53B Hull (Botanic	56A **Wakefield**
51C West Hartlepool	Gardens)	56B Ardsley
51D Middlesbrough	53C Hull (Springhead)	56C Copley Hill
51E Stockton	Alexandra Dock	56D Mirfield
51F West Auckland	53D Bridlington	56E Sowerby Bridge
51G Haverton Hill	53E Goole	56F Low Moor
51H Kirkby Stephen		56G Bradford
51J Northallerton	54A **Sunderland**	
51K Saltburn	Durham	

60A **Inverness**	62C Dunfermline	65C Parkhead
Dingwall	Alloa	65D Dawsholm
Kyle of Lochalsh		Dumbarton
60B Aviemore		65E Kipps
Boat of Garten	63A **Perth South**	65F Grangemouth
60C Helmsdale	Aberfeldy	65G Yoker
Dornoch	Crieff	65H Helensburgh
Tain	63B Stirling South	65I Balloch
60D Wick	Killin	65J Fort William
Thurso	Stirling (Shore	Mallaig
60E Forres	Road)	
	63C Forfar	66A **Polmadie (Glasgow)**
	63D Oban	66B Motherwell
61A **Kittybrewster**	Ballachulish	66C Hamilton
Ballater		66D Greenock (Ladyburn)
Fraserburgh		Greenock (Princes
Inverurie	64A **St. Margarets**	Pier)
Peterhead	**(Edinburgh)**	
61B Aberdeen (Ferryhill)	Dunbar	
61C Keith	Galashiels	67A **Corkerhill**
Banff	Longniddry	**(Glasgow)**
Elgin	North Berwick	67B Hurlford
	64B Haymarket	Beith
	64C Dalry Road	Muirkirk
	64D Carstairs	67C Ayr
62A **Thornton**	64E Polmont	67D Ardrossan
Anstruther	64F Bathgate	
Burntisland	64G Hawick	
Ladybank	Riccarton	68A **Carlisle (Kingmoor)**
Methil	St. Boswells	68B Dumfries
62B Dundee (Tay Bridge)		68C Stranraer
Arbroath		Newton Stewart
Dundee West	65A **Eastfield (Glasgow)**	68D Beattock
Montrose	Arrochar	68E Carlisle Canal
St. Andrews	65B St. Rollox	

ROUTE AVAILABILITY OF LOCOMOTIVES

Restrictions on the working of locomotives over the routes of the former L.N.E.R. are denoted by Route availability numbers. In general a locomotive is not permitted to work over a line of lower R.A. number than it bears. The scheme is as follows :

R.A.1 : J15, J71, Y1, Y3, Y8, Y10, Z4, DM1, Standard 2 2-6-2T.

R.A.2 : E4, J67/1, J72, J77, Y9, Z5.

R.A.3 : F5, J10, J21, J25, J36, J66, J67/2, J68, J69, J88, N10, Standard 2 2-6-0.

R.A.4 : B12/3, D40, F6, G5, J17, J26, J55, J83, N5/2, N14, V4, Standard 4 4-6-0, Standard 4 2-6-0, Standard 3 2-6-2T.

R.A.5 : A5, A8, B1, B2, B17, C12, C13, C14, D16, J6, J11, J19, J20, J27, J52, J73, J94, K2, N1, N7, Standard 4 2-6-4T.

R.A.6 : C15, C16, D11, D20, D30, D34, J35, J39, J50, K1, K4, N2, N15, O1, O2, O4, WD 2-8-0, Q6, V1, Y4.

R.A.7 : A7, B16/1, L1, Q7, V3, Standard 6P5F 4-6-2, Standard S 4-6-0.

R.A.8 : B16/2, B16/3, D49, J37, J38, K3, K5, Q1, T1, Standard 7P6F 4-6-2.

R.A.9 : A1, A2, A3, A4, V2, W1.

NUMERICAL LIST OF ENGINES

The Code given in smaller bold type at the head of each class, e.g. " 4MT "
denotes its British Railways power classification.

4-6-2 8P6F **Class A4**

Introduced 1935. Gresley streamlined
design with corridor tender (except
those marked †).
*Inside cylinder reduced to 17".
‡Kylchap blast pipe and double
chimney.
Weight: Loco. 102 tons 19 cwt.
Tender $\begin{cases} 64 \text{ tons } 19 \text{ cwt.} \\ 60 \text{ tons } 7 \text{ cwt.†} \end{cases}$
Pressure: 250 lb. Su.
Cyls.: $\begin{cases} (3) \ 18\frac{1}{2}'' \times 26''. \\ (2) \ 18\frac{1}{2}'' \times 26''. \ (1) \ 17'' \times 26''.* \end{cases}$
Driving Wheels: 6' 8".
T.E.: $\begin{cases} 35,455 \text{ lb.} \\ 33,616 \text{ lb.*} \end{cases}$
Walschaerts valve gear and derived
motion. P.V.

60001†	Sir Ronald Matthews
60002†	Sir Murrough Wilson
60003	Andrew K. McCosh
60004	William Whitelaw
60005†‡	Sir Charles Newton
60006†	Sir Ralph Wedgwood
60007	Sir Nigel Gresley
60008	Dwight D. Eisenhower
60009	Union of South Africa
60010	Dominion of Canada
60011	Empire of India
60012*	Commonwealth of Australia
60013	Dominion of New Zealand
60014	Silver Link
60015	Quicksilver
60016†	Silver King
60017	Silver Fox
60018†	Sparrow Hawk
60019†	Bittern
60020*†	Guillemot
60021†	Wild Swan
60022‡	Mallard
60023†	Golden Eagle
60024	Kingfisher
60025	Falcon

60026†	Miles Beevor
60027	Merlin
60028	Walter K. Whigham
60029	Woodcock
60030	Golden Fleece
60031*	Golden Plover
60032	Gannet
60033‡	Seagull
60034‡	Lord Faringdon

Total 34

4-6-2 7P6F **Class A3**

Introduced 1927. Development of
Gresley G.N. 180 lb. Pacific (intro-
duced 1922, L.N.E.R. A1, later A10)
with 220 lb. pressure (prototype and
others rebuilt from A10). Some have
G.N.-type tender† with coal rails,
remainder L.N.E.R. pattern.
*Kylchap blast pipe and double chimney.
Weight: Loco. 96 tons 5 cwt.
Tender $\begin{cases} 56 \text{ tons } 6 \text{ cwt.†} \\ 57 \text{ tons } 18 \text{ cwt.} \end{cases}$
Pressure:220 lb. Su. Cyls.:(3) $19'' \times 26''$
Driving Wheels: 6' 8". T.E.: 32,910 lb.
Walschaerts valve gear and derived
motion. P.V.

60035	Windsor Lad
60036	Colombo
60037	Hyperion
60038	Firdaussi
60039	Sandwich
60040	Cameronian
60041	Salmon Trout
60042	Singapore
60043	Brown Jack
60044	Melton
60045	Lemberg
60046	Diamond Jubilee
60047	Donovan
60048	Doncaster
60049	Galtee More
60050	Persimmon
60051	Blink Bonny
60052	Prince Palatine
60053	Sansovino
60054	Prince of Wales
60055	Woolwinder

60056	Centenary		60104	Solario
60057	Ormonde		60105	Victor Wild
60058	Blair Athol		60106	Flying Fox
60059	Tracery		60107	Royal Lancer
60060	The Tetrarch		60108	Gay Crusader
60061	Pretty Polly		60109	Hermit
60062	Minoru		60110	Robert the Devil
60063	Isinglass		60111	Enterprise
60064	Tagalie		60112	St. Simon
60065	Knight of Thistle			
60066	Merry Hampton			**Total 78**
60067	Ladas			
60068	Sir Visto			
60069	Sceptre			

4-6-2   8P6F   **Class A1**

A1/1* Introduced 1945. Thompson rebuild of A10.
A1   Peppercorn development of A1/1 for new construction.
A1†   Fitted with roller bearings.
Weight: Loco. { 101 tons.* 104 tons 2 cwt.
Tender 60 tons 7 cwt.
Pressure: 250 lb. Su.
Cyls.: (3) 19″ × 26″.
Driving Wheels: 6′ 8″. T.E.: 37,400 lb.
Walschaerts valve gear. P.V

60070	Gladiateur		60113*	Great Northern
60071	Tranquil		60114	W. P. Allen
60072	Sunstar		60115	Meg Merrilies
60073	St. Gatien		60116	Hal o' the Wynd
60074	Harvester		60117	Bois Roussel
60075	St. Frusquin		60118	Archibald Sturrock
60076	Galopin		60119	Patrick Stirling
60077	The White Knight		60120	Kittiwake
60078	Night Hawk		60121	Silurian
60079	Bayardo		60122	Curlew
60080	Dick Turpin		60123	H. A. Ivatt
60081	Shotover		60124	Kenilworth
60082	Neil Gow		60125	Scottish Union
60083	Sir Hugo		60126	Sir Vincent Raven
60084	Trigo		60127	Wilson Worsdell
60085	Manna		60128	Bongrace
60086	Gainsborough		60129	Guy Mannering
60087	Blenheim		60130	Kestrel
60088	Book Law		60131	Osprey
60089	Felstead		60132	Marmion
60090	Grand Parade		60133	Pommern
60091	Captain Cuttle		60134	Foxhunter
60092	Fairway		60135	Madge Wildfire
60093	Coronach		60136	Alcazar
60094	Colorado		60137	Redgauntlet
60095	Flamingo			
60096	Papyrus			
60097*	Humorist			
60098	Spion Kop			
60099	Call Boy			
60100	Spearmint			
60101	Cicero			
60102	Sir Frederick Banbury			
60103	Flying Scotsman			

60138	Boswell
60139	Sea Eagle
60140	Balmoral
60141	Abbotsford
60142	Edward Fletcher
60143	Sir Walter Scott
60144	King's Courier
60145	Saint Mungo
60146	Peregrine
60147	North Eastern
60148	Aboyeur
60149	Amadis
60150	Willbrook
60151	Midlothian
60152	Holyrood
60153†	Flamboyant
60154†	Bon Accord
60155†	Borderer
60156†	Great Central
60157†	Great Eastern
60158	Aberdonian
60159	Bonnie Dundee
60160	Auld Reekie
60161	North British
60162	Saint Johnstoun

Total 50

4-6-2 8P7F
(A2/1: 7P6F) Class A2

A2/2* Introduced 1943. Original Thompson Pacific, rebuilt from Gresley Class P2 2-8-2 (introduced 1934).
Weight: Loco. 101 tons 10 cwt.
Pressure: 225 lb. Su.
Cyls.: (3) 20″ × 26″.
Driving Wheels: 6′ 2″. T.E.: 40,320 lb.

A2/1† Introduced 1944. Development of Class A2/2, incorporating Class V2 2-6-2 boiler.
Weight: Loco. 98 tons.
Pressure: 225 lb. Su.
Cyls.: (3) 19″ × 26″.
Driving Wheels: 6′ 2″. T.E. 36,385 lb.

A2/3‡ Introduced 1946. Development of Class A2/2 for new construction.
Weight: Loco. 101 tons 10 cwt.
Pressure: 250 lb. Su.
Cyls.: (3) 19″ × 26″.
Driving Wheels: 6′ 2″. T.E. 40,430 lb.

A2§ Introduced 1947. Peppercorn development of Class A2/2 with shorter wheelbase. (No. 60539 built with double blast pipe.)

A2** Rebuilt with double blast pipe and multiple valve regulator.
Weight: Loco. 101 tons.
Pressure: 250 lb. Su.
Cyls.: (3) 19″ × 26″.
Driving Wheels: 6′ 2″. T.E.: 40,430 lb.
Tender weight (all parts): 60 tons 7 cwt.
Walschaerts valve gear. P.V.

60500‡	Edward Thompson
60501*	Cock o' the North
60502*	Earl Marischal
60503*	Lord President
60504*	Mons Meg
60505*	Thane of Fife
60506*	Wolf of Badenoch
60507†	Highland Chieftain
60508†	Duke of Rothesay
60509†	Waverley
60510†	Robert the Bruce
60511‡	Airborne
60512‡	Steady Aim
60513‡	Dante
60514‡	Chamossaire
60515‡	Sun Stream
60516‡	Hycilla
60517‡	Ocean Swell
60518‡	Tehran
60519‡	Honeyway
60520‡	Owen Tudor
60521‡	Watling Street
60522‡	Straight Deal
60523‡	Sun Castle
60524‡	Herringbone
60525§	A. H. Peppercorn
60526**	Sugar Palm
60527§	Sun Chariot
60528§	Tudor Minstrel
60529**	Pearl Diver
60530§	Sayajirao
60531§	Bahram
60532**	Blue Peter
60533**	Happy Knight
60534§	Irish Elegance
60535§	Hornet's Beauty
60536§	Trimbush

60537§ Bachelor's Button
60538** Velocity
60539§ Bronzino

Total : Class **A2**   15
Class **A2/1**   4
Class **A2/2**   6
Class **A2/3**   13

4-6-4   8P7F   Class **W1**

Introduced 1937. Rebuilt from Gresley
experimental high-pressure 4-cyl.
compound with water-tube boiler,
introduced 1929.
Weight: Loco.   107 tons 17 cwt.
Tender   60 tons 7 cwt.
Pressure: 250 lb. Su.
Cyls.: (3) 19" × 26".
Driving Wheels: 6' 8". T.E.: 37,400 lb.
Walschaerts valve gear and derived
motion. P.V.

60700   Total 1

2-6-2   7P6F   Class **V2**

Introduced 1936. Gresley design.
Weight: Loco.   93 tons 2 cwt.
Tender   52 tons.
Pressure: 220 lb. Su
Cyls.: (3) 18½" × 26".
Driving Wheels: 6' 2". T.E. 33,730 lb.
Walschaerts valve gear and derived
motion. P.V.

60800   Green Arrow
60801
60802
60803
60804
60805
60806
60807
60808
60809   The Snapper, The East
Yorkshire Regiment,
The Duke of York's Own
60810
60811

60812
60813
60814
60815
60816
60817
60813
60819
60820
60821
60822
60823
60824
60825
60826
60827
60828
60829
60830
60831
60832
60833
60834
60835   The Green Howard,
Alexandra, Princess of
Wales's Own York-
shire Regiment
60836
60837
60838
60839
60840
60841
60842
60843
60844
60845
60846
60847   St. Peter's School, York,
A.D. 627
60848
60849
60850
60851
60852
60853
60854
60855

9

60856			
60857			
60858			
60859			
60860	Durham School		
60861			
60862			
60863			
60864			
60865			
60866			
60867			
60868			
60869			
60870			
60871			
60872	King's Own Yorkshire Light Infantry		
60873	Coldstreamer		
60874	60902	60930	60958
60875	60903	60931	60959
60876	60904	60932	60960
60877	60905	60933	60961
60878	60906	60934	60962
60879	60907	60935	60963
60880	60908	60936	60964
60881	60909	60937	60965
60882	60910	60938	60966
60883	60911	60939	60967
60884	60912	60940	60968
60885	60913	60941	60969
60886	60914	60942	60970
60887	60915	60943	60971
60888	60916	60944	60972
60889	60917	60945	60973
60890	60918	60946	60974
60891	60919	60947	60975
60892	60920	60948	60976
60893	60921	60949	60977
60894	60922	60950	60978
60895	60923	60951	60979
60896	60924	60952	60980
60897	60925	60953	60981
60898	60926	60954	60982
60899	60927	60955	60983
60900	60928	60956	
60901	60929	60957	

Total 184

4-6-0   SMT   Class B1

Introduced 1942. Thompson design.
Weight: Loco.   71 tons 3 cwt.
            Tender 52 tons.
Pressure: 225 lb. Su.
Cyls.: (O) 20″ × 26″.
Driving Wheels: 6′ 2″. T.E. 26,880 lb.
Walschaerts valve gear. P.V.

61000	Springbok
61001	Eland
61002	Impala
61003	Gazelle
61004	Oryx
61005	Bongo
61006	Blackbuck
61007	Klipspringer
61008	Kudu
61009	Hartebeeste
61010	Wildebeeste
61011	Waterbuck
61012	Puku
61013	Topi
61014	Oribi
61015	Duiker
61016	Inyala
61017	Bushbuck
61018	Gnu
61019	Nilghal
61020	Gemsbok
61021	Reitbok
61022	Sassaby
61023	Hirola
61024	Addax
61025	Pallah
61026	Ourebi
61027	Madoqua
61028	Umseke
61029	Chamois
61030	Nyala
61031	Reedbuck
61032	Stembok
61033	Dibatag
61034	Chiru
61035	Pronghorn
61036	Ralph Assheton
61037	Jairou
61038	Blacktail
61039	Steinbok
61040	Roedeer

61041	61079	61116	61153	61200
61042	61080	61117	61154	61201
61043	61081	61118	61155	61202
61044	61082	61119	61156	61203
61045	61083	61120	61157	61204
61046	61084	61121	61158	61205
61047	61085	61122	61159	61206
61048	61086	61123	61160	61207
61049	61087	61124	61161	61208
61050	61088	61125	61162	61209
61051	61089	61126	61163	61210
61052	61090	61127	61164	61211
61053	61091	61128	61165	61212
61054	61092	61129	61166	61213
61055	61093	61130	61167	61214
61056	61094	61131	61168	61215 William Henton Carver
61058	61095	61132	61169	61216
61059	61096	61133	61170	61217
61060	61097	61134	61171	61218
61061	61098	61135	61172	61219
61062	61099	61136	61173	61220
61063	61100	61137	61174	61221 Sir Alexander Erskine-Hill
61064	61101	61138	61175	
61065	61102	61139	61176	61222
61066	61103	61140	61177	61223
61067	61104	61141	61178	61224
61068	61105	61142	61179	61225
61069	61106	61143	61180	61226
61070	61107	61144	61181	61227
61071	61108	61145	61182	61228
61072	61109	61146	61183	61229
61073	61110	61147	61184	61230
61074	61111	61148	61185	61231
61075	61112	61149	61186	61232
61076	61113	61150	61187	61233
61077	61114	61151	61188	61234
61078	61115	61152		61235
61189 Sir William Gray				61236
61190				61237 Geoffrey H. Kitson
61191				61238 Leslie Runciman
61192				61239
61193				61240 Harry Hinchcliffe
61194				61241 Viscount Ridley
61195				61242 Alexander Reith Gray
61196				61243 Sir Harold Mitchell
61197				61244 Strang Steel
61198				61245 Murray of Elibank
61199				61246 Lord Balfour of Burleigh

61247	Lord Burghley		
61248	Geoffrey Gibbs		
61249	FitzHerbert Wright		
61250	A. Harold Bibby		
61251	Oliver Bury		

61252	61284	61316	61348
61253	61285	61317	61349
61254	61286	61318	61350
61255	61287	61319	61351
61256	61288	61320	61352
61257	61289	61321	61353
61258	61290	61322	61354
61259	61291	61323	61355
61260	61292	61324	61356
61261	61293	61325	61357
61262	61294	61326	61358
61263	61295	61327	61359
61264	61296	61328	61360
61265	61297	61329	61361
61266	61298	61330	61362
61267	61299	61331	61363
61268	61300	61332	61364
61269	61301	61333	61365
61270	61302	61334	61366
61271	61303	61335	61367
61272	61304	61336	61368
61273	61305	61337	61369
61274	61306	61338	61370
61275	61307	61339	61371
61276	61308	61340	61372
61277	61309	61341	61373
61278	61310	61342	61374
61279	61311	61343	61375
61280	61312	61344	61376
61281	61313	61345	61377
61282	61314	61346	61378
61283	61315	61347	

61379	Mayflower

61380	61388	61396	61404
61381	61389	61397	61405
61382	61390	61398	61406
61383	61391	61399	61407
61384	61392	61400	61408
61385	61393	61401	61409
61386	61394	61402	
61387	61395	61403	

Total 409

4-6-0   5MT   Class B16

B16/1 Introduced 1920. Raven N.E. design with Stephenson valve gear.

B16/2* Introduced 1937. Gresley rebuild of B16/1 with Walschaerts valve gear and derived motion for inside cylinder.

B16/3† Introduced 1944. Thompson rebuild of B16/1 with individual sets of Walschaerts valve gear for each cylinder.

Weight: Loco. $\begin{cases} 77 \text{ tons } 14 \text{ cwt.} \\ 79 \text{ tons } 4 \text{ cwt.*} \\ 78 \text{ tons } 19 \text{ cwt.†} \end{cases}$
Tender 46 tons 12 cwt.

Pressure: 180 lb. Su

Cyls.: (3) $18\frac{1}{2}'' \times 26''$.

Driving Wheels: 5' 8"   T.E.: 30,030 lb. P.V.

61410	61428	61446	61464†
61411	61429	61447	61465
61412	61430	61448†	61466
61413	61431	61449†	61467†
61414	61432	61450	61468†
61415	61433	61451	61469
61416	61434†	61452	61470
61417†	61435*	61453†	61471
61418†	61436	61454†	61472†
61419	61437*	61455*	61473
61420†	61438*	61456	61474
61421*	61439†	61457*	61475*
61422	61440	61458	61476†
61423	61441	61459	61477
61424	61442	61460	61478
61425	61443	61461†	
61426	61444†	61462	
61427	61445	61463†	

Total : Class B16/1 45
        Class B16/2   7
        Class B16/3 17

IMPORTANT NOTE
A careful reading of the notes on page 2 is essential to understand the use of reference marks in this book.

4-6-0 4P3F Class B12

B12/3 Introduced 1932. Gresley rebuild of Holden G.E. design of 1911 with large boiler, round-topped firebox and long-travel valves.
(B12/2 was a development of B12/1 with Lentz valves, since rebuilt to B12/3.)

Weight: Loco. 69 tons 10 cwt.
Tender 39 tons 6 cwt.

Pressure: 180 lb. Su. Cyls.: 20″ × 28″.

Driving Wheels: 6′ 6″. T.E.: 21,970 lb. P.V

61514	61540	61556	61571
61516	61542	61558	61572
61519	61546	61561	61573
61520	61547	61564	61575
61530	61549	61566	61576
61533	61553	61567	61577
61535	61554	61568	61580
61537	61555	61570	

Total 31

4-6-0 4MT (B2 and B17/6; 5P4F) Classes B2 & B17

B17/1¹ Introduced 1928. Gresley design for G.E. section with G.E.-type tender.

B17/6² Introduced 1947. B17/1 fitted with 100A (B1 type) boiler.

B17/4⁵ Introduced 1936. Locos with L.N.E.R. 4,200-gallon tender.

B17/6⁴ Introduced 1943. B17/4 fitted with 100A (B1 type) boiler.

B17/5⁵ Rebuild of streamlined B17/5 introduced in 1937. Rebuilt with 100A boiler and de-streamlined in 1951

Weight: Loco. 77 tons 5 cwt.
Tender $\begin{cases} 39 \text{ tons } 6 \text{ cwt.}^{12} \\ 52 \text{ tons.}^{34} \end{cases}$

Pressure: $\begin{cases} 180 \text{ lb.}^{15} \\ 225 \text{ lb.}^{245} \end{cases}$ Su.

Cyls.: (3) 17½″ × 26″.

Driving Wheels: 6′ 8″.

T.E.: $\begin{cases} 22,485 \text{ lb.}^{15} \\ 28,555 \text{ lb.}^{245} \end{cases}$

Walschaerts valve gear and derived motion. P.V.

B2⁶ Introduced 1945. Thompson 2-cyl. rebuild of B17, with 100A boiler and N.E. tender.

B2⁷ Introduced 1945, with L.N.E.R. tender.

Weight: Loco. 73 tons 10 cwt.
Tender $\begin{cases} 46 \text{ tons } 12 \text{ cwt.}^6 \\ 52 \text{ tons.}^7 \end{cases}$

Pressure: 225 lb Su.

Cyls.: (O) 20″ × 26″.

Driving Wheels: 6′ 8″. T.E.: 24,865 lb.

Walschaerts valve gear. P.V.

61600²	Sandringham
61601²	Holkham
61602²	Walsingham
61603⁶	Framlingham
61605²	Lincolnshire Regiment
61606²	Audley End
61607⁶	Blickling
61608²	Gunton
61609²	Quidenham
61610²	Honingham Hall
61611²	Raynham Hall
61612²	Houghton Hall
61613²	Woodbastwick Hall
61614⁶	Castle Hedingham
61615⁷	Culford Hall
61616⁶	Fallodon
61617⁶	Ford Castle
61618¹	Wynyard Park
61619²	Welbeck Abbey
61620²	Clumber
61621¹	Hatfield House
61622²	Alnwick Castle
61623²	Lambton Castle
61625¹	Raby Castle
61626²	Brancepeth Castle
61627²	Aske Hall
61629¹	Naworth Castle
61630²	Tottenham Hotspur
61631²	Serlby Hall
61632⁷	Belvoir Castle
61633³	Kimbolton Castle
61634¹	Hinchingbrooke
61635²	Milton
61636⁸	Harlaxton Manor
61637¹	Thorpe Hall

13

61638²	Melton Hall
61639⁶	Norwich City
61640²	Somerleyton Hall
61641²	Gayton Hall
61642²	Kilverstone Hall
61643²	Champion Lodge
61644⁶	Earlham Hall
61645²	The Suffolk Regiment
61646²	Gilwell Park
61647¹	Helmingham Hall
61648³	Arsenal
61649⁴	Sheffield United
61650⁴	Grimsby Town
61651⁴	Derby County
61652³	Darlington
61653⁴	Huddersfield Town
61654⁴	Sunderland
61655⁴	Middlesbrough
61656⁴	Leeds United
61657⁴	Doncaster Rovers
61658⁴	The Essex Regiment
61659⁵	East Anglian
61660⁵	Hull City
61661⁴	Sheffield Wednesday
61662⁴	Manchester United
61663⁴	Everton
61664⁴	Liverpool
61665⁴	Leicester City
61666⁴	Nottingham Forest
61667³	Bradford
61668⁴	Bradford City
61669⁴	Barnsley
61670⁵	City of London
61671⁷	Royal Sovereign
61672⁴	West Ham United

Total : Class B2   10
        Class B17/1   8
        Class B17/4   4
        Class B17/6   48

2-6-2   4MT   Class V4

Introduced 1941. Gresley design.
Weight: Loco. 70 tons 8 cwt.
        Tender 42 tons 15 cwt.
Pressure: 250 lb. Su.
Cyls.: (3) 15″ × 26″.
Driving Wheels: 5′ 8″. T.E.: 27,420 lb.
Walschaerts valve gear and derived motion. P.V.

61700	Bantam Cock
61701	**Total 2**

2-6-0   4MT   Class K2

K2/2 Introduced 1914. Gresley G.N. design.
K2/1* Introduced 1931. Rebuilt from small-boilered K1 (introduced 1>12).
† K2/2 with side-window cab.
‡ K2/1 with side-window cab.
Weight: Loco. 64 tons 8 cwt.
        Tender 43 tons 2 cwt.
Pressure: 180 lb. Su.
Cyls.: (O) 20″ × 26″.
Driving Wheels: 5′ 8″. T.E.: 23,400 lb.
Walschaerts valve gear. P.V.

61721‡	61732	61745	61754
61723*	61733†	61746	61755†
61724*	61736	61747	61756
61725*	61738	61748	61757
61726*	61739	61749	61758†
61728*	61740	61750	61759
61729‡	61741†	61751	61760
61730	61742	61752	61761
61731	61743	61753	61762

61763	
61764†	Loch Arkaig
61765	
61766	
61767	
61768	
61769†	
61770†	
61771	
61772†	Loch Lochy
61773	
61774†	Loch Garry
61775†	Loch Treig
61776†	
61777	
61778	
61779†	
61780	
61781†	Loch Morar
61782†	Loch Eil
61783†	Loch Shiel
61784†	
61785†	

61786†			
61787† Loch Quoich			
61788† Loch Rannoch			
61789† Loch Laidon			
61790† Loch Lomond			
61791† Loch Laggan			
61792†			
61793†			
61794† Loch Oich			

Total : Class K2/1   7
Class K2/2   61

Classes
2-6-0   5P6F   K3 & K5

K3/2 Introduced 1924. Development of Gresley G.N. design, built to L.N.E.R. loading gauge.
K3/3* Introduced 1929. Differ in details only, such as springs, from K3/2.
‡ K3/2 fitted with G.N. tender. (K3/1 were G.N. locos (introduced 1920), with G.N. cabs, and K3/4, K3/5 and K3/6 were variations of K3/2 differing in weight and details. These locos have now been modified to K3/2.)

Weight: Loco.   72 tons 12 cwt.
Tender $\begin{cases} 52 \text{ tons.} \\ 43 \text{ tons } 2 \text{ cwt.}‡ \end{cases}$

Pressure: 180 lb. Su.
Cyls.: (3) 18½″ × 26″.
Driving Wheels: 5′ 8″.   T.E. 30,030 lb.
Walschaerts valve gear and derived motion P.V.
K5† Introduced 1945.   Thompson 2-cyl. rebuild of K3.
Weight: Loco.   71 tons 5 cwt.
Tender 52 tons.
Pressure: 225 lb. Su.
Cyls.: (O) 20″ × 26″.
Driving Wheels: 5′ 8″.   T.E.: 29,250 lb.
Walschaerts valve gear.   P.V.

61800	61804	61808	61812‡
61801	61805	61809	61813
61802	61806	61810	61814
61803	61807	61811	61815

61816	61861	61906	61951
61817	61862	61907	61952
61818	61863†	61908	61953
61819	61864	61909	61954
61820	61865	61910	61955
61821	61866	61911	61956
61822	61867	61912	61957
61823	61868	61913	61958
61824	61869	61914	61959
61825	61870*	61915	61960
61826	61871*	61916	61961
61827	61872*	61917	61962
61828	61873*	61918	61963
61829	61874*	61919	61964
61830	61875*	61920	61965
61831	61876*	61921	61966
61832	61877*	61922	61967
61833	61878*	61923	61968
61834	61879*	61924	61969
61835	61880*	61925	61970
61836	61881*	61926	61971
61837	61882*	61927	61972
61838	61883*	61928	61973
61839	61884*	61929	61974
61840	61885*	61930	61975
61841‡	61886*	61931	61976
61842	61887*	61932	61977
61843	61888*	61933	61978
61844	61889*	61934	61979
61845	61890	61935	61980
61846	61891	61936	61981
61847	61892	61937	61982
61848	61893	61938	61983
61849	61894	61939	61984
61850	61895	61940	61985
61851	61896	61941	61986
61852	61897	61942	61987
61853	61898	61943	61988
61854‡	61899	61944	61989
61855‡	61900	61945	61990
61856‡	61901	61946	61991
61857‡	61902	61947	61992
61858‡	61903	61948	
61859‡	61904	61949	
61860	61905	61950	

Total :   Class K3/2   172
Class K3/3   20
Class K5   1

Classes

2-6-0   5P6F   K1 & K4

K4* Introduced 1937. Gresley locos. for West Highland line.

Weight: Loco.   68 tons 8 cwt.
Tender   44 tons 4 cwt.

Pressure: 200 lb. Su.

Cyls.: (3) $18\frac{1}{2}'' \times 26''$.

Driving Wheels: 5′ 2″. T.E.: 36,600 lb.

Walschaerts valve gear and derived motion. P.V.

K1/1† Introduced 1945. Thompson 2-cyl. loco. Rebuilt from K4.

K1 Introduced 1949. Peppercorn development of Thompson K1/1 (No. 61997) for new construction, with increased length.

Weight: Loco.   66 tons 17 cwt.
Tender   44 tons 4 cwt.

Pressure: 225 lb. Su.

Cyls.: (O) $20'' \times 26''$.

Driving Wheels: 5′ 2″. T.E.: 32,080 lb.

Walschaerts valve gear. P.V.

61993* Loch Long
61994* The Great Marquess
61995* Cameron of Lochiel
61996* Lord of the Isles
61997† MacCailin Mor
61998* Macleod of Macleod

62001	62019	62037	62055
62002	62020	62038	62056
62003	62021	62039	62057
62004	62022	62040	62058
62005	62023	62041	62059
62006	62024	62042	62060
62007	62025	62043	62061
62008	62026	62044	62062
62009	62027	62045	62063
62010	62028	62046	62064
62011	62029	62047	62065
62012	62030	62048	62066
62013	62031	62049	62067
62014	62032	62050	62068
62015	62033	62051	62069
62016	62034	62052	62070
62017	62035	62053	
62018	62036	62054	

Total : Class K1   70
Class K1/1   1
Class K4   5

4-4-0   1P   Class D40

Introduced 1899. Pickersgill G.N. of S. design.
*Introduced 1920. Heywood superheated loco.

Weight: Loco. $\begin{cases} 46 \text{ tons } 7 \text{ cwt.} \\ 48 \text{ tons } 13 \text{ cwt.*} \end{cases}$
Tender   37 tons 8 cwt.

Pressure: 165 lb. SS. Cyls.: $18'' \times 26''$.
Driving Wheels: 6′ 1″. T.E.: 16,185 lb.

62264

62277* Gordon Highlander

Total 2

4-4-0   2P   Class D20

D20/1 Introduced 1899. W. Worsdell N.E. design. Since superheated.
D20/2* Introduced 1936. D20/1 rebuilt with long-travel valves.
† Locos. with tender rebuilt with J39-type tank.

Weight: Loco. $\begin{cases} 54 \text{ tons } 2 \text{ cwt.} \\ 55 \text{ tons } 9 \text{ cwt.*} \end{cases}$
Tender $\begin{cases} 41 \text{ tons } 4 \text{ cwt.} \\ 43 \text{ tons.†} \end{cases}$

Pressure: 175 lb. Su. Cyls.: $19'' \times 26''$.
Driving Wheels: 6′ 10″. T.E.: 17,025 lb. P.V.

62375*	62383†	62395	62396
62381	62387†		

Total : Class D20/1   5
Class D20/2   1

4-4-0   3P   Class D30

D30/2 Introduced 1914. Development of D30/1, introduced 1912 (Reid N.B. "Scott" class) with detail differences.
Weight: Loco.   57 tons 16 cwt.
Tender   46 tons 13 cwt.
Pressure: 165 lb. Su. Cyls.: $20'' \times 26''$.
Driving Wheels: 6′ 6″. T.E.: 18,700 lb. P.V.

62418 The Pirate
62419 Meg Dods
62420 Dominie Sampson
62421 Laird o' Monkbarns
62422 Caleb Balderstone
62423 Dugald Dalgetty

Class A1 4-6-2 No. 60162 *Saint Johnstoun* [T. K. Widd

Class A2/3 4-6-2 No. 60515 *Sun Stream* [P. Ransome-Wallis

Class A2 4-6-2 No. 60536 *Trimbush* [J. R. Paterson

Class A3 4-6-2 No. 60054 *Prince of Wales*   [*R. K. Evans*

Class A4 4-6-2 No. 60028 *Walter K. Whigham*   [*A. E. Brown*

Class V2 2-6-2 No. 60982   [*John Robertson*

Class B1 4-6-0 No. 61033 *Dibatag*   [D. Penney

Class B16/1 4-6-0 No. 61419   [R. K. Evans

Class B16/3 4-6-0 No. 61448   [T. K. Widd

Class B17/6 4-6-0 No. 61636 *Harlaxton Manor* [R. E. Vincent

Class B2 4-6-0 No. 61603 *Framlingham* [G. Wheeler

Class B12/3 4-6-0 No. 61540 [G. Wheeler

Class K1 2-6-0 No. 62015   [P. H. Groom

Class K4 2-6-0 No. 61995 *Cameron of Lochiel* (fitted with snowplough) [David A. Anderson

Class K2/1 2-6-0 No. 61721 (with side-window cab)   [David A. Anderson

Class K3/2 2-6-0 No. 61942   [R. E. Vincent

Class 3 2-6-0 No. 77018   [E. M. Patterson

Class D20/I 4-4-0 No. 62383 (with rebuilt tender)   [D. Penney

Class D49/1 4-4-0 No. 62713 *Aberdeenshire* [J. R. Paterson

Class D49/2 4-4-0 No. 62773 *The South Durham* [John Robertson

Class D16/3 4-4-0 No. 62530 [A. R. Carpenter

Class D11/2 4-4-0 No. 62691 *Laird of Balmawhapple* [W. S. Sellar

Class D30/2 4-4-0 No. 62441 *Black Duncan* [J. L. Stevenson

Class D34 4-4-0 No. 62487 *Glen Arklet* [W. S. Sellar

62424	Claverhouse
62425	Ellangowan
62426	Cuddie Headrigg
62427	Dumbiedykes
62428	The Talisman
62429	The Abbot
62431	Kenilworth
62432	Quentin Durward
62434	Kettledrummle
62435	Norna
62436	Lord Glenvarloch
62437	Adam Woodcock
62438	Peter Poundtext
62439	Father Ambrose
62440	Wandering Willie
62441	Black Duncan
62442	Simon Glover

Total 23

4-4-0   3P   Class D34

Introduced 1913. Reid N.B. " Glen "
class.

Weight: Loco.   57 tons 4 cwt.
         Tender 46 tons 13 cwt.
Pressure: 165 lb. Su. Cyls.: 20″ × 26″.
Driving Wheels: 6′ 0″. T.E.: 20,260 lb.
P.V.

62467	Glenfinnan
62468	Glen Orchy
62469	Glen Douglas
62470	Glen Roy
62471	Glen Falloch
62472	Glen Nevis
62474	Glen Croe
62475	Glen Beasdale
62477	Glen Dochart
62478	Glen Quoich
62479	Glen Sheil
62480	Glen Fruin
62482	Glen Mamie
62483	Glen Garry
62484	Glen Lyon
62485	Glen Murran
62487	Glen Arklet
62488	Glen Aladale
62489	Glen Dessary
62490	**Glen Fintaig**

62492	Glen Garvin
62493	Glen Gloy
62494	Glen Gour
62495	Glen Luss
62496	Glen Loy
62497	Glen Mallie
62498	Glen Moidart

Total 27

4-4-0   3P1F   Class D16

D16/3[1] Introduced 1933. Gresley rebuild of D15 with larger boiler,
round-topped firebox and modified
footplating.   D15 was Belpaire
firebox development of original
J. Holden (G.E.) " Claud Hamilton "
Class.

D16/3[2] Introduced 1933. Rebuild of
D15 with larger boiler, round-topped
firebox, modified footplate and 8″
piston valves.

D16/3[3] Introduced 1936. Rebuild of
D15 with larger boiler, round-topped
firebox, modified footplating and
9½″ piston valves.

D16/3[4] Introduced 1938. Rebuild of
D16/2 with round-topped firebox,
but retaining original footplating and
slide valves.

D16/3[5] Introduced 1939. Rebuild of
D16/2 with round-topped firebox
and modified footplating, retaining
slide valves.

Weight: Loco.   55 tons 18 cwt.
         Tender 39 tons 5 cwt.

Pressure: 180 lb. Su. Cyls.: 19″ × 26″.

Driving Wheels: 7′ 0″. T.E.: 17,095 lb.

62510[1]	62530[1]	62558[4]	62580[4]
62511[1]	62533[1]	62561[1]	62582[1]
62513[1]	62534[1]	62562[4]	62584[1]
62515[1]	62535[3]	62564[4]	62586[1]
62516[1]	62539[1]	62566[1]	62588[2]
62517[1]	62540[1]	62568[2]	62589[4]
62518[1]	62543[4]	62570[4]	62592[4]
62521[1]	62544[4]	62571[1]	62593[1]
62522[1]	62545[1]	62572[1]	62596[4]
62524[1]	62546[2*]	62575[1]	62597[1]
62526[1]	62548[1]	62576[3]	62599[3]
62529[1]	62555[1]	62578[4]	62604[1]

* **Named** *Claud Hamilton.*

62605⁴	62612⁴	62615⁴	62619⁴
62606⁴	62613⁴	62617⁴	
62610¹	62614⁵	62618⁴	

Total 58

4-4-0   3P2F   Class D11

D11/1* Introduced 1920. Robinson G.C. " Large Director " development of D10 (introduced 1913).

D11/2 Introduced 1924. Post-grouping locos built to Scottish loading gauge. From 1938 the class has been rebuilt with long-travel valves.

Weight: Loco.   61 tons 3 cwt.
Tender 48 tons 6 cwt.

Pressure: 180 lb. Su. Cyls.: 20″ × 26″.

Driving Wheels: 6′ 9″. T.E.: 19,645 lb. P.V.

62660* Butler-Henderson
62661* Gerard Powys Dewhurst
62662* Prince of Wales
62663* Prince Albert
62664* Princess Mary
62665* Mons
62666* Zeebrugge
62667* Somme
62668* Jutland
62669* Ypres
62670* Marne
62671 Bailie MacWheeble
62672 Baron of Bradwardine
62673 Evan Dhu
62674 Flora MacIvor
62675 Colonel Gardiner
62676 Jonathan Oldbuck
62677 Edie Ochiltree
62678 Luckie Mucklebackit
62679 Lord Glenallan
62680 Lucy Ashton
62681 Captain Craigengelt
62682 Haystoun of Bucklaw
62683 Hobbie Elliott

62684 Wizard of the Moor
62685 Malcolm Graeme
62686 The Fiery Cross
62687 Lord James of Douglas
62688 Ellen Douglas
62689 Maid of Lorn
62690 The Lady of the Lake
62691 Laird of Balmawhapple
62692 Allan-Bane
62693 Roderick Dhu
62694 James Fitzjames

Total : Class D11/1   11
Class D11/2   24

4-4-0   4P   Class D49

D49/1* Introduced 1927. Gresley design with piston valves. Walschaerts valve gear and derived motion.

D49/2† Introduced 1928. Development of D49/1 with Lentz Rotary Cam poppet valves.

D49/2‡ Introduced 1949. Fitted with Reidinger R.R. Rotary valve gear (D49/3 comprised locos. 62720-5 as built with Lentz Oscillating Cam poppet valves. From 1938 these locos were converted to D49/1. 62751-75 have larger valves than the earlier D49/2, and were at first classified D49/4).

¹Fitted with G.C. tender.
²Fitted with N.E. tender.
⁵The remainder have L.N.E.R. tenders.

Weight: Loco. { 66 tons.*†
{ 64 tons 10 cwt.‡
Tender { 48 tons 6 cwt.¹
{ 44 tons 2 cwt.²
{ 52 tons.⁵

Pressure: 180 lb. Su.
Cyls.: (3) 17″ × 26″.
Driving Wheels: 6′ 8″. T.E.: 21,555 lb.

62700*¹ Yorkshire
62701*¹ Derbyshire
62702*¹ Oxfordshire
62703*² Hertfordshire
62704*¹ Stirlingshire
62705*¹ Lanarkshire
62706*¹ Forfarshire

62707*[1]	Lancashire
62708*[1]	Argyllshire
62709*[1]	Berwickshire
62710*[1]	Lincolnshire
62711*[1]	Dumbartonshire
62712*[1]	Morayshire
62713*[1]	Aberdeenshire
62714*[1]	Perthshire
62715*[1]	Roxburghshire
62716*[1]	Kincardineshire
62717*[1]	Banffshire
62718*[1]	Kinross-shire
62719*[1]	Peebles-shire
62720*[1]	Cambridgeshire
62721*[1]	Warwickshire
62722*[1]	Huntingdonshire
62723*[2]	Nottinghamshire
62724*[1]	Bedfordshire
62725*[1]	Inverness-shire
62726†[3]	The Meynell
62727†[2]	The Quorn
62728*[1]	Cheshire
62729*[1]	Rutlandshire
62730*[1]	Berkshire
62731*[1]	Selkirkshire
62732*[1]	Dumfries-shire
62733*[1]	Northumberland
62734*[2]	Cumberland
62735*[2]	Westmorland
62736†[3]	The Bramham Moor
62737†[3]	The York and Ainsty
62738†[3]	The Ze land
62739†[3]	The Badsworth
62740†[3]	The Bedale
62741†[3]	The Blankney
62742†[3]	The Braes of Derwent
62743†[3]	The Cleveland
62744†[3]	The Holderness
62745†[3]	The Hurworth
62746†[3]	The Middleton
62747†[3]	The Percy
62748†[3]	The Southwold
62749†[3]	The Cottesmore
62750†[3]	The Pytchley
62751†[3]	The Albrighton
62752†[2]	The Atherstone
62753†[3]	The Belvoir
62754†[3]	The Berkeley

62755†[3]	The Bilsdale
62756†[2]	The Brocklesby
62757†[3]	The Burton
62758†[3]	The Cattistock
62759†[3]	The Craven
62760†[3]	The Cotswold
62761†[3]	The Derwent
62762†[3]	The Fernie
62763‡[3]	The Fitzwilliam
62764‡[3]	The Garth
62765†[3]	The Goathland
62766†[3]	The Grafton
62767†[3]	The Grove
62769†[3]	The Oakley
62770†[3]	The Puckeridge
62771†[3]	The Rufford
62772†[3]	The Sinnington
62773†[3]	The South Durham
62774†[3]	The Staintondale
62775†[3]	The Tynedale

Total : Class D49/1   34
Class D49/2   41

2-4-0   1MT   Class E4

Introduced 1891. J. Holden G.E.
design.
*Fitted with side-window cab.
Weight: Loco.   40 tons 6 cwt.
             Tender 30 tons 13 cwt.
Pressure: 160 lb. Cyls.: 17½" × 24".
Driving Wheels: 5' 8". T.E.: 14,700 lb

62785	62789	62796	62797
62788*			

Total 5

0-8-0   6F   Class Q6

Introduced 1913. Raven N.E. design.
* Some locos. are fitted with tender
  from withdrawn B15 locos.
Weight: Loco.   65 tons 18 cwt.
             Tender { 44 tons 2 cwt.
                       44 tons.*
Pressure: 180 lb. Su.
Cyls.: (O) 20" × 26".
Driving Wheels: 4' 7½".   T.E. 28,800 lb.
P.V.

63340	63341	63342	63343

63344	63373	63402	63431
63345	63374	63403	63432
63346	63375	63404	63433
63347	63376	63405	63434
63348	63377	63406	63435
63349	63378	63407	63436
63350	63379	63408	63437
63351	63380	63409	63438
63352	63381	63410	63439
63353	63382	63411	63440
63354	63383	63412	63441
63355	63384	63413	63442
63356	63385	63414	63443
63357	63386	63415	63444
63358	63387	63416	63445
63359	63388	63417	63446
63360	63389	63418	63447
63361	63390	63419	63448
63362	63391	63420	63449
63363	63392	63421	63450
63364	63393	63422	63451
63365	63394	63423	63452
63366	63395	63424	63453
63367	63396	63425	63454
63368	63397	63426	63455
63369	63398	63427	63456
63370	63399	63428	63457
63371	63400	63429	63458
63372	63401	63430	63459

Total 120

0-8-0 8F Class Q7

Introduced 1919. Raven N.E. design.

Weight: Loco. 71 tons 12 cwt.
Tender 44 tons 2 cwt

Pressure: 180 lb. Su.

Cyls.: (3) 18½″ × 26″.

Driving Wheels: 4′ 7¼″. T.E.: 36,965 lb. P.V.

63460	63464	63468	63472
63461	63465	63469	63473
63462	63466	63470	63474
63463	63467	63471	

Total 15

Classes O1 & O4

2-8-0 8F (O1) 7F (O4)

O4/1[1] Introduced 1911. Robinson G.C. design with small boiler, Belpaire firebox, steam and vacuum brakes and water scoop.

O4/3[2] Introduced 1917. R.O.D. locos. with steam brake only and no scoop.

O4/2[3] Introduced 1925. O4/3 with cab and boiler mountings reduced.

O4/5[4] Introduced 1932. Rebuilt with shortened O2-type boiler and separate smokebox saddle.

O4/6[5] Introduced 1924. Rebuilt from O5 retaining higher cab (63914-20 with side-windows)

O4/7[6] Introduced 1939. Rebuilt with shortened O2-type boiler retaining G.C. smokebox.

O4/8[7] Introduced 1944. Rebuilt with 100A (B1) boiler, retaining original cylinders.

(O4/4 were rebuilds with O2 boilers, since rebuilt again ; O5 was a G.C. development of O4 with larger boiler and Belpaire firebox.)

Weight: Loco. 73 tons 4 cwt.[1]
73 tons 4 cwt.[2]
73 tons 4 cwt.[3]
74 tons 13 cwt.[4]
73 tons 4 cwt.[5]
73 tons 17 cwt.[6]
72 tons 10 cwt.[7]

Tender 48 tons 6 cwt. (with scoop)
47 tons 6 cwt. (without scoop)

Pressure: 180 lb. Su.

Cyls.: (O) 21″ × 26″.

Driving Wheels: 4′ 8″. T.E.: 31,325 lb. P.V.

O1[8] Introduced 1944. Thompson rebuild with 100A boiler, Walschaerts valve gear and new cylinders.

Weight: Loco. 73 tons 6 cwt.
Tender as O4.

Pressure: 225 lb. Su.

Cyls.: (O) 20″ × 26″.

Driving Wheels: 4′ 8″. T.E.: 35,520 lb.

Walschaerts valve gear P.V.

63570[6]	63579[8]	63589[8]	63598[1]
63571[8]	63581[1]	63590[8]	63599[1]
63572[1]	63582[8]	63591[8]	63600[6]
63573[7]	63583[1]	63592[8]	63601[1]
63574[1]	63584[1]	63593[1]	63602[1]
63575[7]	63585[1]	63594[8]	63603[8]
63576[1]	63586[1]	63595[8]	63604[7]
63577[1]	63587[1]	63596[8]	63605[1]
63578[8]	63588[6]	63597[1]	63606[7]

63607⁷	63656²	63704⁷	63752⁸	63801⁷	63836⁷	63862²	63889²
63608¹	63657²	63705⁶	63753²	63802⁷	63837⁷	63863⁸	63890³
63609¹	63658¹	63706⁷	63754²	63803⁸	63838⁷	63864²	63891⁶
63610⁸	63659²	63707¹	63755⁸	63804²	63839⁶	63865⁸	63893⁷
63611²	63660¹	63708⁶	63756²	63805⁷	63840²	63867⁸	63894⁶
63612⁷	63661⁸	63709³	63757¹	63806⁸	63841⁷	63868⁸	63895⁷
63613⁷	63662⁶	63710¹	63758⁶	63807⁷	63842²	63869⁵	63897⁷
63614¹	63663⁸	63711⁸	63759²	63808⁸	63843⁶	63870³	63898²
63615⁶	63664¹	63712⁸	63760⁸	63812²	63845²	63872⁸	63899⁷
63616⁶	63665²	63713²	63761⁶	63813²	63846²	63873⁷	63900²
63617¹	63666²	63714²	63762¹	63816⁷	63847³	63874⁸	63901⁸
63618¹	63667²	63715²	63763⁷	63817⁸	63848⁶	63876⁶	63902⁵
63619⁸	63668²	63716²	63764²	63818⁷	63850⁷	63877²	63904⁵
63620¹	63669⁶	63717²	63765²	63819⁷	63851¹	63878²	63905⁵
63621¹	63670⁸	63718⁷	63766²	63821²	63852⁷	63879⁸	63906⁵
63622²	63671¹	63719¹	63767²	63822²	63853⁷	63880⁶	63907⁵
63623¹	63672²	63720⁷	63768⁸	63823²	63854⁸	63881²	63908⁵
63624⁷	63673⁶	63721⁷	63769²	63824⁶	63855²	63882⁷	63911⁵
63625¹	63674⁸	63722¹	63770⁶	63827²	63856⁸	63883²	63912⁵
63626¹	63675²	63723¹	63771²	63828⁷	63857⁷	63884⁶	63913⁵
63628⁷	63676⁸	63724²	63772⁶	63829²	63858⁷	63885⁷	63914⁷
63629²	63677¹	63725⁸	63773⁸	63832²	63859²	63886⁸	63915⁷
63630⁸	63678⁸	63726⁴	63774²	63833²	63860⁶	63887⁸	63917⁵
63631⁷	63679²	63727¹	63775⁶	63835³	63861²	63888²	63920⁵
63632¹	63680³	63728⁷	63776⁷				
63633⁷	63681⁷	63729²	63777³				
63634⁶	63682³	63730³	63779²				
63635¹	63683⁷	63731⁷	63780⁸				
63636²	63684¹	63732⁷	63781²				
63637²	63685²	63733²	63782²				
63638²	63686²	63734⁷	63783²				
63639⁷	63687⁸	63735⁴	63784⁸				
63640¹	63688⁷	63736¹	63785⁷				
63641²	63689⁸	63737²	63786³				
63642²	63690³	63738⁷	63787²				
63643⁶	63691⁷	63739²	63788⁷				
63644⁷	63692¹	63740⁸	63789³				
63645⁷	63693¹	63741²	63790²				
63646⁸	63694²	63742⁷	63791⁷				
63647³	63695²	63743¹	63792³				
63648³	63696²	63744²	63793³				
63649²	63697²	63745⁴	63794⁶				
63650⁸	63698¹	63746⁸	63795⁸				
63651⁷	63699⁶	63747⁶	63796⁸				
63652⁸	63700¹	63748⁶	63797¹				
63653⁷	63701²	63749⁶	63798³				
63654¹	63702²	63750⁷	63799¹				
63655⁷	63703⁷	63751²	63800²				

Total :

Class O1	58	Class O4/5	3
Class O4/1	55	Class O4/6	11
Class O4/2	9	Class O4/7	36
Class O4/3	87	Class O4/8	65

2-8-0   6F   Class O2

O2/1* Introduced 1921. Development of experimental Gresley G.N. 3-cyl. loco. (L.N.E.R. 3921). Subsequently rebuilt with side-window cab, and reduced boiler mountings.

O2/2† Introduced 1924. Development of O2/1 with detail differences.

O2/3 Introduced 1932. Development of O2/2 with side-window cab and reduced boiler mountings

O2/4‡ Introduced 1943. Rebuilt with 100A (B1 type) boiler and smokebox extended backwards (63924 retaining G.N. tender).

Weight: Loco. { 75 tons 16 cwt.*†
78 tons 13 cwt.
74 tons 2 cwt.‡

Tender { 43 tons 2 cwt. (63922-46)
52 tons. (63947-87)

Pressure: 180 lb. Su.

63922-64381

Cyls.: (3) 18½" × 26".
Driving Wheels: 4′ 8″. T.E.: 36,740 lb.
Walschaerts valve gear and derived motion. P.V.

63922*	63939†	63956	63973
63923*	63940†	63957	63974
63924‡	63941†	63958	63975
63925*	63942†	63959	63976
63926*	63943†	63960	63977
63927*	63944†	63961	63978
63928*	63945‡	63962‡	63979
63929*	63946†	63963	63980
63930*	63947	63964	63981
63931*	63948	63965	63982
63932‡	63949‡	63966	63983‡
63933†	63950‡	63967	63984
63934†	63951	63968	63985
63935†	63952	63969	63986
63936†	63953	63970	63987
63937†	63954	63971	
63938†	63955	63972	

	Total :		
	Class O2/1	9
	Class O2/2	13
	Class O2/3	37
	Class O2/4	7

0-6-0   2P3F   Class J6

Introduced 1911. Gresley G.N. design.
Weight: Loco. 50 tons 10 cwt.
        Tender 43 tons 2 cwt.
Pressure: 170 lb. Su. Cyls.: 19″ × 26″.
Driving Wheels: 5′ 2″. T.E. 21,875 lb. P.V.

64170	64185	64201	64217
64171	64186	64202	64218
64172	64187	64203	64219
64173	64188	64204	64220
64174	64189	64205	64221
64175	64190	64206	64222
64176	64191	64207	64223
64177	64192	64208	64224
64178	64193	64209	64225
64179	64195	64210	64226
64180	64196	64211	64227
64181	64197	64213	64228
64182	64198	64214	64229
64183	64199	64215	64230
64184	64200	64216	64231

64232	64245	64257	64269
64233	64246	64258	64270
64234	64247	64259	64271
64235	64248	64260	64272
64236	64249	64261	64273
64237	64250	64262	64274
64238	64251	64263	64275
64239	64252	64264	64276
64240	64253	64265	64277
64241	64254	64266	64278
64243	64255	64267	64279
64244	64256	64268	

Total 107

0-6-0   2P3F   Class J11

Introduced 1901. Robinson G.C. design. Parts 1 and 4 have 3,250 gallon tenders; Parts 2 and 5, 4,000 gallon. Parts 1 and 2 have higher boiler mountings; Parts 4 and 5 low. All Parts 4 and 5 are superheated, and some of Parts 1 and 2. There are frequent changes between parts.
J11/3* Introduced 1942. Rebuilt with long-travel piston valves and boiler higher pitched.
Weight: Loco. { 51 tons 19 cwt. (Sat.) / 52 tons 2 cwt. (Su.) / 53 tons 6 cwt.*
Tender { 44 tons 3 cwt. (3,250 gall.) / 48 tons 6 cwt. (4,000 gall.)
Pressure: 180 lb. SS. Cyls.: 18½" × 26".
Driving Wheels: 5′ 2″. T.E.: 21,960 lb.

64280	64305	64329	64354*
64281	64306	64331	64355
64283*	64308	64332*	64357
64284*	64310	64333*	64359*
64285	64311	64336	64361
64287	64313	64337	64362*
64288	64314*	64338	64363
64290	64315	64340	64364*
64292	64316*	64341	64365
64293	64317*	64343	64368
64294	64318*	64344	64371
64295	64319	64345	64372
64296	64320	64346*	64373*
64297	64321	64348	64375*
64298	64322	64349	64376
64300	64324*	64351	64377
64302	64325	64352*	64379*
64304*	64328	64353	64381

64382	64401	64420*	64439*
64383	64402*	64421	64440
64384	64403	64422	64441*
64385	64404	64423	64442*
64386*	64405	64424	64443
64387	64406*	64425	64444
64388	64407	64427*	64445
64389	64409	64428	64446
64392	64411	64429	64447
64393*	64412	64430	64450*
64394*	64414	64433	64451
64395*	64416	64434	64452
64396	64417*	64435	64453
64397	64418*	64437	
64399	64419	64438	

Total : Class J11/3 33
Class J11 (other parts) 97

0-6-0   3F   Class J35

J35/5* Introduced 1906.   Reid N.B. design with piston valves.

J35/4 Introduced 1908.   Slide valves. (Parts 1, 2 and 3 were variations of Parts 4 and 5 before superheating.)

Weight: Loco. $\begin{cases} 51 \text{ tons.*} \\ 50 \text{ tons 15 cwt.} \end{cases}$
Tender $\begin{cases} 38 \text{ tons 1 cwt.*} \\ 37 \text{ tons 15 cwt.} \end{cases}$
Pressure: 180 lb. Su. Cyls.: $18\frac{1}{4}'' \times 26''$.
Driving Wheels: 5' 0".   T.E. 22,080 lb.

64460*	64478	64494	64511
64461*	64479	64495	64512
64462*	64480	64496	64513
64463*	64482	64497	64514
64464*	64483	64498	64515
64466*	64484	64499	64516
64468*	64485	64500	64517
64470*	64486	64501	64518
64471*	64487	64502	64519
64472*	64488	64504	64520
64473*	64489	64505	64521
64474*	64490	64506	64522
64475*	64491	64507	64523
64476*	64492	64509	64524
64477*	64493	64510	64525

64526	64529	64532	64535
64527	64530	64533	
64528	64531	64534	

Total : Class J35/4 55
Class J35/5 15

0-6-0   5F   Class J37

Introduced 1914.   Reid N.B. design. Superheated development of J35.
Weight: Loco.   54 tons 14 cwt.
Tender 40 tons 19 cwt.
Pressure: 180 lb. Su. Cyls.: $19\frac{1}{4}'' \times 26''$.
Driving Wheels: 5' 0".   T.E. 25,210 lb. P.V.

64536	64562	64588	64614
64537	64563	64589	64615
64538	64564	64590	64616
64539	64565	64591	64617
64540	64566	64592	64618
64541	64567	64593	64619
64542	64568	64594	64620
64543	64569	64595	64621
64544	64570	64596	64622
64545	64571	64597	64623
64546	64572	64598	64624
64547	64573	64599	64625
64548	64574	64600	64626
64549	64575	64601	64627
64550	64576	64602	64628
64551	64577	64603	64629
64552	64578	64604	64630
64553	64579	64605	64631
64554	64580	64606	64632
64555	64581	64607	64633
64556	64582	64608	64634
64557	64583	64609	64635
64558	64584	64610	64636
64559	64585	64611	64637
64560	64586	64612	64638
64561	64587	64613	64639

Total 104

0-6-0   3P5F   Class J19

Introduced 1912.   S. Holden G.E. design rebuilt with round-topped firebox from 1934.
* Rebuilt with 19" cyls. and 180 lb. pressure.
† Rebuilt with 19" cyls. and 160 lb. pressure.

31

64640-64871

Weight: Loco.   50 tons 7 cwt.
           Tender 38 tons 5 cwt.
Pressure $\begin{cases} 170 \text{ lb. Su.} \\ 180 \text{ lb. Su.*} \\ 160 \text{ lb. Su.†} \end{cases}$

Cyls. $\begin{cases} 20'' \times 26''. \\ 19'' \times 26''.*† \end{cases}$

Driving Wheels: 4' 11".

T.E. $\begin{cases} 27,430 \text{ lb.} \\ 26,215 \text{ lb.*} \\ 23,300 \text{ lb.†} \end{cases}$

64640	64649	64658	64667
64641	64650	64659	64668
64642	64651	64660	64669
64643	64652	64661	64670
64644	64653	64662	64671*
64645	64654	64663	64672†
64646	64655	64664*	64673
64647	64656	64665	64674
64648	64657	64666	

Total 35

0-6-0   5F   Class J20

J20/1 Introduced 1943. Hill G.E. design with Belpaire firebox (introduced 1920) rebuilt with B12/1 type boiler with round-topped firebox.
Weight: Loco.   54 tons 15 cwt.
           Tender 38 tons 5 cwt.
Pressure: 180 lb. Su. Cyls.: 20" × 28".
Driving Wheels: 4' 11". T.E. 29,045 lb. P.V.

64675	64682	64688	64694
64676	64683	64689	64695
64677	64684	64690	64696
64678	64685	64691	64697
64679	64686	64692	64698
64680	64687	64693	64699
64681			

Total 25

0-6-0   4P5F   Class J39

ntroduced 1926. Gresley design.
J39/1 Standard 3,500 gallon tender.
J39/2* Standard 4,200 gallon tender.
J39/3† Various N.E. tenders (3,940 gallon on 64843-5, 4,125 gallon on 64855-9).

Weight: Loco.   57 tons 17 cwt.
Tender $\begin{cases} 44 \text{ tons } 4 \text{ cwt.} \\ 52 \text{ tons } 13 \text{ cwt.*} \end{cases}$ and others
Pressure: 180 lb. Su. Cyls.: 20" × 26".
Driving Wheels: 5' 2". T.E. 25,665 lb. P.V.

64700†	64743	64786*	64829
64701	64744	64787*	64830
64702	64745	64788*	64831
64703	64746	64789*	64832
64704	64747	64790*	64833
64705	64748	64791*	64834
64706	64749	64792*	64835
64707	64750	64793*	64836
64708	64751	64794*	64837
64709	64752	64795*	64838*
64710	64753	64796	64839*
64711	64754	64797	64840*
64712	64755	64798	64841*
64713	64756	64799	64842*
64714	64757	64800	64843†
64715	64758	64801	64844†
64716	64759	64802	64845†
64717	64760	64803	64846
64718	64761	64804	64847
64719	64762	64805	64848
64720	64763	64806	64849
64721	64764	64807	64850
64722	64765	64808	64851
64723	64766	64809	64852
64724	64767	64810	64853
64725	64768	64811	64854
64726	64769	64812	64855†
64727	64770	64813	64856†
64728	64771	64814	64857†
64729	64772	64815	64858†
64730	64773	64816	64859†
64731	64774	64817	64860
64732	64775	64818	64861
64733	64776	64819	64862
64734	64777	64820*	64863
64735	64778	64821*	64864
64736	64779	64822*	64865
64737	64780	64823	64866
64738	64781	64824	64867
64739	64782	64825	64868
64740	64783	64826	64869
64741	64784*	64827	64870
64742	64785*	64828	64871

Class O2/2 2-8-0 No. 63938   [E. M. Patterson

Class O2/3 2-8-0 No. 63983   [G. Wheeler

Class Q6 0-8-0 No. 63389   [R. E. Vincent

Class O4/1 2-8-0 No. 63583   [E. M. Patterson

Class O4/8 2-8-0 No. 63728   [P. H. Groom

Class O4/5 2-8-0 No. 63745   [R. A. Panting

Class O4/6 2-8-0 No. 63902　　　　　　　　　　　　　　　　　[P. Ransome-Wallis

Class O4/7 2-8-0 No. 63699　　　　　　　　　　　　　　　　　[Brian E. Morrison

Class O1 2-8-0 No. 63901　　　　　　　　　　　　　　　　　　[A. R. Carpenter

Class J38 0-6-0 No. 65927   [*D. Marriott*

Class J39/1 0-6-0 No. 64783   [*R. E. Vincent*

Class J6 0-6-0 No. 64223   [*P. H. Groom*

Class J25 0-6-0 No. 65695   *[P. H. Groom*

Class J27 0-6-0 No. 65859   *[R. Goult*

Class J11 0-6-0 No. 64349   *[Brian E. Morrison*

Class J15 0-6-0 No. 65391 (with side-window cab)　　　　[D. Penney

Class J17 0-6-0 No. 65534　　　　[D. Penney

Class J20/1 0-6-0 No. 64687　　　　[R. E. Vincent

Class J36 0-6-0 No. 65270

[L. Marshall

Class J35/4 0-6-0 No. 64489

[I. S. Swanson

Class J37 0-6-0 No. 64558

[David A. Anderson

Class C12 4-4-2T No. 67365   [R. K. Evans

Class C16 4-4-2T No. 67502   [David A. Anderson

Class C13 4-4-2T No. 67424   [K. R. Pirt

64872*	64902*	64932*	64962*
64873*	64903*	64933	64963*
64874*	64904*	64934	64964*
64875*	64905*	64935	64965*
64876*	64906*	64936	64966*
64877*	64907*	64937	64967*
64878*	64908*	64938	64968*
64879*	64909*	64939	64969*
64880*	64910*	64940	64970*
64881*	64911*	64941	64971†
64882*	64912*	64942	64972†
64883*	64913*	64943	64973†
64884*	64914*	64944	64974†
64885*	64915*	64945*	64975†
64886*	64916*	64946*	64976†
64887*	64917*	64947*	64977†
64888*	64918*	64948*	64978†
64889*	64919*	64949*	64979†
64890*	64920*	64950*	64980†
64891*	64921*	64951*	64981†
64892*	64922*	64952*	64982†
64893*	64923*	64953*	64983†
64894*	64924*	64954*	64984†
64895*	64925*	64955*	64985†
64896*	64926†	64956*	64986†
64897*	64927*	64957*	64987†
64898*	64928*	64958*	64988†
64899*	64929*	64959*	
64900*	64930*	64960*	
64901*	64931*	64961*	

Total : Class J39/1 155

Class J39/2 106

Class J39/3 28

0-6-0   2F   Class J21

Introduced 1886. T. W. Worsdell N.E. design. Majority built as 2-cyl. compounds and later rebuilt as simple locos.

* Rebuilt with superheater, Stephenson valve gear and piston valves.

† Rebuilt with piston valves, superheater removed.

Weight: Loco. $\begin{cases} 43 \text{ tons } 15 \text{ cwt.*} \\ 42 \text{ tons } 9 \text{ cwt.†} \end{cases}$
Tender 36 tons 19 cwt.
Pressure: 160 lb. SS.
Cyls.: 19″ × 24″.
T.E. : 19,240 lb.
Driving Wheels: 5′ 1¼″.

65033†	65064*	65099†	65110
65039†	65070†	65103*	65117†
65061*	65091*		

Total 10

0-6-0   2F   Class J10

J10/4* Introduced 1896. Pollitt development of J10/2 with larger bearings and larger tender.

J10/6 Introduced 1901. Robinson locos. with larger bearings and small tender.

Weight: Loco.   41 tons 6 cwt.
Tender $\begin{cases} 37 \text{ tons } 6 \text{ cwt.} \\ 43 \text{ tons.*} \end{cases}$
Pressure: 160 lb.   Cyls.: 18″ × 26″.
Driving Wheels: 5′ 1″.   T.E.: 18,780 lb.

65131	65146*	65170*	65196
65132*	65147*	65175	65198
65133*	65157*	65177	65199
65134*	65157*	65178*	65200
65135*	65158*	65184	65202
65138*	65159*	65186	65208
65140*	65160*	65187	65209
65142*	65166*	65191	
65144*	65167*	65192	
65145*	65169*	65194	

Total : Class J10/4 21

Class J10/6 16

0-6-0   2F   Class J36

Introduced 1888. Holmes N.B. design.
Weight : Loco. 41 tons 19 cwt.
Tender 33 tons 9 cwt.
Pressure : 165 lb.   Cyls. : 18¼″ × 26″.
Driving Wheels : 5′ 0″.   T.E. : 19,690 lb.

65210	65211	65213	65214

41

65216	Byng		
65217	French		
65218			
65221			
65222	Somme		
65224	Mons		
65225			
65227			
65228			
65229			
65230			
65232			
65233	Plumer		
65234			
65235	Gough		
65237			
65239			
65241			
65242			
65243	Maude		
65244			
65246			
65247			
65249			
65251			
65252			
65253	Joffre		
65257			
65258			
65259			
65260			
65261			
65265			
65266			
65267			
65268	Allenby		
65270	65281	65293	65304
65273	65282	65295	65305
65275	65285	65296	65306
65276	65287	65297	65307
65277	65288	65300	65309
65280	65290	65303	65310
65311	Haig		
65312	65318	65324	65331
65313	65319	65325	65333
65315	65320	65327	65334
65316	65321	65329	65335
65317	65323	65330	65338

65339	65342	65344	65346
65341	65343	65345	

Total 92

0-6-0   1P2F   Class J15

Introduced 1883. Worsdell G.E. design, modified by J. Holden.

* Fitted with side-window cab for Colne Valley line.

Weight: Loco.   37 tons 2 cwt.
         Tender 30 tons 13 cwt.

Pressure: 160 lb. Cyls.: $17\frac{1}{2}'' \times 24''$.

Driving Wheels: 4' 11". T.E.: 16,940 lb.

65356	65441	65455	65469
65361	65442	65456	65470
65388	65443	65457	65471
65389	65444	65458	65472
65390	65445	65459	65473
65391*	65446	65460	65474
65405*	65447	65461	65475
65420	65448	65462	65476
65424*	65449	65463	65477
65432*	65450	65464	65478
65433	65451	65465	65479
65434	65452	65466	
65438*	65453	65467	
65440	65454	65468	

Total 53

0-6-0   2P4F   Class J17

Introduced 1901. J. Holden G.E. design. Many rebuilt from round-top firebox J16, introduced 1900.

* Fitted with small tender.

Weight: Loco.   45 tons 8 cwt.
         Tender $\begin{cases} 38 \text{ tons } 5 \text{ cwt.} \\ 30 \text{ tons } 12 \text{ cwt.*} \end{cases}$

Pressure: 180 lb. Su. Cyls.: 19" × 26".

Driving Wheels: 4' 11". T.E.: 24,340 lb.

65500	65523	65546	65570
65501*	65525	65548	65571
65502*	65526	65549	65572
65503*	65527	65551	65573
65504*	65528*	65553	65575
65505	65529	65554	65576
65506*	65530	65555	65577
65507*	65531	65556	65578
65508*	65532	65557	65580
65509	65533	65558	65581
65511*	65534	65559	65582
65512*	65535	65560	65583
65513*	65536	65561	65584
65514*	65538	65562	65586
65515*	65539	65563	65587
65518*	65540	65564	65588
65519*	65541	65565	65589
65520	65542	65566	
65521	65544	65567	
65522	65545	65568	

65695*	65699*	65712*	65720*
65696*	65700*	65713*	65726*
65697*	65702‡	65714*	65727*
65698*	65706†	65717†	65728*

Total 36

Total 77

0-6-0   5F   Class J26

Introduced 1904. W. Worsdell N.E. design.

Weight: Loco.   46 tons 16 cwt.
           Tender 36 tons 19 cwt.

Pressure: 180 lb.   Cyls.: $18\frac{1}{2}'' \times 26''$.
Driving Wheels: 4' 7$\frac{1}{4}$".   T.E.: 24,640 lb.

65730	65743	65756	65769
65731	65744	65757	65770
65732	65745	65758	65771
65733	65746	65759	65772
65734	65747	65760	65773
65735	65748	65761	65774
65736	65749	65762	65775
65737	65750	65763	65776
65738	65751	65764	65777
65739	65752	65765	65778
65740	65753	65766	65779
65741	65754	65767	
65742	65755	65768	

Total 50

0-6-0   3F   Class J25

Introduced 1898. W. Worsdell N.E. design.

* Original design, saturated, with slide valves.

† Rebuilt with superheater and piston valves.

‡ Rebuilt with piston valves, superheater removed.

Weight: Loco. { 39 tons 11 cwt.*
               41 tons 14 cwt.†
               40 tons 17 cwt.‡
        Tender 36 tons 19 cwt.

Pressure: 160 lb. SS. Cyls.: $18\frac{1}{2}'' \times 26''$.
Driving Wheels: 4' 7$\frac{1}{4}$".   T.E.: 21,905 lb.

65645†	65656*	65670*	65683‡
65648*	65657*	65673‡	65685*
65650*	65662†	65675*	65687*
65654‡	65663*	65677‡	65691*
65655*	65666*	65680*	65693*

0-6-0   5F   Class J27

Introduced 1906. W. Worsdell N.E. design developed from J26.

* Introduced 1921.   Raven locos. Superheated, with piston valves.

† Introduced 1943.   Piston valves, superheater removed.

Weight: Loco. { 47 tons Sat.
               49 tons 10 cwt. Su.
        Tender 36 tons 19 cwt.

Pressure: 180 lb. SS. Cyls.: $18\frac{1}{2}'' \times 26''$.
Driving Wheels: 4' 7$\frac{1}{4}$".   T.E. 24,640 lb.

65780	65782	65784	65786
65781	65783	65785	65787

65788	65815	65842	65869†
65789	65816	65843	65870†
65790	65817	65844	65871*
65791	65818	65845	65872*
65792	65819	65846	65873†
65793	65820	65847	65874*
65794	65821	65848	65875†
65795	65822	65849	65876†
65796	65823	65850	65877†
65797	65824	65851	65878*
65798	65825	65852	65879†
65799	65826	65853	65880*
65800	65827	65854	65881*
65801	65828	65855	65882†
65802	65829	65856	65883*
65803	65830	65857	65884†
65804	65831	65858	65885*
65805	65832	65859	65886*
65806	65833	65860†	65887*
65807	65834	65861†	65888†
65808	65835	65862†	65889*
65809	65836	65863*	65890*
65810	65837	65864†	65891†
65811	65838	65865†	65892*
65812	65839	65866*	65893*
65813	65840	65867†	65894*
65814	65841	65868†	

Total 115

0-6-0   6F   Class J38

Introduced 1926. Gresley design.
Predecessor of J39, with 4' 8" wheels,
boiler 6" longer than J39 and smoke-
box 6" shorter.
* Rebuilt with J39 boiler.
Weight: Loco. 58 tons 19 cwt.
         Tender 44 tons 4 cwt.
Pressure: 180 lb. Su. Cyls.: 20" × 26"
Driving Wheels: 4' 8". T.E.: 28,415 lb.
P.V.

65900	65909	65918*	65927*
65901	65910	65919	65928
65902	65911	65920	65929
65903*	65912	65921	65930
65904	65913	65922	65931
65905	65914	65923	65932
65906*	65915	65924	65933
65907	65916	65925	65934
65908*	65917*	65926*	

Total 35

2-4-2T   IMT   Class F5

Introduced 1911. S. D. Holden G. E.
design. (Rebuilt from Worsdell G. E.
F4.)

* Introduced 1949, Push-and-pull fitted.

Weight: 53 tons 19 cwt.

Pressure: 180 lb. Cyls.: 17½" × 24".

Driving Wheels: 5' 4". T.E.: 17,570 lb.

67192	67200*	67203*	67214
67193*	67202*	67212	67218*
67195			

Total 9

2-4-2T   IMT   Class F6

Introduced 1911. S.D. Holden G. E.
design, development of Worsdell G. E.
F4 with higher pressure and larger
tanks.

Weight: 56 tons 9 cwt.

Pressure: 180 lb. Cyls.: 17½" × 24".

Driving Wheels: 5' 4". T.E.: 17,570 lb.

67221	67228	67230	67231
67227	67229		

Total 6

0-4-4T   IMT   Class G5

Introduced 1894. W. Worsdell N.E. design.
* Push-and-pull fitted.
† Push-and-pull fitted and rebuilt with larger tanks.
Weight: 54 tons 4 cwt.
Pressure: 160 lb.   Cyls.: 18″ × 24″.
Driving Wheels: 5′ 1¼″.   T.E. 17,265 lb.

67246	67263	67297*	67329
67248	67265	67305*	67338*
67250*	67270	67311*	67339*
67253*	67273*	67315	67340†
67254	67274	67319	67341
67256	67277*	67320	67342
67258	67278	67323*	67343
67259	67280*	67324	
67261*	67281*	67325	
67262	67282*	67326	

Total 37

4-4-2T   IMT   Class C12

Introduced 1898. Ivatt G.N. design.
*†Boiler pressure reduced to 170 lb.
†‡Push-and-pull fitted.
Weight: 62 tons 6 cwt.
Pressure: $\begin{cases} 175 \text{ lb.} \\ 170 \text{ lb.}*† \end{cases}$
Cyls.: 18″ × 26″.
Driving Wheels: 5′ 8″.
T.E. $\begin{cases} 18,425 \text{ lb.} \\ 17,900 \text{ lb.}*† \end{cases}$

67352	67365	67376	67391
67357	67366	67379	67394
67362	67367	67380	67397
67363†	67374†	67386‡	67398*

Total 16

4-4-2T   2PIF   Class C13

Introduced 1903. Robinson G.C. design, later rebuilt with superheater.
* Push-and-pull fitted.
Weight: 66 tons 13 cwt.
Pressure: 160 lb. Su.   Cyls.: 18″ × 26″.
Driving Wheels: 5′ 7″.   T.E.: 17,100 lb.

67413	67419	67424	67434
67416*	67420*	67427	67437
67417*	67421*	67428	67438*
67418*	67423	67433*	67439

Total 16

4-4-2T   2PIF   Class C14

Introduced 1907. Robinson G.C. design, later superheated, development of C13, with detail differences.
Weight: 71 tons.
Pressure: 160 lb. Su.   Cyls.: 18″ × 26″.
Driving Wheels: 5′ 7″.   T.E.: 17,100 lb.

67440	67443	67446	67449
67441	67444	67447	67450
67442	67445	67448	

Total 11

4-4-2T   2P   Class C15

Introduced 1911.   Reid N.B. design.
Push-and-pull fitted.
Weight: 68 tons 15 cwt.
Pressure: 175 lb.   Cyls.: 18″ × 26″.
Driving Wheels: 5′ 9″.   T.E.: 18,160 lb.

67460   67474

Total 2

4-4-2T   2P   Class C16

Introduced 1915.   Reid N.B. design, superheated development of C15.
Weight: 72 tons 10 cwt.
Pressure: 165 lb. Su.   Cyls.: 19″ × 26″.
Driving Wheels: 5′ 9″.   T.E.: 19,080 lb.
P.V.

67482	67487	67491	67497
67484	67488	67492	67500
67485	67489	67494	67501
67486	67490	67496	67502

Total 16

Classes

2-6-2T V1 (3MT) V1 & V3
V3 (4MT)

V1 Introduced 1930. Gresley design.
V3* Introduced 1939. Development of V1 with higher pressure (locos. numbered below 67682 rebuilt from V1).

Weight: { 84 tons.
{ 86 tons 16 cwt.*

Pressure: { 180 lb. Su.
{ 200 lb. Su.*

Cyls.: (3) 16″ × 26″.
Driving Wheels: 5′ 8″.

T.E.: { 22,465 lb.
{ 24,960 lb.*

Walschaerts valve gear and derived motion. P.V.

67600*	67623	67646*	67669*
67601	67624*	67647	67670*
67602	67625*	67648	67671
67603	67626*	67649	67672*
67604*	67627*	67650	67673
67605*	67628*	67651*	67674
67606*	67629	67652*	67675*
67607	67630	67653*	67676
67608	67631	67654*	67677
67609*	67632	67655	67678
67610	67633	67656*	67679*
67611*	67634*	67657*	67680
67612*	67635	67658	67681
67613	67636*	67659	67682*
67614	67637	67660*	67683*
67615*	67638*	67661	67684*
67616	67639	67662*	67685*
67617	67640	67663*	67686*
67618	67641	67664	67687*
67619*	67642	67665	67688*
67620*	67643*	67666	67689*
67621	67644	67667	67690*
67622	67645	67668*	67691*

Total : Class V1   47
Class V3   45

2-6-4T   4MT   Class L1

Introduced 1945. Thompson design.
* Introduced 1954. Boiler pressure reduced to 200 lb.
† Introduced 1954. Cylinder diameter reduced.

Weight: 89 tons 9 cwt.

Pressure: { 225 lb.
{ 200 lb.*

Cyls.: { (O) 20″ × 26″.
{ (O) 18½″ × 26″.†

Driving Wheels: 5′ 2″.

T.E.: { 32,080 lb.
{ 28,515 lb.*
{ 28,180 lb.†

Walschaerts valve gear. P.V.

67701	67726	67751	67776†
67702	67727	67752	67777
67703	67728	67753	67778
67704	67729	67754	67779†
67705	67730	67755	67780
67706	67731	67756	67781
67707	67732	67757	67782
67708	67733	67758	67783
67709	67734	67759	67784
67710	67735	67760	67785
67711	67736	67761*	67786
67712	67737	67762	67787
67713	67738	67763	67788
67714	67739	67764	67789
67715	67740	67765	67790
67716	67741	67766	67791
67717	67742	67767	67792
67718	67743	67768	67793
67719	67744	67769	67794
67720	67745	67770†	67795
67721	67746	67771†	67796
67722	67747*	67772†	67797
67723	67748	67773	67798*
67724	67749	67774	67799
67725	67750	67775	67800

Total 100

0-6-0ST   4F   Class J94

Introduced 1943. Riddles M.o.S. design. (Bought from M.o.S. 1946.)

Weight: 48 tons 5 cwt.
Pressure: 170 lb. Cyls.: 18″ × 26″.
Driving Wheels: 4′ 3″. T.E.: 23,870 lb.

68006	68025	68044	68063
68007	68026	68045	68064
68008	68027	68046	68065
68009	68028	68047	68066
68010	68029	68048	68067
68011	68030	68049	68068
68012	68031	68050	68069
68013	68032	68051	68070
68014	68033	68052	68071
68015	68034	68053	68072
68016	68035	68054	68073
68017	68036	68055	68074
68018	68037	68056	68075
68019	68038	68057	68076
68020	68039	68058	68077
68021	68040	68059	68078
68022	68041	68060	68079
68023	68042	68061	68080
68024	68043	68062	

Total 75

0-4-0ST OF Class Y9

Introduced 1882. Holmes N.B. design.
* Locos. running permanently attached
to wooden tender.
Weight: Loco.   27 tons 16 cwt.
        Tender   6 tons.*
Pressure: 130 lb. Cyls.: (O) 14″ × 20″.
Driving Wheels: 3′ 8″. T.E.: 9,845 lb.

68095	68104	68114*	68119*
68097*	68106*	68115	68123
68100*	68108*	68116*	68124
68101	68110	68117*	
68102*	68113	68118*	

Total 18

0-4-0T Dock Tank Class Y4

Introduced 1913.   Hill G.E. design.
Weight: 38 tons 1 cwt.
Pressure: 180 lb. Cyls.: (O) 17″ × 20″.
Driving Wheels: 3′ 10″. T.E : 19,225 lb.
Walschaerts valve gear.
(See also page 48)

68126

Total 2

0-4-0T Unclass. Class Y1

Sentinel Wagon Works design. Single-
speed Geared Sentinel locomotives.
The parts of this class differ in details,
including size of boiler and fuel
capacity.
Y1/1* Introduced 1925.
Y1/2† Introduced 1927.
Y1/4‡ Introduced 1927.
§ Sprocket gear ratio 9: 25 (remainder
11: 25).
Weight: { 20 tons 17 cwt.*
         { 19 tons 16 cwt.†
         { 19 tons 7 cwt.‡
Pressure: 275 lb. Su. Cyls.: 6¾″ × 9″.
Driving Wheels: 2′ 6″.
T.E.: { 7,260 lb.*†‡
      { 8,870 lb.§
Poppet valves.
(See also page 48)

68138†	68149†§	68150†§
68142†		

Total : Class Y1/1   5
        Class Y1/2   5
        Class Y1/4   1

0-4-0T Unclass. Class Y3

Sentinel Wagon Works design. Two-
speed Geared Sentinel locos.
Introduced 1927.
* Sprocket gear ratio 15 : 19 (re-
mainder 19 : 19).
Weight: 20 tons 16 cwt.
Pressure: 275 lb. Su. Cyls. 6¼″ × 9″.
Driving Wheels: 2′ 6″.
T.E. { Low Gear :   12,600 lb.
      { High Gear :   4,705 lb.
      { Low Gear : 15,960 lb.*
      { High Gear :   5.960 lb.*
Poppet valves.
(See also page 48)

68164   68182*

Total 12

0-4-2T OF Class Z4

Introduced   1915.   Manning-Wardle
design for G.N. of S.
Weight: 25 tons 17 cwt.
Pressure: 160 lb. Cyls : (O) 13″ × 20″.
Driving Wheels: 3′ 6″. T.E.: 10,945 lb.
68190   68191

Total 2

47

DEPARTMENTAL LOCOMOTIVES

In addition to service locomotives (denoted by a bold "S" in these pages) that are still shown with numbers in the British Railways series, a number of E. & N.E. Region departmental locomotives have been renumbered between 1 and 100. These are shown below with their former B.R. number in brackets.

0-6-0ST 3F Class J52/2

(For dimensions see page 59)

1 (68845)	2 (68816)

0-4-0T Un-class. Class Y3

(15:19 gear ratio—for dimensions see page 47)

3 (68181)	38 (68168)
5 (68165)	40 (68173)
7 (68166)	41 (68177)
8 (68183)	42 (68178)
21 (68162)	57 (68160)

0-4-0T Un-class. Class Y1/1

(For dimensions see page 47)

4 (68132)	37 (68130)
6 (68133)	39 (68131)
	53 (68152)

0-6-0T 2F Class J66

Introduced 1886. J. Holden G.E. design.
Weight: 40 tons 6 cwt.
Pressure: 160 lb. Cyls.: $16\frac{1}{2}'' \times 22''$.
Driving Wheels: 4' 0".
T.E.: 16,970 lb.

31 (68382)	36 (68378)
32 (68370)	**Total 3**

0-4-0T Dock Tank Class Y4

(For dimensions see page 47)

33 (68129)

0-4-0T Un-class. Class Y1/4

(For dimensions see page 47)

51 (68136)

0-4-0 Diesel Mechanical

Introduced 1950, Hibberd & Co. for North Eastern Region.
Weight: 11 tons.
Engine: English National Gas type DA 4, 4-cyls., 52 h.p. at 1,250 r.p.m. Transmission spur type gear box with roller chains: three forward and three reverse gears.

52 (11104)	**Total 1**

0-4-0T Un-class. Class Y1/2

(For dimensions see page 47)

54 (68153)

0-4-0T Dock Tank Class Y8

Introduced 1890. T. W. Worsdell N.E. design.
Weight: 15 tons 10 cwt.
Pressure: 140 lb. Cyls.: $11'' \times 15''$.
Driving Wheels: 3' 0".
T.E.: 6,000 lb.

55 (68091)	**Total 1**

0-4-0 Diesel Mechanical

Introduced 1956. Ruston & Hornsby 88 h.p. Shunting locomotive.

56

Above : Class J50/1
0-6-0T No. 68897
　　　　[*G. Wheeler*

Right : Class J88
0-6-0T No. 68345
　　　　[*David A. Anderson*

Below : Class J83
0-6-0T No. 68454
　　　　[*David A. Anderson*

Class J72 0-6-0T No. 68700   [I. S. Swanson

Class J71 0-6-0T No. 68283   [D. Marriott

Class J77 0-6-0T No. 68391   [T. K. Widd

Class F5 2-4-2T No. 67193

[G. Wheeler

Class J68 0-6-0T No. 68658

[Brian E. Morrison

Class J69/1 0-6-0T No. 68588

[R. E. Vincent

Class N1 0-6-2T No. 69472 [D. Penney

Class N2/2 0-6-2T No. 69532 [G. Wheeler

Class N10 0-6-2T No. 69099 P. H. Groom

Class N7/5 0-6-2T No. 69635   [J. A. Young

Class N7/3 0-6-2T No. 69673   [J. Davenport

Class N15/1 0-6-2T No. 69173   [David A. Anderson

Class A8 4-6-2T No. 69869 [T. B. Paisley

Class A7 4-6-2T No. 69786 [P. H. Groom

Class T1 4-8-0T No. 69913 [F. J. Saunders

Class Q1/1 0-8-0T No. 69926   [P. H. Groom

Class A5/1 4-6-2T No. 69822   [D. Marriott

Class V1 2-6-2T No. 67680   [R. K. Evans

Class Y4 0-4-0T No. 68126

[*P. Ransome-Wallis*

Class Y9 0-4-0ST No. 68114 (permanently coupled to wooden tender)

[*J. R. Paterson*

Class Z5 0-4-2T No. 68192

[*J. R. Paterson*

0-4-2T 0F Class Z5

Introduced 1915. Manning-Wardle design for G.N. of S.

Weight: 30 tons 18 cwt.

Pressure: 160 lb. Cyls.: (O) 14″ × 20″.

Driving Wheels: 4′ 0″. T.E.: 11,105 lb.

68192   **Total 1**

68320	68329	68338	68347
68321	68330	68339	68348
68322	68331	68340	68349
68324	68332	68342	68350
63325	68333	68343	68352
68326	68334	68344	68353
68327	68335	68345	68354
68328	68336	68346	

Total 31

0-6-0T Unclass. Class J71

Introduced 1886. T. W. Worsdell N.E. design.

*†Altered cylinder dimensions.

Weight: 37 tons 12 cwt. Dr. Wheels: 4′ 7½″.

Cyls.: $\begin{cases} 16″ × 22″. \\ 16\frac{1}{2}″ × 22″.* \\ 18″ × 22″.† \end{cases}$ T.E.: $\begin{cases} 12,130 \text{ lb.} \\ 13,300 \text{ lb.}* \\ 15,355 \text{ lb.}† \end{cases}$

68230*	68253*	68273	68305*
68233	68254	68275	68306*
68235	68260	68278	68308*
68242	68262	68279	68309*
68244	68263	68280*	68312†
68245	68264	68283	68314
68246*	68265	68290	68316*
68250*	68267	68295	
68251	68269	68296	
68252*	68272	68298	

Total 37

0-6-0T 3F Class J73

Introduced 1891. W. Worsdell N.E. design.

Weight: 46 tons 15 cwt.

Pressure: 160 lb. Cyls.: 19″ × 24″.

Driving Wheels: 4′ 7½″. T.E.: 21,320 lb.

68355	68359	68361	68363
68356	68360	68362	68364
68357			

Total 9

0-6-0T 2F Class J77

Introduced 1899. W. Worsdell N.E. rebuild of Fletcher 0-4-4T originally built 1874-84.

Some engines of this class have square-cornered and some round-cornered cab-roofs.

Weight: 43 tons.

Pressure: 160 lb. Cyls.: 17″ × 22″.

Driving Wheels: 4′ 1¼″. T.E.: 17,560 lb.

68391	68405	68414	68427
68392	68406	68423	68431
68397	68408	68424	68435
68399	68409	68425	68438
68402	68410	68426	

Total 19

0-6-0T 0F Class J88

Introduced 1904. Reid N.B. design with short wheelbase.

Weight: 38 tons 14 cwt.

Pressure: 130 lb. Cyls.: (O) 15″ × 22″.

Driving Wheels: 3′ 9″. T.E.: 12,155 lb.

0-6-0T 2F Class J83

Introduced 1900. Holmes N.B. design.
Weight: 45 tons 5 cwt.
Pressure: 150 lb. Cyls.: 17" × 26".
Driving Wheels: 4' 6". T.E.: 17,745 lb.

68442	68452	68463	68474
68443	68453	68464	68475
68444	68454	68465	68477
68445	68456	68466	68478
68447	68457	68467	68479
68448	68458	68468	68480
68449	68459	68470	68481
68450	68460	68471	
68451	68461	68472	

Total 34

Classes
0-6-0T 2F J67 & J69

67/1* Introduced 1890. J. Holden G.E. design with 160 lb. pressure.

J69/1† Introduced 1902. Development of J67 with 180 lb. pressure, larger tanks and larger firebox (some rebuilt from J67).

J67/2‡ Introduced 1937. Rebuild of J69 with 160 lb. boiler and small firebox.

J69/2§ Introduced 1950. J67/1 rebuilt with 180 lb. boiler and large firebox.

Weight: $\begin{cases} 40 \text{ tons.*‡} \\ 40 \text{ tons 9 cwt.†§} \end{cases}$

Pressure: $\begin{cases} 160 \text{ lb.*‡} \\ 180 \text{ lb.†§} \end{cases}$

Cyls.: 16½" × 22".

Driving Wheels: 4' 0".

T.E.: $\begin{cases} 16,970 \text{ lb.*‡} \\ 19,090 \text{ lb.†§} \end{cases}$

68490§	68498§	68507†	68516*
68491†	68499†	68508†	68518*
68494†	68500†	68510§	68519§
68495†	68501†	68512§	68520§
68497†	68502†	68513§	68522§

68524†	68553†	68577†	68609†
68526†	68554†	68578†	68612†
68527†	68555†	68579†	68613†
68528†	68556†	68581†	68616*
68529†	68557†	68583*	68617†
68530†	68558†	68585†	68618†
68532†	68560†	68587†	68619†
68535†	68561†	68588†	68621†
68536‡	68563†	68591†	68623†
68537†	68565†	68593*	68625†
68538†	68566†	68596†	68626†
68541†	68567†	68598†	68628‡
68542†	68568†	68599†	68629†
68543†	68569†	68600†	68630†
68545†	68570†	68601†	68631†
68546†	68571†	68602†	68632†
68549†	68573†	68603†	68633†
68550†	68574†	68605†	68635†
68551†	68575†	68607†	68636†
68552†	68576†	68608*	

Total : Class J67/1 6

Class J67/2 2

Class J69/1 83

Class J69/2 8

0-6-0T 2F Class J68

Introduced 1912. Hill G.E. development of J69 with side-window cab.
Weight: 42 tons 9 cwt.
Pressure: 180 lb. Cyls.: 16½" × 22".
Driving Wheels: 4' 0". T.E.: 19,090 lb.

68638	68646	68654	68662
68639	68647	68655	68663
68640	68648	68656	68664
68641	68649	68657	68665
68642	68650	68658	68666
68643	68651	68659	
68644	68652	68660	
68645	68653	68661	

Total 29

0-6-0T 2F Class J72

Introduced 1898. W. Worsdell N.E. design.
* Altered cylinder dimensions.
Weight: 38 tons 12 cwt.
Pressure: 140 lb. Cyls.: $\left\{\begin{array}{l}17'' \times 24''. \\ 18'' \times 24''.*\end{array}\right.$
Driving Wheels: 4' 1¼".
T.E.: $\left\{\begin{array}{l}16,760 \text{ lb.} \\ 18,790 \text{ lb.*}\end{array}\right.$

68670	68692	68714	68736
68671	68693	68715	68737
68672	68694	68716	68738
68673	68695	68717	68739
68674	68696	68718	68740
68675	68697	68719	68741
68676	68698	68720	68742
68677	68699	68721	68743
68678	68700	68722	68744
68679	68701	68723	68745
68680	68702	68724	68746
68681	68703	68725	68747
68682	68704	68726	68748
68683	68705	68727	68749
68684	68706	68728	68750
68685*	68707	68729	68751
68686	68708	68730	68752
68687	68709	68731	68753
68688	68710	68732	68754
68689	68711	68733	
68690	68712	68734	
68691	68713	68735	

(Class continued with No. 69001)

0-6-0ST 3F Class J52

J52/2 Introduced 1897. Ivatt standard G.N. saddletank with domed boiler.
J52/1* Introduced 1922. Rebuild of Stirling domeless saddletank (introduced 1892)—non-condensing.
J52/1† Introduced 1922. Condensing rebuild of Stirling locos.
‡ J52/2 with boiler pressure raised to 175 lb.
Weight: 51 tons 14 cwt.
Pressure: $\left\{\begin{array}{l}170 \text{ lb.} \\ 175 \text{ lb.‡}\end{array}\right.$ Cyls.: $18'' \times 26''$.
Driving Wheels: 4' 8".
T.E.: $\left\{\begin{array}{l}21,735 \text{ lb.} \\ 22,370 \text{ lb.‡}\end{array}\right.$
(See also page 45)

68761†	68828	68846	68870
68768*	68829	68847	68871
68778†	68831	68848	68874
68784†	68832	68849	68875
68785†	68834	68851	68882
68800*	68835	68857	68886
68808	68837	68860‡	68887
68811	68839	68862	68888
68815	68840‡	68863	
68817	68841	68866	
68823	68842	68867	
68824	68843	68869	

Total : Class J52/1 6
         Class J52/2 40

0-6-0T 4F Class J50

J50/2* Introduced 1922. Gresley G.N. design (68900-19 rebuilt from smaller J51, built 1915-22).
J50/3† Introduced 1926. Post-grouping development with detail differences.
J50/1‡ Introduced 1929. Rebuilt from smaller J51, built 1913-14.
J50/4§ Introduced 1937. Development of J50/3 with larger bunker.
Weight: $\left\{\begin{array}{l}57 \text{ tons.}* \\ 56 \text{ tons 6 cwt.‡} \\ 58 \text{ tons 3 cwt.†§}\end{array}\right.$
Pressure: 175 lb. Cyls.: $18\frac{1}{2}'' \times 26''$.
Driving Wheels: 4' 8". T.E.: 23,635 lb.

68890‡	68903*	68916*	68929*
68891‡	68904*	68917*	68930*
68892‡	68905*	68918*	68931*
68893‡	68906*	68919*	68932*
68894‡	68907*	68920*	68933*
68895‡	68908*	68921*	68934*
68896‡	68909*	68922*	68935*
68897‡	68910*	68923*	68936*
68898‡	68911*	68924*	68937*
68899‡	68912*	68925*	68938*
68900*	68913*	68926*	68939*
68901*	68914*	68927*	68940†
68902*	68915*	68928*	68941†

68942†	68955†	68968†	68981§
68943†	68956†	68969†	68982§
68944†	68957†	68970†	68983§
68945†	68958†	68971†	68984§
68946†	68959†	68972†	68985§
68947†	68960†	68973†	68986§
68948†	68961†	68974†	68987§
68949†	68962†	68975†	68988§
68950†	68963†	68976†	68989§
68951†	68964†	68977†	68990§
68952†	68965†	68978§	68991§
68953†	68966†	68979§	
68954†	68967†	68980§	

Total : Class J50/1   10
Class J50/2   40
Class J50/3   38
Class J50/4   14

0-6-0T   2F   Class J72

(Continued from 68754)

69001	69008	69015	69022
69002	69009	69016	69023
69003	69010	69017	69024
69004	69011	69018	69025
69005	69012	69019	69026
69006	69013	69020	69027
69007	69014	69021	69028

Total 113

0-6-2T   3F   Class N10

Introduced 1902.   W. Worsdell N.E. design.

Weight: 57 tons 14 cwt.

Pressure: 160 lb.   Cyls.: $18\frac{1}{2}'' \times 26''$.

Driving Wheels: 4′ 7½″.   T.E.: 21,905 lb.

69092	69097	69101	69106
69093	69098	69102	69107
69094	69099	69104	69108
69096	69100	69105	69109

Total 16

0-6-2T   3MT   Class N15

N15/2* Introduced 1910. Reid N.B. design developed from N14. Cowlairs Incline banking locos.

N15/1 Introduced 1910. Development of N15/2 with smaller bunker for normal duties.

Weight $\begin{cases} 62 \text{ tons} & 1 \text{ cwt.*} \\ 60 \text{ tons} & 18 \text{ cwt.} \end{cases}$

Pressure : 175 lb.

Cyls.: 18″ × 26″.

Driving Wheels: 4′ 6″.

T.E.: 23,205 lb.

69126*	69151	69176	69201
69127*	69152	69177	69202
69128*	69153	69178	69203
69129*	69154	69179	69204
69130*	69155	69180	69205
69131*	69156	69181	69206
69132	69157	69182	69207
69133	69158	69183	69208
69134	69159	69184	69209
69135	69160	69185	69210
69136	69161	69186	69211
69137	69162	69187	69212
69138	69163	69188	69213
69139	69164	69189	69214
69140	69165	69190	69215
69141	69166	69191	69216
69142	69167	69192	69217
69143	69168	69193	69218
69144	69169	69194	69219
69145	69170	69195	69220
69146	69171	69196	69221
69147	69172	69197	69222
69148	69173	69198	69223
69149	69174	69199	69224
69150	69175	69200	

Total : Class N15/1 93
Class N15/2   6

0-6-2T   2MT   Class N5

N5/2 Introduced 1891. Parker M.S. & L. design developed from N4.

* Push-and-pull fitted.

Weight: 62 tons 7 cwt.

Pressure: 160 lb.   Cyls.: 18″ × 26″.

Driving Wheels: 5′ 1″.   T.E.: 18,780 lb.

69257*	69283	69307	69342
69258	69284	69308	69343
69259	69286	69309	69344
69261	69290	69312	69346
69262	69292	69314	69347
69263	69293	69315	69349
69265	69294	69319	69354
69266	69295	69320	69355
69267	69296	69322	69360
69268	69297	69326	69361
69269	69298	69327	69362
69271	69299	69329	69370
69274	69300	69332	
69276	69302	69335	
69281	69305	69341	

Total 57

0-6-2T   2MT   Class N1

†‡§ Introduced 1907. Standard Ivatt G.N. design.

§ Rebuilt with superheater and reduced pressure.

‡ Fitted with condensing apparatus.

Weight: 65 tons 17 cwt.

Pressure: $\begin{cases} 175 \text{ lb.†‡} \\ 170 \text{ lb. Su.§} \end{cases}$

Cyls.: $18'' \times 26''$.

Driving Wheels: 5′ 8″.

T.E.: $\begin{cases} 18,430 \text{ lb.†‡} \\ 17,900 \text{ lb.§} \end{cases}$

69434‡	69452§	69469‡	69484‡
69440†	69453‡	69472§	
69443†	69457‡	69474†	
69450†	69462‡	69477‡	

Total 13

0-6-2T   3P2F   Class N2

N2/2* Introduced 1925. Post-grouping development of Gresley G.N. N2/1, introduced 1920, which class is now included in N2/2. Built with condensing gear and small chimney.

N2/2† Condensing gear removed.

N2/3‡ Introduced 1925. Locos. built non-condensing, originally fitted with large chimney. Some now with small chimney.

N2/4§ Introduced 1928. Development of N2/2, slightly heavier. Built with condensing gear and small chimney.

(The small chimneys are to suit the Metropolitan loading gauge, for working to Moorgate. Condensing gear has been removed from or added to certain locos. transferred from or to the London area).

Weight: $\begin{cases} 70 \text{ tons 5 cwt.*†} \\ 70 \text{ tons 8 cwt.‡} \\ 71 \text{ tons 9 cwt.§} \end{cases}$

Pressure: 170 lb. Su. Cyls.: $19'' \times 26''$. Driving Wheels: 5′ 8″. T.E.: 19,945 lb. P.V.

69490*	69518†	69544*	69571§
69491*	69519†	69545*	69572§
69492*	69520*	69546*	69573§
69493*	69521*	69547*	69574§
69494*	69522*	69548*	69575§
69495*	69523*	69549*	69576§
69496*	69524*	69550†	69577§
69497*	69525*	69551†	69578§
69498*	69526*	69552†	69579§
69499*	69527*	69553†	69580§
69500†	69528*	69554†	69581§
69501†	69529*	69555†	69582§
69502†	69530*	69556§	69583§
69504*	69531*	69557†	69584§
69505†	69532*	69558†	69585§
69506*	69533*	69559†	69586§
69507*	69534*	69560†	69587§
69508†	69535*	69561†	69588§
69509†	69536*	69563‡	69589§
69510†	69537*	69564‡	69590§
69511†	69538*	69565‡	69591§
69512*	69539*	69566‡	69592§
69513*	69540*	69567‡	69593§
69515†	69541*	69568§	69594‡
69516†	69542*	69569§	69595‡
69517*	69543*	69570§	69596‡

Total :   Class N2/2   69

       Class N2/3   8

       Class N2/4   27

0-6-2T 3MT Class N7

N7/1[1] Introduced 1925. Post-grouping development of Hill G.E. design with detail differences.

N7/2[2] Introduced 1926. Development of N7/1 with long-travel valves.

N7/3[3] Introduced 1927. Doncaster-built version of N7/2 with round-topped firebox.

N7/4[4] Introduced 1940. Pre-grouping N7 (G.E.) rebuilt with round-topped firebox, retaining short-travel valves.

N7/5[5] Introduced 1943. N7/1 rebuilt with round-topped firebox, retaining short-travel valves.

N7/3[6] Introduced 1943. N7/2 rebuilt with round-topped firebox.

Weight:
$\begin{cases} \text{63 tons 13 cwt.}[1] \\ \text{64 tons 17 cwt.}[2] \\ \text{64 tons.}[3] \\ \text{61 tons 16 cwt.}[4] \\ \text{64 tons.}[5] \\ \text{64 tons.}[6] \end{cases}$

Pressure: 180 lb. Su. Cyls.: 18″ × 24″.

Driving Wheels: 4′ 10″. T.E.: 20,515 lb.

Walschaerts gear. P.V.

69600[4]	69623[5]	69646[5]	69669[5]
69601[4]	69624[5]	69647[5]	69670[5]
69602[4]	69625[5]	69648[5]	69671[5]
69603[4]	69626[5]	69649[5]	69672[6]
69604[4]	69627[1]	69650[5]	69673[6]
69605[4]	69628[5]	69651[5]	69674[6]
69606[4]	69629[5]	69652[5]	69675[6]
69607[4]	69630[5]	69653[5]	69676[6]
69608[4]	69631[5]	69654[5]	69677[6]
69609[4]	69632[5]	69655[5]	69678[6]
69610[4]	69633[5]	69656[5]	69679[6]
69611[4]	69634[5]	69657[5]	69680[6]
69612[4]	69635[5]	69658[5]	69681[6]
69613[4]	69636[5]	69659[5]	69682[6]
69614[4]	69637[5]	69660[5]	69683[6]
69615[4]	69638[5]	69661[5]	69684[6]
69616[4]	69639[5]	69662[5]	69685[6]
69617[4]	69640[5]	69663[5]	69686[6]
69618[4]	69641[5]	69664[5]	69687[6]
69619[4]	69642[5]	69665[5]	69688[6]
69620[4]	69643[5]	69666[5]	69689[2]
69621[4]	69644[5]	69667[5]	69690[6]
69622[5]	69645[5]	69668[5]	69691[6]
69692[6]	69703[3]	69714[3]	69725[3]
69693[6]	69704[3]	69715[3]	69726[3]
69694[6]	69705[3]	69716[3]	69727[3]
69695[2]	69706[3]	69717[3]	69728[3]
69696[6]	69707[3]	69718[3]	69729[3]
69697[6]	69708[3]	69719[3]	69730[3]
69698[6]	69709[3]	69720[3]	69731[3]
69699[6]	69710[3]	69721[3]	69732[3]
69700[6]	69711[3]	69722[3]	69733[3]
69701[3]	69712[3]	69723[3]	
69702[3]	69713[3]	69724[3]	

Total :
Class N7/1	1
Class N7/2	2
Class N7/3	60
Class N7/4	22
Class N7/5	49

4-6-2T 3F Class A7

Introduced 1910. Raven N.E. design, later rebuilt with superheater and reduced pressure.

Weight: 87 tons 10 cwt.

Pressure: 160 lb. Su.

Cyls.: (3) 16½″ × 26″.

Driving Wheels: 4′ 7¼″.

T.E.: 26,140 lb.

P.V.

69772	69782	69786

Total 3

4-6-2T 3MT Class A5

A5/1 Introduced 1911. Robinson G.C. design.

A5/2* Introduced 1925. Post-grouping development of A5/1 with reduced boiler mountings and detail differences.

Weight: $\begin{cases} \text{85 tons 18 cwt.} \\ \text{90 tons 11 cwt.*} \end{cases}$

Pressure: 180 lb. Su. Cyls.: 20″ × 26″.

Driving Wheels: 5′ 7″. T.E.: 23,750 lb.

P.V.

69800	69811	69822	69833*
69801	69812	69823	69834*
69802	69813	69824	69835*
69803	69814	69825	69836*
69804	69815	69826	69837*
69805	69816	69827	69838*
69806	69817	69828	69839*
69807	69818	69829	69840*
69808	69819	69830*	69841*
69809	69820	69831*	69842*
69810	69821	69832*	

Total : Class A5/1   30
Class A5/2   13

4-6-2T   3MT   Class A8

Introduced 1931. Gresley rebuild of Raven N.E. Class " D " 4-4-4T (introduced 1913).
Weight: 86 tons 18 cwt.
Pressure: 175 lb. Su.
Cyls.: (3) 16½″ × 26″.
Driving Wheels: 5′ 9″. T.E.: 22,940 lb. P.V.

69850	69862	69874	69886
69851	69863	69875	69887
69852	69864	69876	69888
69853	69865	69877	69889
69854	69866	69878	69890
69855	69867	69879	69891
69856	69868	69880	69892
69857	69869	69881	69893
69858	69870	69882	69894
69859	69871	69883	
69860	69872	69884	
69861	69873	69885	

Total 45

4-8-0T   5F   Class T1

Introduced 1909.   W. Worsdell N.E. design.
Weight: 85 tons 8 cwt.
Pressure: 175 lb.
Cyls.: (3) 18″ × 26″.
Driving Wheels: 4′ 7¼″. T.E. 34,080 lb. P.V.

69910	69913	69917	69921
69911	69915	69918	
69912	69916	69920	

Total 10

0-8-0T   5F   Class Q1

Thompson rebuild of Robinson G.C. Q4 0-8-0, introduced 1902.

Q1/1* Introduced 1942.   1,500 gallon tanks.

Q1/2 Introduced 1943.   2,000 gallon tanks.

Weight: $\begin{cases} 69 \text{ tons } 18 \text{ cwt.*} \\ 73 \text{ tons } 13 \text{ cwt.} \end{cases}$
Pressure: 180 lb. Cyls.: (O) 19″ × 26″.
Driving Wheels: 4′ 8″. T.E.: 25,645 lb.

69926*	69930	69933	69936
69928*	69931	69934	
69929	69932	69935	

Total 10

BRITISH RAILWAYS STANDARD LOCOMOTIVES

Chief Officer (Mechanical Engineering) :
R. C. BOND

4-6-2 **7P6F**

Introduced 1951. Designed at Derby
Weight Loco. 94 tons 0 cwt.
    Tender (see page 71)
Pressure : 250 lb Su.
Cyls. : (O) 20″ × 28″.
Driving Wheels: 6′ 2″. T.E.: 32,150 lb.
Walschaerts valve gear. P V.

70000	Britannia
70001	Lord Hurcomb
70002	Geoffrey Chaucer
70003	John Bunyan
70004	William Shakespeare
70005	John Milton
70006	Robert Burns
70007	Coeur-de-Lion
70008	Black Prince
70009	Alfred the Great
70010	Owen Glendower
70011	Hotspur
70012	John of Gaunt
70013	Oliver Cromwell
70014	Iron Duke
70015	Apollo
70016	Ariel
70017	Arrow
70018	Flying Dutchman
70019	Lightning
70020	Mercury
70021	Morning Star
70022	Tornado
70023	Venus
70024	Vulcan
70025	Western Star
70026	Polar Star
70027	Rising Star
70028	Royal Star
70029	Shooting Star
70030	William Wordsworth
70031	Byron
70032	Tennyson
70033	Charles Dickens
70034	Thomas Hardy
70035	Rudyard Kipling
70036	Boadicea
70037	Hereward the Wake
70038	Robin Hood
70039	Sir Christopher Wren
70040	Clive of India
70041	Sir John Moore
70042	Lord Roberts
70043	
70044	Earl Haig
70045	
70046	
70047	
70048	
70049	
70050	Firth of Clyde
70051	Firth of Forth
70052	Firth of Tay
70053	Moray Firth
70054	Dornoch Firth

Total 55

4-6-2 **8P**

Introduced 1954. Designed at Derby.
Weight: Loco. 101 tons 5 cwt.
    Tender (see page 71)
Pressure: 250 lb. Su.
Cyls.: (3) 18″ × 28″.
Driving Wheels: 6′ 2″. T.E.: 39,080 lb.
Caprotti valve gear.

71000 Duke of Gloucester

Total 1

4-6-2 **6P5F**

Introduced 1952. Designed at Derby.
Weight: Loco. 86 tons 19 cwt.
    Tender (see page 71).
Pressure: 225 lb. Su.
Cyls.: (O) 19½″ × 28″.
Driving Wheels: 6′ 2″. T.E.: 27,520 lb.
Walschaerts valve gear. P.V.

72000	Clan Buchanan
72001	Clan Cameron
72002	Clan Campbell
72003	Clan Fraser
72004	Clan Macdonald
72005	Clan Macgregor
72006	Clan Mackenzie
72007	Clan Mackintosh
72008	Clan Macleod
72009	Clan Stewart

Total 10

4-6-0   5

Introduced 1951. Designed at Doncaster.
*Introduced 1956. Fitted with Caprotti valve gear.
Weight: Loco.   76 tons 4 cwt.
        Tender (see page 71).
Pressure: 225 lb. Su.
Cyls.: (O) 19″ × 28″.
Driving Wheels: 6′ 2″. T.E.: 26,120 lb.
Walschaerts valve gear. P.V.

73000	73024	73048	73072
73001	73025	73049	73073
73002	73026	73050	73074
73003	73027	73051	73075
73004	73028	73052	73076
73005	73029	73053	73077
73006	73030	73054	73078
73007	73031	73055	73079
73008	73032	73056	73080
73009	73033	73057	73081
73010	73034	73058	73082
73011	73035	73059	73083
73012	73036	73060	73084
73013	73037	73061	73085
73014	73038	73062	73086
73015	73039	73063	73087
73016	73040	73064	73088
73017	73041	73065	73089
73018	73042	73066	73090
73019	73043	73067	73091
73020	73044	73068	73092
73021	73045	73069	73093
73022	73046	73070	73094
73023	73047	73071	73095

73096	73115	73134*	73153*
73097	73116	73135*	73154*
73098	73117	73136*	73155
73099	73118	73137*	73156
73100	73119	73138*	73157
73101	73120	73139*	73158
73102	73121	73140*	73159
73103	73122	73141*	73160
73104	73123	73142*	73161
73105	73124	73143*	73162
73106	73125*	73144*	73163
73107	73126*	73145*	73164
73108	73127*	73146*	73165
73109	73128*	73147*	73166
73110	73129*	73148*	73167
73111	73130*	73149*	73168
73112	73131*	73150*	73169
73113	73132*	73151*	73170
73114	73133*	73152*	73171

Engines of this class are still being delivered.

4-6-0   4

Introduced 1951. Designed at Brighton.
Weight: Loco.   69 tons 0 cwt.
        Tender (see page 71).
Pressure: 225 lb. Su.
Cyls.: (O) 18″ × 28″.
Driving Wheels: 5′ 8″. T.E.: 25,100 lb.
Walschaerts valve gear. P.V.

75000	75017	75034	75051
75001	75018	75035	75052
75002	75019	75036	75053
75003	75020	75037	75054
75004	75021	75038	75055
75005	75022	75039	75056
75006	75023	75040	75057
75007	75024	75041	75058
75008	75025	75042	75059
75009	75026	75043	75060
75010	75027	75044	75061
75011	75028	75045	75062
75012	75029	75046	75063
75013	75030	75047	75064
75014	75031	75048	75065
75015	75032	75049	75066
75016	75033	75050	75067

75068	75074	75080	75086
75069	75075	75081	75087
75070	75076	75082	75088
75071	75077	75083	75089
75072	75078	75084	
75073	75079	75085	

Engines of this class are still being delivered.

2-6-0   4

Introduced 1953. Designed at Doncaster.
Weight: Loco.   59 tons 2 cwt.
         Tender (see page 71).
Pressure: 225 lb. Su.
Cyls.: (O) 17½″ × 26″.
Driving Wheels: 5′ 3″.   T.E.: 24,170 lb.
Walschaerts valve gear.   P.V.

76000	76029	76058	76087
76001	76030	76059	76088
76002	76031	76060	76089
76003	76032	76061	76090
76004	76033	76062	76091
76005	76034	76063	76092
76006	76035	76064	76093
76007	76036	76065	76094
76008	76037	76066	76095
76009	76038	76067	76096
76010	76039	76068	76097
76011	76040	76069	76098
76012	76041	76070	76099
76013	76042	76071	76100
76014	76043	76072	76101
76015	76044	76073	76102
76016	76045	76074	76103
76017	76046	76075	76104
76018	76047	76076	76105
76019	76048	76077	76106
76020	76049	76078	76107
76021	76050	76079	76108
76022	76051	76080	76109
76023	76052	76081	76110
76024	76053	76082	76111
76025	76054	76083	76112
76026	76055	76084	76113
76027	76056	76085	76114
76028	76057	76086	

Engines of this class are still being delivered.

2-6-0   3

Introduced 1954. Designed at Swindon.
Weight: Loco.   57 tons 10 cwt.
         Tender (see page 71).
Pressure: 200 lb. Su.
Cyls.: (O) 17½″ × 26″.
Driving Wheels: 5′ 3″.   T.E.: 21,490 lb.
Walschaerts valve gear.   P.V.

77000	77007	77014	77021
77001	77008	77015	77022
77002	77009	77016	77023
77003	77010	77017	77024
77004	77011	77018	
77005	77012	77019	
77006	77013	77020	

Engines of this class are still being delivered.

2-6-0   2

Introduced 1953. Designed at Derby.
Weight: Loco.   49 tons 5 cwt.
         Tender (see page 71).
Pressure: 200 lb. Su.
Cyls.: (O) 16½″ × 24″.
Driving Wheels: 5′ 0″.   T.E.: 18,515 lb.
Walschaerts valve gear.   P.V.

78000	78017	78034	78051
78001	78018	78035	78052
78002	78019	78036	78053
78003	78020	78037	78054
78004	78021	78038	78055
78005	78022	78039	78056
78006	78023	78040	78057
78007	78024	78041	78058
78008	78025	78042	78059
78009	78026	78043	78060
78010	78027	78044	78061
78011	78028	78045	78062
78012	78029	78046	78063
78013	78030	78047	78064
78014	78031	78048	
78015	78032	78049	
78016	78033	78050	

Total 65

2-6-4T   4

Introduced 1951. Designed at Brighton.
Weight: 88 tons 10 cwt.
Pressure: 225 lb. Su.
Cyls.: (O) 18″ × 28″.
Driving Wheels: 5′ 8″. T.E.: 25,100 lb.
Walschaerts valve gear. P.V.

80000	80039	80078	80117
80001	80040	80079	80118
80002	80041	80080	80119
80003	80042	80081	80120
80004	80043	80082	80121
80005	80044	80083	80122
80006	80045	80084	80123
80007	80046	80085	80124
80008	80047	80086	80125
80009	80048	80087	80126
80010	80049	80088	80127
80011	80050	80089	80128
80012	80051	80090	80129
80013	80052	80091	80130
80014	80053	80092	80131
80015	80054	80093	80132
80016	80055	80094	80133
80017	80056	80095	80134
80018	80057	80096	80135
80019	80058	80097	80136
80020	80059	80098	80137
80021	80060	80099	80138
80022	80061	80100	80139
80023	80062	80101	80140
80024	80063	80102	80141
80025	80064	80103	80142
80026	80065	80104	80143
80027	80066	80105	80144
80028	80067	80106	80145
80029	80068	80107	80146
80030	80069	80108	80147
80031	80070	80109	80148
80032	80071	80110	80149
80033	80072	80111	80150
80034	80073	80112	80151
80035	80074	80113	80152
80036	80075	80114	80153
80037	80076	80115	80154
80038	80077	80116	

Total 155

2-6-2T   3

Introduced 1952. Designed at Swindon.
Weight: 73 tons 10 cwt.
Pressure: 200 lb. Su.
Cyls.: (O) 17½″ × 26″.
Driving Wheels: 5′ 3″. T.E.: 21,490 lb.
Walschaerts valve gear. P.V.

82000	82012	82024	82036
82001	82013	82025	82037
82002	82014	82026	82038
82003	82015	82027	82039
82004	82016	82028	82040
82005	82017	82029	82041
82006	82018	82030	82042
82007	82019	82031	82043
82008	82020	82032	82044
82009	82021	82033	
82010	82022	82034	
82011	82023	82035	

Total 45

2-6-2T   2

Introduced 1953. Designed at Derby.
Weight: 63 tons 5 cwt.
Pressure: 200 lb. Su.
Cyls.: (O) 16½″ × 24″.
Driving Wheels: 5′ 0″. T.E.: 18,515 lb.
Walschaerts valve gear. P.V.

84000	84008	84016	84024
84001	84009	84017	84025
84002	84010	84018	84026
84003	84011	84019	84027
84004	84012	84020	84028
84005	84013	84021	84029
84006	84014	84022	
84007	84015	84023	

Engines of this class are still being delivered.

2-8-0 8F WD

Ministry of Supply " Austerity " 2-8-0 locomotives purchased by British Railways, 1948.
Introduced 1943. Riddles M.o.S. design.
Weight: Loco. 70 tons 5 cwt.
       Tender 55 tons 10 cwt.
Pressure: 225 lb. Su.
Cyls.: (O) 19″ × 28″.
Driving Wheels: 4′ 8½″. T.E.: 34,215 lb.
Walschaerts valve gear. P.V.

90000	90038	90076	90114	90152	90200	90248	90296
90001	90039	90077	90115	90153	90201	90249	90297
90003	90040	90078	90116	90154	90202	90250	90298
90004	90041	90079	90117	90155	90203	90251	90299
90005	90042	90080	90118	90156	90204	90252	90300
90006	90043	90081	90119	90157	90205	90253	90301
90007	90044	90082	90120	90158	90206	90254	90302
90008	90045	90083	90121	90159	90207	90255	90303
90009	90046	90084	90122	90160	90208	90256	90304
90010	90047	90085	90123	90161	90209	90257	90305
90011	90048	90086	90124	90162	90210	90258	90306
90012	90049	90087	90125	90163	90211	90259	90307
90013	90050	90088	90126	90164	90212	90260	90308
90014	90051	90089	90127	90165	90213	90261	90309
90015	90052	90090	90128	90166	90214	90262	90310
90016	90053	90091	90129	90167	90215	90263	90311
90017	90054	90092	90130	90168	90216	90264	90312
90018	90055	90093	90131	90169	90217	90265	90313
90019	90056	90094	90132	90170	90218	90266	90314
90020	90057	90095	90133	90171	90219	90267	90315
90021	90058	90096	90134	90172	90220	90268	90316
90022	90059	90097	90135	90173	90221	90269	90317
90023	90060	90098	90136	90174	90222	90270	90318
90024	90061	90099	90137	90175	90223	90271	90319
90025	90062	90100	90138	90176	90224	90272	90320
90026	90063	90101	90139	90177	90225	90273	90321
90027	90064	90102	90140	90178	90226	90274	90322
90028	90065	90103	90141	90179	90227	90275	90323
90029	90066	90104	90142	90180	90228	90276	90324
90030	90067	90105	90143	90181	90229	90277	90325
90031	90068	90106	90144	90182	90230	90278	90326
90032	90069	90107	90145	90183	90231	90279	90327
90033	90070	90108	90146	90184	90232	90280	90328
90034	90071	90109	90147	90185	90233	90281	90329
90035	90072	90110	90148	90186	90234	90282	90330
90036	90073	90111	90149	90187	90235	90283	90331
90037	90074	90112	90150	90188	90236	90284	90332
	90075	90113	90151	90189	90237	90285	90333
				90190	90238	90286	90334
				90191	90239	90287	90335
				90192	90240	90288	90336
				90193	90241	90289	90337
				90194	90242	90290	90338
				90195	90243	90291	90339
				90196	90244	90292	90340
				90197	90245	90293	90341
				90198	90246	90294	90342
				90199	90247	90295	90343

90344	90392	90440	90488	90536	90584	90632	90680
90345	90393	90441	90489	90537	90585	90633	90681
90346	90394	90442	90490	90538	90586	90634	90682
90347	90395	90443	90491	90539	90587	90635	90683
90348	90396	90444	90492	90540	90588	90636	90684
90349	90397	90445	90493	90541	90589	90637	90685
90350	90398	90446	90494	90542	90590	90638	90686
90351	90399	90447	90495	90543	90591	90639	90687
90352	90400	90448	90496	90544	90592	90640	90688
90353	90401	90449	90497	90545	90593	90641	90689
90354	90402	90450	90498	90546	90594	90642	90690
90355	90403	90451	90499	90547	90595	90643	90691
90356	90404	90452	90500	90548	90596	90644	90692
90357	90405	90453	90501	90549	90597	90645	90693
90358	90406	90454	90502	90550	90598	90646	90694
90359	90407	90455	90503	90551	90599	90647	90695
90360	90408	90456	90504	90552	90600	90648	90696
90361	90409	90457	90505	90553	90601	90649	90697
90362	90410	90458	90506	90554	90602	90650	90698
90363	90411	90459	90507	90555	90603	90651	90699
90364	90412	90460	90508	90556	90604	90652	90700
90365	90413	90461	90509	90557	90605	90653	90701
90366	90414	90462	90510	90558	90606	90654	90702
90367	90415	90463	90511	90559	90607	90655	90703
90368	90416	90464	90512	90560	90608	90656	90704
90369	90417	90465	90513	90561	90609	90657	90705
90370	90418	90466	90514	90562	90610	90658	90706
90371	90419	90467	90515	90563	90611	90659	90707
90372	90420	90468	90516	90564	90612	90660	90708
90373	90421	90469	90517	90565	90613	90661	90709
90374	90422	90470	90518	90566	90614	90662	90710
90375	90423	90471	90519	90567	90615	90663	90711
90376	90424	90472	90520	90568	90616	90664	90712
90377	90425	90473	90521	90569	90617	90665	90713
90378	90426	90474	90522	90570	90618	90666	90714
90379	90427	90475	90523	90571	90619	90667	90715
90380	90428	90476	90524	90572	90620	90668	90716
90381	90429	90477	90525	90573	90621	90669	90717
90382	90430	90478	90526	90574	90622	90670	90718
90383	90431	90479	90527	90575	90623	90671	90719
90384	90432	90480	90528	90576	90624	90672	90720
90385	90433	90481	90529	90577	90625	90673	90721
90386	90434	90482	90530	90578	90626	90674	90722
90387	90435	90483	90531	90579	90627	90675	90723
90388	90436	90484	90532	90580	90628	90676	90724
90389	90437	90485	90533	90581	90629	90677	90725
90390	90438	90486	90534	90582	90630	90678	90726
90391	90439	90487	90535	90583	90631	90679	90727

90728	90730	90732 Vulcan
90729	90731	

Total 733

2-10-0   8F   WD

Ministry of Supply " Austerity " 2-10-0 locomotives purchased by British Railways, 1948.

Introduced 1943. Riddles M.o.S. design.

Weight: Loco.   78 tons   6 cwt.
          Tender   55 tons 10 cwt.

Pressure: 225 lb. Su.

Cyls.: (O) 19" × 28".

Driving Wheels: 4' 8½". T.E.: 34,215 lb

Walschaerts valve gear. P.V.

90750	90757	90763	90769
90751	90758	90764	90770
90752	90759	90765	90771
90753	90760	90766	90772
90754	90761	90767	90773
90755	90762	90768	90774
90756			Total 25

2-10-0   9F

Introduced 1954. Designed at Brighton

* Introduced 1955. Fitted with Crosti boiler.

Weight: Loco. $\begin{cases} 86 \text{ tons } 14 \text{ cwt.} \\ 90 \text{ tons } \ 4 \text{ cwt.*} \end{cases}$

       Tender (see page 71).

Pressure: 250 lb. Su.

Cyls.: (O) 20" × 28".

Driving Wheels: 5' 0". T.E. 39,670 lb.

Walschaerts valve gear. P.V.

92000	92005	92010	92015
92001	92006	92011	92016
92002	92007	92012	92017
92003	92008	92013	92018
92004	92009	92014	92019
92020*	92066	92112	92158
92021*	92067	92113	92159
92022*	92068	92114	92160
92023*	92069	92115	92161
92024*	92070	92116	92162
92025*	92071	92117	92163
92026*	92072	92118	92164
92027*	92073	92119	92165
92028*	92074	92120	92166
92029*	92075	92121	92167
92030	92076	92122	92168
92031	92077	92123	92169
92032	92078	92124	92170
92033	92079	92125	92171
92034	92080	92126	92172
92035	92081	92127	92173
92036	92082	92128	92174
92037	92083	92129	92175
92038	92084	92130	92176
92039	92085	92131	92177
92040	92086	92132	92178
92041	92087	92133	92179
92042	92088	92134	92180
92043	92089	92135	92181
92044	92090	92136	92182
92045	92091	92137	92183
92046	92092	92138	92184
92047	92093	92139	92185
92048	92094	92140	92186
92049	92095	92141	92187
92050	92096	92142	92188
92051	92097	92143	92189
92052	92098	92144	92190
92053	92099	92145	92191
92054	92100	92146	92192
92055	92101	92147	92193
92056	92102	92148	92194
92057	92103	92149	92195
92058	92104	92150	92196
92059	92105	92151	92197
92060	92106	92152	92198
92061	92107	92153	92199
92062	92108	92154	92200
92063	92109	92155	92201
92064	92110	92156	92202
92065	92111	92157	

Engines of this class are still being delivered.

BRITISH RAILWAYS STANDARD TENDERS

N.B.—These pairings are not permanent and are liable to alteration with changed operating conditions

Type	Capacity		Weight in Full W.O.		Locos. to which Allocated
	Water galls.	Coal tons	tons	cwt.	
BRI ...	4,250	7	49	3	70000–24 30–44 72000–9 73000–49
BRIA ...	5,000	7	52	10	70025–9
BRIB ...	4,725	7	50	5	73080–9 73100–9/20–34/45–71 75065–79 76053–69 92020–9/60–6/97–9
BRIC ...	4,725	9	53	5	73065–79/90–9 73135–44 92015–9/45–59 77–86 92100–39/50–67
BRID ...	4,725	9	54	10	70045–54
BRIE ...	4,725	10	55	10	71000
BRIF ...	5,625	7	55	5	73110–9 92010–4 30–44 67–76 92087–96 92140–9/68–92202
BRIG ...	5,000	7	52	10	73050–2 92000–9
BRIH ...	4,250	7	49	3	73053–64
BR2 ...	3,500	6	42	3	75000–49 76000–44
BR2A ...	3,500	6	42	3	75050–64 80–9 76045–52/70–76114 77000–24
BR3 ...	3,000	4	36	17	78000–64

THE ABC

Locoshed Book

LONDON

Ian Allan Ltd

NOTES ON THE USE OF THIS BOOK

The *ABC Locoshed Book* is not designed to be used on its own, but as a companion to the *ABC of British Railways Locomotives*. As it is difficult to include shed allocations in the latter without harm to the format which has proved popular with *ABC* users, we introduce this all-in-one *Locoshed Book* wherein the number of *all* British Railways locomotives are listed with the code number of the shed to which each engine is allocated.

1. No details of wheel arrangements, dimensions or locomotive names are provided in the *Locoshed Book*. All these details are readily ascertained from the *ABC of British Railways Locomotives*, as follows :

PART I	... ...	Locomotives Nos. 1—9999
PART II	... ...	,, ,, 10000—39999
PART III	... ...	,, ,, 40000—59999
PART IV	... ...	,, ,, 60000—99999
		Each 2/6

In this publication, however, named locomotives are indicated by an asterisk.

2. Against each locomotive in this booklet is shown the code of its home shed, which the locomotive carries on a small plate at the bottom of the smokebox door. A key to the British Railways shed code is found on pp. 4—9.

3. Sub-sheds, which are not given a special code number by British Railways are included in this list, but locomotives allocated to them carry the shed code of the parent depot, whose number appears immediately above them in the list of shed codes. Sheds listed in bold type are chief sheds of a motive power district.

4. Locomotives not given a shed code were on order, under construction or not yet allocated at the time of compilation.

5. All locomotives solely employed on service or departmental work, whether numbered in the British Railways or in individual departmental series, are listed on page 94.

6. The shed allocations given in this booklet are as they were reported to the following dates :— E. & N.E.R. to May 11th 1957 ; L.M.R. to April 20th 1957 ; Sc.R. to April 13th 1957 ; S.R. to April 1st 1957 ; W.R. to April 20th 1957. To enable the user to keep the booklet up to date, full details of all alterations in shed allocations are published each month in the Ian Allan periodical, *Trains Illustrated* price 2s. 0d., obtainable from any bookstall or newsagent.

3

BRITISH RAILWAYS LOCOMOTIVE
SHEDS AND SHED CODES

THIS LIST INCLUDES ONLY THOSE DEPOTS WHICH HAVE ENGINES
ALLOCATED TO THEM. IT DOES NOT INCLUDE OVERNIGHT
STABLING OR SIGNING-ON POINTS.

ALL B.R. LOCOMOTIVES CARRY THE CODE OF THEIR HOME DEPOT
ON A SMALL PLATE AFFIXED TO THE SMOKEBOX DOOR.

LONDON MIDLAND REGION

1A **Willesden**	9A **Longsight**
1B Camden	9B Stockport (Edgeley)
1C Watford	9C Macclesfield
1D Devons Road (Bow)	9D Buxton
1E Bletchley	9G Northwich
Leighton Buzzard	
	10A **Springs Branch (Wigan)**
2A **Rugby**	10B Preston
Seaton	10C Patricroft
2B Nuneaton	10D Sutton Oak
2C Warwick	
2D Coventry	11A **Carnforth**
2E Northampton	11B Barrow
2F Market Harborough	Coniston
	11C Oxenholme
3A **Bescot**	11D Tebay
3B Bushbury	
3C Walsall	12A **Carlisle (Upperby)**
3D Aston	12B Penrith
3E Monument Lane	12C Workington
5A **Crewe North**	14A **Cricklewood**
Whitchurch	14B Kentish Town
5B Crewe South	14C St. Albans
5C Stafford	
5D Stoke	15A **Wellingborough**
5E Alsager	15B Kettering
5F Uttoxeter	15C Leicester
	15D Bedford
6A **Chester**	
6B Mold Junction	16A **Nottingham**
6C Birkenhead	16B Kirkby
6D Chester (Northgate)	16C Mansfield
6E Wrexham	
6F Bidston	17A **Derby**
6G Llandudno Junction	17B Burton
6H Bangor	Horninglow
6J Holyhead	Overseal
6K Rhyl	17C Coalville
	17D Rowsley
8A **Edge Hill**	Cromford
8B Warrington	Middleton
Warrington (Arpley)	Sheep Pasture
8C Speke Junction	17E Heaton Mersey
8D Widnes	17F Trafford Park
8E Brunswick (Liverpool)	

18A	**Toton**		24C	Lostock Hall
18B	Westhouses		24D	Lower Darwen
18C	Hasland		24E	Blackpool
18D	Staveley			Blackpool North
	Sheepbridge		24F	Fleetwood
			24G	Skipton
19A	**Sheffield**		24H	Hellifield
19B	Millhouses		24J	Lancaster
19C	Canklow			
			26A	**Newton Heath**
21A	**Saltley**		26B	Agecroft
21B	Bournville		26C	Bolton
21C	Bromsgrove		26D	Bury
			26E	Lees
22A	**Bristol**			
22B	Gloucester		27A	**Bank Hall**
	Dursley		27B	Aintree
	Tewkesbury		27C	Southport
			27D	Wigan (L. & Y.)
24A	**Accrington**		27E	Walton
24B	Rose Grove			

EASTERN REGION

30A	Stratford		32A	**Norwich**
	Brentwood			Cromer Beach
	Chelmsford			Dereham
	Enfield Town			Swaffham
	Epping			Wymondham
	Ilford		32B	Ipswich
	Wood St.			Felixstowe Town
	(Walthamstow)			Stowmarket
30B	Hertford East		32C	Lowestoft
	Buntingford		32D	Yarmouth (South Town)
	Ware		32E	Yarmouth (Vauxhall)
30C	Bishops Stortford		32F	Yarmouth Beach
30E	Colchester		32G	**Melton Constable**
	Braintree			Norwich City
	Clacton			
	Maldon		33A	**Plaistow**
	Walton-on-Naze		33B	Tilbury
30F	Parkeston		33C	Shoeburyness
			34A	**Kings Cross**
			34B	Hornsey
31A	**Cambridge**		34C	Hatfield
	Ely		34D	Hitchin
	Huntingdon East		34E	Neasden
	Saffron Walden			Aylesbury
31B	March			Chesham
	Wisbech			
31C	Kings Lynn		35A	**New England**
	Hunstanton			Spalding
31D	South Lynn			Stamford
31E	**Bury St. Edmunds**		35B	Grantham
	Sudbury (Suffolk)		35C	Peterborough (Spital)

36A	**Doncaster**		39A	**Gorton**
36B	Mexborough			Dinting
	Wath			Hayfield
36C	Frodingham			
36D	Barnsley		40A	**Lincoln**
36E	Retford			Lincoln (St. Marks)
	Newark		40B	Immingham
				Grimsby
				New Holland
			40D	Tuxford
			40E	Langwith Junction
38A	**Colwick**		40F	Boston
38B	Annesley			Sleaford
38C	Leicester (G.C.)			
38D	Staveley			
38E	Woodford Halse		41A	**Sheffield (Darnall)**

NORTH-EASTERN REGION

50A	**York**		52E	Percy Main
50B	Leeds (Neville Hill)		52F	North Blyth
50C	Selby			South Blyth
50D	Starbeck			
50E	Scarborough		53A	**Hull (Dairycoates)**
50F	Malton		53B	Hull (Botanic Gardens)
	Pickering		53C	Hull (Springhead)
50G	Whitby			Alexandra Dock
			53D	Bridlington
			53E	Goole
51A	**Darlington**			
	Middleton-in-Teesdale		54A	**Sunderland**
51B	Newport (Yorks)			Durham
51C	West Hartlepool		54B	Tyne Dock
51D	Middlesbrough		54C	Borough Gardens
51E	Stockton		54D	Consett
51F	West Auckland			
51G	Haverton Hill		55A	**Leeds (Holbeck)**
51H	Kirkby Stephen		55B	Stourton
51J	Northallerton		55C	Farnley Junction
51K	Saltburn		55D	Royston
			55E	Normanton
			55F	Manningham
52A	**Gateshead**		55G	Huddersfield
	Bowes Bridge			
52B	Heaton		56A	**Wakefield**
52C	Blaydon		56B	Ardsley
	Alston		56C	Copley Hill
	Hexham		56D	Mirfield
52D	Tweedmouth		56E	Sowerby Bridge
	Alnmouth		56F	Low Moor
			56G	Bradford

SCOTTISH REGION

60A	**Inverness**	**64A**	**St. Margarets**
	Dingwall		**(Edinburgh)**
	Kyle of Lochalsh		Dunbar
60B	Aviemore		Galashiels
	Boat of Garten		Longniddry
60C	Helmsdale		North Berwick
	Dornoch	**64B**	Haymarket
	Tain	**64C**	Dalry Road
60D	Wick	**64D**	Carstairs
	Thurso	**64E**	Polmont
60E	Forres	**64F**	Bathgate
		64G	Hawick
			Riccarton
			St. Boswells
61A	**Kittybrewster**	**65A**	**Eastfield (Glasgow)**
	Ballater		Arrochar
	Fraserburgh	**65B**	St. Rollox
	Inverurie	**65C**	Parkhead
	Peterhead	**65D**	Dawsholm
61B	Aberdeen (Ferryhill)		Dumbarton
61C	Keith	**65E**	Kipps
	Banff	**65F**	Grangemouth
	Elgin	**65G**	Yoker
		65H	Helensburgh
		65 I	Balloch
		65 J	Fort William
			Mallaig
62A	**Thornton**		
	Anstruther		
	Burntisland		
	Ladybank	**66A**	**Polmadie (Glasgow)**
	Methil	**66B**	Motherwell
62B	Dundee (Tay Bridge)	**66C**	Hamilton
	Arbroath	**66D**	Greenock (Ladyburn)
	Dundee West		Greenock (Princes Pier)
	Montrose		
	St. Andrews		
62C	Dunfermline		
	Alloa	**67A**	**Corkerhill (Glasgow)**
		67B	Hurlford
			Beith
			Muirkirk
		67C	Ayr
63A	**Perth South**	**67D**	Ardrossan
	Aberfeldy		
	Crieff		
63B	Stirling South	**68A**	**Carlisle (Kingmoor**
	Killin	**68B**	Dumfries
	Stirling (Shore Road)	**68C**	Stranraer
63C	Forfar		Newton Stewart
63D	Oban	**68D**	Beattock
	Ballachulish	**68E**	Carlisle Canal

SOUTHERN REGION

70A **Nine Elms**
70B Feltham
70C Guildford
70D Basingstoke
70E Reading
70F Fratton
70G Newport (I.O.W.)
70H Ryde (I.O.W.)

71A **Eastleigh**
    Andover Junction
    Lymington
    Winchester
71B Bournemouth
    Branksome
71G Bath (S. & D.)
    Radstock
71H Templecombe
71I Southampton Docks
71J Highbridge

72A **Exmouth Junction**
    Bude
    Exmouth
    Lyme Regis
    Okehampton
    Seaton

72B Salisbury
72C Yeovil
72D Plymouth
    Callington
72E Barnstaple Junction
    Ilfracombe
    Torrington
72F Wadebridge

73A **Stewarts Lane**
73B Bricklayers Arms
73C Hither Green
73D Gillingham (Kent)
73E Faversham

74A **Ashford (Kent)**
74B Ramsgate
74C Dover
    Folkestone
74D Tonbridge
74E St. Leonards

75A **Brighton**
75B Redhill
75C Norwood Junction
75D Horsham
75E Three Bridges
75F Tunbridge Wells West

WESTERN REGION

81A **Old Oak Common**
81B Slough
    Marlow
    Watlington
81C Southall
81D Reading
    Henley-on-Thames
81E Didcot
81F Oxford
    Fairford

82A **Bristol (Bath Road)**
    Bath
    Wells
    Weston-super-Mare
    Yatton
82B St. Philip's Marsh

82C Swindon
    Chippenham
82D Westbury
    Frome
82E Yeovil
82F Weymouth
    Bridport

83A **Newton Abbot**
    Ashburton
    Kingsbridge
83B Taunton
    Bridgwater
83C Exeter
    Tiverton Junction
83D Laira (Plymouth)
    Launceston

83E	**St. Blazey**
	Bodmin
	Moorswater
83F	Truro
83G	Penzance
	Helston
	St. Ives
84A	**Wolverhampton**
	(Stafford Road)
84B	Oxley
84C	Banbury
84D	Leamington Spa
84E	Tyseley
	Stratford-on-Avon
84F	Stourbridge Junc.
84G	Shrewsbury
	Builth Road
	Clee Hill
	Craven Arms
	Knighton
84H	Wellington (Salop)
84J	Croes Newydd
	Bala
	Penmaenpool
	Trawsfynydd
84K	Chester
85A	**Worcester**
	Evesham
	Kingham
85B	Gloucester
	Brimscombe
	Cheltenham
	Cirencester
	Lydney
	Tetbury
85C	Hereford
	Ledbury
	Leominster
	Ross
85D	Kidderminster
86A	**Newport**
	(Ebbw Junction)
86B	Newport (Pill)
86C	Cardiff (Canton)
86D	Llantrisant
86E	Severn Tunnel Junction
86F	Tondu
86G	Pontypool Road
	Abergavenny

86H	Aberbeeg
86J	Aberdare
86K	Tredegar
87A	**Neath**
	Glyn Neath
	Neath (N. & B.)
87B	Duffryn Yard
87C	Danygraig
87D	Swansea East Dock
87E	Landore
87F	Llanelly
	Burry Port
	Pantyfynnon
87G	Carmarthen
87H	Neyland
	Cardigan
	Milford Haven
	Pembroke Dock
	Whitland
87J	Goodwick
87K	Swansea (Victoria)
	Gurnos
	Llandovery
	Upper Bank
88A	**Cardiff (Cathays)**
	Radyr
88B	Cardiff East Dock
88C	Barry
88D	Merthyr
	Cae Harris
	Dowlais Central
	Rhymney
88E	Abercynon
88F	Treherbert
	Ferndale
89A	**Oswestry**
	Llanidloes
	Moat Lane
89B	Brecon
	Builth Wells
89C	Machynlleth
	Aberayron
	Aberystwyth
	Aberystwyth (V. of R.)
	Portmadoc
	Pwllheli

ABBREVIATIONS USED

C W — Crewe Works
H W — Horwich Works
R W — St. Rollox Works
R T S — Rugby Testing Station

SHED ALLOCATIONS OF BRITISH RAILWAYS LOCOMOTIVES

IN NUMERICAL ORDER

7 * 89C	1015 * 83D	1406 81C	1455 85C
8 * 89C	1016 * 84G	1407 81D	1456 85C
9 * 89C	1017 * 84G	1408 83D	1457 6C
36 88B	1018 * 83G	1409 82A	1458 84F
38 88B	1019 * 82C	1410 82C	1459 89A
42 88B	1020 * 87H	1412 82A	1461 85A
304 88E	1021 * 83D	1417 6C	1462 82C
365 88E	1022 * 84K	1418 85A	1463 82A
370 88E	1023 * 83F	1419 83E	1464 85B
373 88E	1024 * 84K	1420 81F	1465 84J
381 88E	1025 * 84G	1421 86A	1466 83A
383 88E	1026 * 84G	1422 82C	1467 82F
390 88E	1027 * 87H	1423 87J	1468 83C
393 88E	1028 * 82A	1424 85B	1469 83C
398 88E	1029 * 87H	1426 . 81C	1470 83A
822 89A	1101 87C	1427 83A	1471 86D
823 89A	1102 87C	1428 85B	1472 83A
	1103 87C	1429 83C	1473 34E
	1104 87C	1430 85B	1474 81C
	1105 87C	1431 87J	1500 81A
	1106 87C	1432 89A	1501 81C
	1140 87D	1433 82C	1502 81E
	1142 87C	1434 83D	1503 81A
	1143 87C	1435 83C	1504 81A
	1144 87D	1436 81C	1505 81A
	1145 87C	1437 81F	1506 86B
	1151 87C	1438 84F	1507 86B
	1152 87K	1439 83A	1508 86C
	1338 83B	1440 83C	1509 86A
	1361 83D	1441 85B	1600 88C
1000 * 82A	1362 83B	1442 81F	1601 87H
1001 * 87H	1363 83D	1443 81C	1602 89A
1002 * 83G	1364 83D	1444 81D	1603 89A
1003 * 84G	1365 82C	1445 85C	1604 89A
1004 * 82C	1366 83B	1446 81C	1605 85A
1005 * 82A	1367 82F	1447 81D	1606 87F
1006 * 83G	1368 82F	1448 81B	1607 87F
1007 * 83F	1369 82C	1449 83C	1608 83A
1008 * 84K	1370 82F	1450 81B	1609 87F
1009 * 82A	1371 82C	1451 83C	1610 88E
1010 * 83D	1400 82C	1452 87J	1611 87H
1011 * 82A	1401 85B	1453 82F	1612 87F
1012 * 82C	1403 82F	1454 82A	1613 87F
1013 * 84G	1405 83C		
1014 * 82A			

1614 87F	2069 6C	2254 85B	2811 82D
1615 87F	2134 6C	2255 89C	2812 84C
1616 85B	2198 87F	2256 84C	2813 85A
1617 85C	2200 89C	2257 84E	2814 86A
1618 87F	2201 82B	2258 82C	2815 86E
1619 84F	2202 89C	2259 84C	2816 84C
1620 88E	2203 82C	2260 89C	2817 84K
1621 84F	2204 89C	2261 82B	2818 82C
1622 87F	2205 85C	2262 81D	2819 84B
1623 85B	2206 85C	2263 87H	2820 86A
1624 83E	2207 85B	2264 89C	2821 86C
1625 85C	2208 82D	2265 82B	2822 84C
1626 83E	2209 84J	2266 85C	2823 84G
1627 85B	2210 89A	2267 89C	2824 81D
1628 87F	2211 83C	2268 82D	2825 85A
1629 85A	2212 83B	2269 82B	2826 86E
1630 85B	2213 82B	2270 84C	2827 82D
1631 85B	2214 81E	2271 89C	2828 86J
1632 85B	2215 82C	2272 87G	2829 84F
1633 87F	2216 87G	2273 87G	2830 84B
1634 87C	2217 89C	2274 85C	2831 86J
1635 84J	2218 86A	2275 89A	2832 86E
1636 89C	2219 89A	2276 81A	2833 84B
1637 87H	2220 87H	2277 85A	2834 84F
1638 87F	2221 81E	2278 85B	2835 81D
1639 85B	2222 81A	2279 84E	2836 86J
1640 87C	2223 87J	2280 86A	2837 86C
1641 87D	2224 87G	2281 85C	2838 86E
1642 85B	2225 85C	2282 81A	2839 86A
1643 87F	2226 87E	2283 87H	2840 84J
1644 87F	2227 86A	2284 87E	2841 85A
1645 87A	2228 87H	2285 89C	2842 86A
1646 60C	2229 87H	2286 89C	2843 83D
1647 87C	2230 83C	2287 89B	2844 86E
1648 87C	2231 86E	2288 87H	2845 86A
1649 82B	2232 89C	2289 89C	2846 83A
1650 83D	2233 89C	2290 87G	2847 84C
1651 87F	2234 84G	2291 85B	2848 84K
1652 87D	2235 89B	2292 86E	2849 84E
1653 86A	2236 81F	2293 82C	2850 84B
1654 87F	2237 89C	2294 81F	2851 84E
1655 87F	2238 84E	2295 85C	2852 82C
1656 86A	2239 89A	2296 84J	2853 81C
1657 85C	2240 81E	2297 84C	2854 85B
1658 82C	2241 85A	2298 89C	2855 85A
1659 84J	2242 85A	2299 81D	2856 84E
1660 84J	2243 81A	2538 89A	2857 84E
1661 85D	2244 89C	2800 86A	2858 86E
1662 85C	2245 81D	2801 86G	2859 86E
1663 84H	2246 84C	2802 86G	2860 86E
1664 83E	2247 85A	2803 86E	2861 86A
1665 87F	2248 85B	2804 84F	2862 86E
1666 87F	2249 85C	2805 86A	2863 86J
1667 85C	2250 82B	2806 86E	2864 86E
1668 83B	2251 82B	2807 85A	2865 82C
1669 82B	2252 81E	2808 87F	2866 86E
2008 6C	2253 81D	2809 85B	2867 81D
2012 6C		2810 86J	2868 86A

2869	86E	3183	86E	3623	82B	3681	88B
2870	86J	3186	83D	3624	84D	3682	82C
2871	84J	3187	83D	3625	84E	3683	86H
2872	86E	3190	86E	3626	6C	3684	82C
2873	86E	3200	89A	3627	86F	3685	86G
2874	86C	3201	89A	3628	86G	3686	83D
2875	83A	3202	89A	3629	83D	3687	87A
2876	86J	3203	85B	3630	84K	3688	81A
2877	86C	3204	85A	3631	84D	3689	84E
2878	84J	3205	85A	3632	82B	3690	86F
2879	82C	3206	81E	3633	87C	3691	86A
2880	81C	3207	89A	3634	86A	3692	82A
2881	83A	3208	89A	3635	83E	3693	84E
2882	84K	3209	85A	3636	86A	3694	88B
2883	86E	3210	81E	3637	87J	3695	86J
2884	86G	3211	81E	3638	89B	3696	82D
2885	84F	3212	81E	3639	83D	3697	81B
2886	84C	3213	85A	3640	86G	3698	87F
2887	86E	3214	85A	3641	87D	3699	86J
2888	86E	3215	82B	3642	87G	3700	86B
2889	86E	3216	85A	3643	82B	3701	87E
2890	81C	3217	85A	3644	86D	3702	83F
2891	86C	3218	85A	3645	82C	3703	86G
2892	86C	3219	81D	3646	84C	3704	81C
2893	86E	3400	88B	3647	86H	3705	83E
2894	86A	3401	88B	3648	81A	3706	89B
2895	86E	3402	88B	3649	84F	3707	88E
2896	86E	3403	88B	3650	88E	3708	86G
2897	84E	3404	88B	3651	86G	3709	81E
2898	84E	3405	88B	3652	86B	3710	84F
2899	81C	3406	88B	3653	81E	3711	86H
		3407	88B	3654	87H	3712	86A
		3408	88B	3655	86J	3713	87E
		3409	88B	3656	86D	3714	86A
		3440	81E	3657	84E	3715	87A
		3600	83A	3658	84F	3716	86J
		3601	85D	3659	83A	3717	86G
		3602	84G	3660	84E	3718	87B
		3603	83C	3661	87F	3719	87F
3011	87G	3604	82B	3662	86A	3720	82A
3015	87G	3605	85A	3663	86B	3721	81E
3024	87G	3606	83C	3664	84A	3722	81F
3036	87G	3607	85A	3665	84K	3723	81D
3041	87G	3608	81F	3666	82C	3724	82C
3100	86F	3609	85B	3667	84F	3725	85A
3101	84E	3610	86J	3668	86F	3726	86A
3102	84A	3611	87A	3669	83B	3727	88A
3103	86A	3612	86D	3670	86C	3728	85C
3104	84A	3613	87B	3671	82E	3729	84F
3150	86E	3614	82D	3672	88A	3730	88B
3163	85B	3615	84A	3673	84E	3731	82B
3170	86A	3616	86F	3674	86H	3732	84H
3171	85B	3617	86D	3675	83D	3733	82E
3172	86E	3618	81C	3676	82A	3734	88B
3174	86E	3619	84D	3677	83C	3735	82D
3176	86E	3620	81C	3678	87E	3736	83B
3177	86E	3621	87A	3679	87C	3737	82F
3180	85B	3622	81E	3680	86D	3738	81D

3739	82C	3797	87E	3855	86G	4112	84D
3740	85B	3798	86A	3856	81F	4113	85A
3741	87A	3799	81C	3857	81F	4114	85D
3742	6C	3800	86A	3858	84K	4115	84K
3743	84F	3801	86C	3859	84C	4116	84E
3744	84H	3802	84B	3860	86C	4117	83B
3745	84F	3803	86C	3861	84B	4118	84D
3746	82C	3804	86A	3862	83D	4119	86A
3747	86H	3805	86A	3863	84B	4120	84H
3748	82A	3806	86A	3864	83A	4121	86E
3749	84H	3807	86A	3865	84B	4122	88A
3750	81C	3808	86A	3866	86E	4123	88A
3751	81E	3809	86C			4124	88A
3752	87F	3810	86C			4125	84E
3753	86J	3811	87F			4126	88A
3754	81A	3812	86E			4127	84E
3755	86C	3813	84B			4128	84K
3756	84A	3814	81C			4129	88A
3757	87A	3815	86E	4000 *	87E	4130	86A
3758	82B	3816	86C	4037 *	83A	4131	82B
3759	82A	3817	86C	4056 *	82A	4132	87H
3760	84H	3818	86E	4073 *	86C	4133	82F
3761	87F	3819	84C	4074 *	87G	4134	87G
3762	87B	3820	84K	4075 *	82A	4135	86G
3763	82C	3821	84F	4076 *	83A	4136	83B
3764	82B	3822	86G	4077 *	83D	4137	86E
3765	82B	3823	86E	4078 *	87E	4138	86H
3766	87A	3824	86G	4079 *	84A	4139	85D
3767	89B	3825	84F	4080 *	82A	4140	84A
3768	87E	3826	86G	4081 *	87E	4141	85B
3769	84A	3827	86A	4082 *	81A	4142	84H
3770	89B	3828	86G	4083 *	84A	4143	88D
3771	87F	3829	84C	4084 *	82A	4144	86E
3772	86A	3830	86A	4085 *	81D	4145	83A
3773	82B	3831	84C	4086 *	82C	4146	84E
3774	87A	3832	86A	4087 *	83D	4147	81F
3775	85A	3833	86A	4088 *	83D	4148	85A
3776	86D	3834	83A	4089 *	81A	4149	84C
3777	87F	3835	86C	4090 *	81A	4150	83A
3778	84A	3836	81C	4091 *	81A	4151	86E
3779	86G	3837	84B	4092 *	84A	4152	88D
3780	82C	3838	86E	4093 *	87E	4153	85D
3781	87C	3839	84E	4094 *	84A	4154	85A
3782	84G	3840	83A	4095 *	87E	4155	84E
3783	88B	3841	83A	4096 *	82A	4156	86E
3784	82B	3842	86C	4097 *	81A	4157	83B
3785	87E	3843	86C	4098 *	83A	4158	84H
3786	84K	3844	86C	4099 *	83G	4159	83B
3787	83D	3845	86C	4100	85D	4160	88D
3788	84G	3846	84B	4101	88A	4161	88D
3789	89A	3847	86E	4102	84K	4162	88D
3790	83D	3848	85A	4103	84A	4163	88D
3791	87B	3849	86E	4104	84F	4164	88D
3792	84A	3850	86E	4105	83A	4165	84K
3793	84A	3851	87F	4106	87E	4166	82F
3794	83C	3852	86E	4107	87E	4167	83E
3795	82B	3853	86E	4108	84A	4168	86A
3796	83A	3854	86C	4109	83A	4169	87A
				4110	84H		
				4111	84E		

4170	84E	4262	82B	4553	85B	4612	82C
4171	84D	4263	86F	4554	83F	4613	85A
4172	84E	4264	87A	4555	89C	4614	85A
4173	84F	4265	87B	4556	87H	4615	81A
4174	83D	4266	86C	4557	87H	4616	88D
4175	85D	4267	86A	4558	87H	4617	84J
4176	83A	4268	86D	4559	83E	4618	88A
4177	88A	4269	86F	4560	89C	4619	82A
4178	83A	4270	86C	4561	83F	4620	86D
4179	83A	4271	86A	4562	82F	4621	87A
4200	86H	4272	86J	4563	83G	4622	86C
4201	86B	4273	86F	4564	85B	4623	84G
4203	86A	4274	87A	4565	83E	4624	82F
4206	83E	4275	87A	4566	83G	4625	85A
4207	86C	4276	86H	4567	82A	4626	88B
4208	86D	4277	86H	4568	83A	4627	85B
4211	86B	4278	87F	4569	83E	4628	85B
4212	87B	4279	87A	4570	83G	4629	85A
4213	87F	4280	86B	4571	85A	4630	88D
4214	86B	4281	87A	4572	82D	4631	88B
4215	86E	4282	87A	4573	85B	4632	88D
4217	86E	4283	86A	4574	83F	4633	86C
4218	86F	4284	87A	4575	89C	4634	88A
4221	87D	4285	86B	4576	87H	4635	88D
4222	86F	4286	86A	4577	82A	4636	82D
4223	87F	4287	86H	4578	88C	4637	86D
4224	86F	4288	87A	4579	87H	4638	81B
4225	86C	4289	86E	4580	88A	4639	86G
4226	86C	4290	86A	4581	86F	4640	87B
4227	86A	4291	86B	4582	82A	4641	85D
4228	86J	4292	87B	4583	83D	4642	86G
4229	86G	4293	87B	4584	83E	4643	86B
4230	86G	4294	86A	4585	83E	4644	81A
4231	86C	4295	87A	4587	83F	4645	84J
4232	87D	4296	87B	4588	83F	4646	84F
4233	86B	4297	86J	4589	88A	4647	82D
4235	86B	4298	87F	4590	83D	4648	84E
4236	86F	4299	87C	4591	83D	4649	81E
4237	86H	4358	85B	4592	83D	4650	81B
4238	86H	4375	84F	4593	86G	4651	82C
4241	86F	4377	89C	4594	87H	4652	86H
4242	87A	4505	83G	4595	82A	4653	83D
4243	87A	4507	82F	4596	85A	4654	87H
4246	86A	4508	83F	4597	82A	4655	82B
4247	83E	4519	87H	4599	89C	4656	83D
4248	86A	4524	82A	4600	86G	4657	85C
4250	86H	4526	83E	4601	88C	4658	83D
4251	86F	4536	82D	4602	84K	4659	85B
4252	87A	4538	82C	4603	82B	4660	82A
4253	86B	4540	83C	4604	83B	4661	81D
4254	86C	4545	83G	4605	84H	4662	86D
4255	86J	4546	89A	4606	81D	4663	83B
4256	87B	4547	83G	4607	82D	4664	85A
4257	86J	4548	83G	4608	81C	4665	81D
4258	86B	4549	89C	4609	81D	4666	87C
4259	86B	4550	87H	4610	88C	4667	88A
4260	87F	4551	82D	4611	86A	4668	86G
4261	86D	4552	83E			4669	86F

4670 81D	4920 * 83B	4978 * 83B	5032 * 84A
4671 86A	4921 * 81F	4979 * 81E	5033 * 84K
4672 88A	4922 * 82B	4980 * 82B	5034 * 81A
4673 81C	4923 * 87E	4981 * 87J	5035 * 81A
4674 86D	4924 * 82A	4982 * 86A	5036 * 81D
4675 86F	4925 * 81A	4983 * 82B	5037 * 85A
4676 81F	4926 * 84A	4984 * 84B	5038 * 81A
4677 87J	4927 * 82A	4985 * 83B	5039 * 87G
4678 85C	4928 * 83B	4986 * 84A	5040 * 81A
4679 83D	4929 * 85B	4987 * 81D	5041 * 87E
4680 81B	4930 * 82D	4988 * 84E	5042 * 85B
4681 87B	4931 * 83G	4989 * 81D	5043 * 81A
4682 86H	4932 * 83B	4990 * 83G	5044 * 81A
4683 84J	4933 * 81E	4991 * 83B	5045 * 84A
4684 87B	4934 * 86C	4992 * 83D	5046 * 86C
4685 86H	4935 * 81E	4993 * 81D	5047 * 84A
4686 88B	4936 * 83D	4994 * 81E	5048 * 82A
4687 84F	4937 * 87E	4995 * 81D	5049 * 83D
4688 82B	4938 * 81F	4996 * 86C	5050 * 84G
4689 82E	4939 * 81E	4997 * 84B	5051 * 87E
4690 88D	4940 * 83B	4998 * 81D	5052 * 81A
4691 81B	4941 * 87F	4999 * 82B	5053 * 83A
4692 88C	4942 * 84C		5054 * 82A
4693 83D	4943 * 84E		5055 * 81A
4694 87C	4944 * 81C		5056 * 81A
4695 81C	4945 * 82D		5057 * 82A
4696 84F	4946 * 86C	5000 * 82C	5058 * 83D
4697 82C	4947 * 82A	5001 * 81A	5059 * 83A
4698 88A	4948 * 83C	5002 * 82C	5060 * 81A
4699 87H	4949 * 83B	5003 * 83D	5061 * 84K
4700 81A	4950 * 83D	5004 * 84G	5062 * 82C
4701 81A	4951 * 81D	5005 * 83A	5063 * 82A
4702 81A	4952 * 85C	5006 * 81A	5064 * 82A
4703 82B	4953 * 82C	5007 * 81A	5065 * 81A
4704 81A	4954 * 81F	5008 * 81A	5066 * 81A
4705 83D	4955 * 83C	5009 * 82C	5067 * 82A
4706 82B	4956 * 82A	5010 * 84A	5068 * 82C
4707 81C	4957 * 86A	5011 * 83A	5069 * 83D
4708 81A	4958 * 82A	5012 * 81F	5070 * 84A
4900 * 81A	4959 * 82C	5013 * 87E	5071 * 83A
4901 * 84B	4960 * 81D	5014 * 81A	5072 * 83D
4902 * 81F	4961 * 81D	5015 * 84A	5073 * 84G
4903 * 81F	4962 * 81D	5016 * 87E	5074 * 81A
4904 * 84E	4963 * 84B	5017 * 85B	5075 * 84A
4905 * 83A	4964 * 86C	5018 * 85B	5076 * 82A
4906 * 83F	4965 * 81D	5019 * 82A	5077 * 87E
4907 * 81F	4966 * 84B	5020 * 86C	5078 * 83A
4908 * 83G	4967 * 83A	5021 * 83D	5079 * 83A
4909 * 82A	4968 * 86C	5022 * 84A	5080 * 87E
4910 * 87E	4969 * 81D	5023 * 83D	5081 * 85A
4912 * 84A	4970 * 83B	5024 * 83A	5082 * 81A
4913 * 84B	4971 * 81B	5025 * 82C	5083 * 85A
4914 * 82B	4972 * 82C	5026 * 81F	5084 * 81A
4915 * 84G	4973 * 86C	5027 * 82A	5085 * 82A
4916 * 86A	4974 * 86C	5028 * 83D	5086 * 85A
4917 * 82D	4975 * 85C	5029 * 81A	5087 * 81A
4918 * 82A	4976 * 83D	5030 * 86C	5088 * 84A
4919 * 81A	4977 * 81A	5031 * 84A	5089 * 83D

5090 *	85A	5189	84F	5247	87F	5361	84C
5091 *	84K	5190	81F	5248	87F	5362	84G
5092 *	81A	5191	84F	5249	87F	5367	82B
5093 *	81A	5192	84E	5250	86B	5368	81D
5094 *	85B	5193	83D	5251	86A	5369	84E
5095 *	86C	5194	84D	5252	86B	5370	84E
5096 *	82A	5195	83A	5253	86E	5371	84F
5097 *	84G	5196	83A	5254	87B	5372	87H
5098 *	83D	5197	82A	5255	86A	5375	84B
5099 *	81A	5198	84E	5256	86A	5376	83D
5101	84F	5199	84F	5257	86B	5377	85C
5102	87A	5200	86B	5258	86J	5378	83E
5103	84K	5201	86A	5259	86A	5379	84C
5104	84D	5202	86B	5260	86E	5380	81E
5105	84F	5203	87F	5261	87F	5381	84B
5106	84A	5204	87F	5262	87D	5382	86A
5107	84F	5205	86A	5263	86J	5384	82F
5108	83A	5206	86H	5264	86J	5385	82D
5109	84F	5207	86C	5306	84C	5386	84E
5110	85D	5208	86F	5310	87G	5388	86G
5148	83D	5209	87F	5311	84K	5390	84B
5150	83A	5210	87D	5312	84B	5392	82F
5151	84A	5211	87D	5313	84B	5393	6C
5152	84C	5212	86E	5314	82F	5394	85D
5153	83A	5213	87F	5315	84K	5396	85A
5154	83A	5214	86E	5318	86A	5397	81E
5155	86E	5215	87F	5319	84J	5398	85B
5156	84E	5216	87B	5321	83B	5399	84K
5157	85B	5217	86A	5322	81E	5400	89A
5158	83A	5218	86C	5323	82B	5402	82D
5160	84K	5219	87F	5324	87H	5403	82D
5162	85B	5220	87B	5325	84E	5404	84C
5163	84E	5221	87D	5326	81D	5405	89A
5164	83A	5222	87A	5328	84G	5406	82D
5165	84F	5223	87F	5330	81E	5407	84C
5166	84E	5224	86E	5331	84G	5409	34E
5167	84H	5225	87A	5332	84C	5410	81C
5168	83A	5226	85C	5333	84E	5411	83B
5169	86E	5227	86A	5334	86C	5412	83C
5170	84C	5228	86A	5335	87F	5413	85B
5171	86F	5229	86A	5336	83D	5414	86A
5172	83B	5230	87F	5337	85A	5415	81C
5173	86A	5231	86B	5338	82D	5416	84J
5174	84K	5232	87D	5339	83A	5417	85B
5175	83D	5233	86A	5341	84B	5418	85B
5176	84F	5234	86A	5344	83B	5419	82D
5177	84K	5235	86B	5345	82B	5420	81C
5178	83A	5236	86E	5347	84G	5421	83B
5179	84K	5237	86J	5350	85A	5422	82D
5180	84F	5238	86A	5351	82C	5423	82D
5181	84E	5239	87A	5353	87G	5424	84C
5182	85B	5240	87D	5355	85C	5500	83F
5183	83A	5241	86H	5356	83D	5501	83B
5184	84D	5242	87A	5357	87H	5502	83E
5185	84D	5243	85C	5358	82D	5503	83B
5186	84F	5244	86A	5360	82B	5504	83B
5187	84A	5245	86J			5505	83F
5188	84A	5246	87D				

5506	83D	5565	82A	5648	88C	5707	86F
5507	89C	5566	82C	5649	86J	5708	86D
5508	82D	5567	83D	5650	88D	5709	86A
5509	82C	5568	88A	5651	84F	5710	88A
5510	82C	5569	83D	5652	88D	5711	88D
5511	88A	5570	89C	5653	88A	5712	84H
5513	87H	5571	83B	5654	88A	5713	87B
5514	85B	5572	88A	5655	88D	5714	86B
5515	83F	5573	86G	5656	87E	5715	81B
5516	86H	5574	88A	5657	86A	5716	87J
5517	89C	5600	88F	5658	84F	5717	81A
5518	85D	5601	88A	5659	86G	5718	82D
5519	83E	5602	86C	5660	88D	5719	84F
5520	87H	5603	88D	5661	88D	5720	87A
5521	83E	5604	87E	5662	88D	5721	83B
5522	83B	5605	88D	5663	88A	5722	87F
5523	82A	5606	84F	5664	88C	5723	84K
5524	86F	5607	88F	5665	88F	5724	88A
5525	82A	5608	88F	5666	88D	5725	84K
5526	83F	5609	88C	5667	88C	5726	89A
5527	88C	5610	88F	5668	88F	5727	81C
5528	82A	5611	88F	5669	88A	5728	88D
5529	88C	5612	87F	5670	88A	5729	86H
5530	85B	5613	88F	5671	88D	5730	87C
5531	83D	5614	88C	5672	88D	5731	87C
5532	82A	5615	88D	5673	87E	5732	86A
5533	83A	5616	87D	5674	88D	5733	86B
5534	88A	5617	88E	5675	81E	5734	86B
5535	82A	5618	88E	5676	88F	5735	81E
5536	83A	5619	88C	5677	88D	5736	86B
5537	83F	5620	86E	5678	88F	5737	81E
5538	85B	5621	88A	5679	86C	5738	84A
5539	86H	5622	88A	5680	88E	5739	84K
5540	82C	5623	88E	5681	88D	5740	86B
5541	89C	5624	86J	5682	88E	5741	86B
5542	83B	5625	86G	5683	88A	5742	84J
5543	83B	5626	88D	5684	84B	5743	87C
5544	86H	5627	88A	5685	86H	5744	81E
5545	88A	5628	87D	5686	88E	5745	84E
5546	82A	5629	81E	5687	88B	5746	81E
5547	82A	5630	88A	5688	87B	5747	86B
5548	82E	5631	87E	5689	82D	5748	87H
5549	87H	5632	88F	5690	84G	5749	86C
5550	87H	5633	86C	5691	88F	5750	86G
5551	83D	5634	84G	5692	88A	5751	83B
5552	83F	5635	88D	5693	88F	5753	81C
5553	82A	5636	88A	5694	88F	5754	84F
5554	82D	5637	88F	5695	88F	5755	81B
5555	86F	5638	86G	5696	88D	5756	86G
5556	89C	5639	81E	5697	81E	5757	82D
5557	83E	5640	88D	5698	86J	5758	84H
5558	83A	5641	88E	5699	88E	5759	86G
5559	82A	5642	82B	5701	82D	5760	83B
5560	86F	5643	88E	5702	87F	5761	87K
5561	82A	5644	86J	5703	87F	5763	81D
5562	83F	5645	86H	5704	87C	5764	81A
5563	82E	5646	88F	5705	87F		
5564	86G	5647	81E	5706	86B		

5765	85C	5903 * 87H	5961 * 87F	6013 * 81A
5766	81B	5904 * 82B	5962 * 84K	6014 * 84A
5767	82D	5905 * 87J	5963 * 82D	6015 * 81A
5768	86G	5906 * 81D	5964 * 82F	6016 * 81A
5769	88D	5907 * 85B	5965 * 81F	6017 * 83D
5770	87B	5908 * 87J	5966 * 81F	6018 * 81A
5771	82D	5909 * 85A	5967 * 83A	6019 * 81A
5772	86A	5910 * 82A	5968 * 84G	6020 * 84A
5773	87K	5911 * 86C	5969 * 81F	6021 * 83D
5774	84J	5912 * 84E	5970 * 86C	6022 * 81A
5775	86G	5913 * 87E	5971 * 85A	6023 * 81A
5776	86C	5914 * 85A	5972 * 83G	6024 * 81A
5777	86B	5915 * 81D	5973 * 81D	6025 * 83D
5778	87A	5916 * 84B	5974 * 82D	6026 * 83D
5779	83B	5917 * 85A	5975 * 82D	6027 * 83D
5780	84A	5918 * 81C	5976 * 83C	6028 * 81A
5781	82E	5919 * 82A	5977 * 85C	6029 * 83D
5782	87F	5920 * 83A	5978 * 83D	6100	81D
5783	81E	5921 * 86A	5979 * 81D	6101	81D
5784	82F	5922 * 82C	5980 * 85B	6102	86A
5785	86H	5923 * 86C	5981 * 85A	6103	81D
5786	86C	5924 * 82B	5982 * 82D	6104	81D
5787	87B	5925 * 86C	5983 * 81C	6105	87H
5788	86D	5926 * 83E	5984 * 84E	6106	81F
5789	86G	5927 * 84E	5985 * 83G	6107	82A
5790	84E	5928 * 87J	5986 * 84G	6108	81B
5791	84K	5929 * 87E	5987 * 81A	6109	81B
5793	88A	5930 * 84C	5988 * 87E	6110	81A
5794	86H	5931 * 81A	5989 * 81C	6111	81F
5795	84F	5932 * 81A	5990 * 87E	6112	81F
5796	83A	5933 * 81D	5991 * 84B	6113	81F
5797	86J	5934 * 83D	5992 * 83B	6114	86A
5798	83B	5935 * 81E	5993 * 81D	6115	81B
5799	81C	5936 * 81A	5994 * 85A	6116	84E
5800	82C	5937 * 87G	5995 * 84B	6117	81D
5801	89C	5938 * 87G	5996 * 81C	6118	84E
5802	82C	5939 * 81A	5997 * 82F	6119	86E
5803	89C	5940 * 81A	5998 * 85C	6120	81A
5804	82C	5941 * 81A	5999 * 83B	6121	81A
5805	82C	5942 * 81D		6122	81B
5806	89A	5943 * 81E		6123	81D
5807	85C	5944 * 84B		6124	81B
5809	89C	5945 * 81A		6125	81C
5810	84J	5946 * 86C		6126	81B
5811	81F	5947 * 84C		6127	81B
5812	89A	5948 * 86G	6000 * 81A	6128	81C
5813	84D	5949 * 82A	6001 * 84A	6129	81D
5814	85C	5950 * 82A	6002 * 81A	6130	81D
5815	84D	5951 * 85B	6003 * 81A	6131	81B
5816	85A	5952 * 85A	6004 * 83D	6132	81A
5817	85C	5953 * 86C	6005 * 84A	6133	81B
5818	85A	5954 * 81A	6006 * 84A	6134	84E
5819	87G	5955 * 87E	6007 * 81A	6135	81A
5900 * 84A	5956 * 85A	6008 * 83D	6136	81B
5901 * 81D	5957 * 81D	6009 * 81A	6137	82A
5902 * 87F	5958 * 84B	6010 * 83D	6138	81F
	5959 * 87E	6011 * 84A	6139	84E
	5960 * 81F	6012 * 81A	6140	81B

6141	81A	6331	84C	6390	83B	6608	88A
6142	81A	6332	84F	6391	82B	6609	84F
6143	81B	6333	86C	6392	84K	6610	84B
6144	81A	6334	85A	6393	84F	6611	84J
6145	81D	6335	89C	6394	81D	6612	88A
6146	81B	6336	81F	6395	85A	6613	87D
6147	81C	6337	84K	6396	87F	6614	88A
6148	81C	6338	82D	6397	83E	6615	88C
6149	81A	6339	84J	6398	83B	6616	87B
6150	81B	6340	85A	6399	82D	6617	84J
6151	81B	6341	85B	6400	86G	6618	88A
6152	81B	6342	84E	6401	86A	6619	88F
6153	81D	6343	83B	6402	88A	6620	87B
6154	81B	6344	84K	6403	86G	6621	86H
6155	86E	6345	84K	6404	84J	6622	86J
6156	81C	6346	6C	6405	84J	6623	87B
6157	81B	6347	87H	6406	83D	6624	84D
6158	81A	6348	85A	6407	83D	6625	82D
6159	81A	6349	85B	6408	88D	6626	88A
6160	81B	6350	6C	6409	86A	6627	81D
6161	81D	6351	82B	6410	86J	6628	86J
6162	81D	6352	88E	6411	88E	6629	87B
6163	82A	6353	86C	6412	86A	6630	82B
6164	81B	6354	85A	6413	86J	6631	84E
6165	81C	6355	82C	6414	83D	6632	84J
6166	84E	6356	82B	6415	86A	6633	88A
6167	81B	6357	85A	6416	88D	6634	86G
6168	81A	6358	82D	6417	86J	6635	88A
6169	81C	6359	85C	6418	84A	6636	86G
6300	83F	6360	82A	6419	83D	6637	88C
6301	83D	6361	86J	6420	83D	6638	88A
6302	81D	6362	86C	6421	83D	6639	82C
6303	84J	6363	82B	6422	84A	6640	84B
6304	81E	6364	83B	6423	88D	6641	88C
6305	83E	6365	85B	6424	86G	6642	86E
6306	82B	6366	81D	6425	86A	6643	88C
6307	82C	6367	87G	6426	86G	6644	86C
6308	86C	6368	86G	6427	88D	6645	84B
6309	82C	6369	86E	6428	86A	6646	84F
6310	87G	6370	86A	6429	86G	6647	88A
6311	84J	6371	89C	6430	86A	6648	88A
6312	82B	6372	83B	6431	86J	6649	86J
6313	81C	6373	85B	6432	86G	6650	87A
6314	85D	6374	82B	6433	88D	6651	86J
6316	84J	6375	83B	6434	88D	6652	86J
6317	84G	6376	6C	6435	88A	6653	86G
6318	86A	6377	83B	6436	88D	6654	81C
6319	83D	6378	89C	6437	86J	6655	81C
6320	82D	6379	81D	6438	88E	6656	82B
6322	83C	6380	84K	6439	86K	6657	84D
6323	83B	6381	85B	6600	86C	6658	88C
6324	84B	6382	85D	6601	82B	6659	88A
6325	86G	6384	86E	6602	87B	6660	88A
6326	85C	6385	83C	6603	88A	6661	86J
6327	82B	6386	86E	6604	87E	6662	87D
6328	83D	6387	84C	6605	86J	6663	86H
6329	87G	6388	85A	6606	88A	6664	81B
6330	85B	6389	87F	6607	88A		

6665	88A	6723	88C	6801 * 83G	6859 * 6C
6666	86E	6724	88C	6802 * 83D	6860 * 83G
6667	84F	6725	86B	6803 * 84F	6861 * 84E
6668	84E	6726	86B	6804 * 82B	6862 * 84B
6669	85B	6727	86B	6805 * 82C	6863 * 82B
6670	82B	6728	86B	6806 * 84B	6864 * 81F
6671	82B	6729	86B	6807 * 85A	6865 * 86A
6672	86E	6730	86B	6808 * 83G	6866 * 84E
6673	86F	6731	86B	6809 * 83G	6867 * 82B
6674	84F	6732	86B	6810 * 87F	6868 * 83B
6675	86G	6733	88C	6811 * 82B	6869 * 82B
6676	86F	6734	87K	6812 * 86G	6870 * 83G
6677	84F	6735	86B	6813 * 83A	6871 * 83F
6678	84F	6736	87K	6814 * 83A	6872 * 86G
6679	85D	6737	82C	6815 * 83B	6873 * 83D
6680	87E	6738	88C	6816 * 83D	6874 * 83B
6681	84G	6739	86B	6817 * 84K	6875 * 83B
6682	88A	6740	88C	6818 * 87F	6876 * 82B
6683	84F	6741	82C	6819 * 86G	6877 * 85A
6684	88A	6742	86B	6820 * 83C	6878 * 6C
6685	86G	6743	86B	6821 * 83D	6879 * 84B
6686	87B	6744	88B	6822 * 82D	6900 * 82A
6687	86J	6745	88C	6823 * 84K	6901 * 84K
6688	87E	6746	88C	6824 * 83G	6902 * 82C
6689	88A	6747	88C	6825 * 83G	6903 * 87E
6690	85B	6748	88C	6826 * 83G	6904 * 84E
6691	87B	6749	87B	6827 * 82B	6905 * 87E
6692	84F	6750	88C	6828 * 84F	6906 * 84C
6693	86G	6751	88B	6829 * 83A	6907 * 84B
6694	84J	6752	88C	6830 * 82B	6908 * 82A
6695	87E	6753	88C	6831 * 6C	6909 * 87F
6696	84J	6754	88C	6832 * 82C	6910 * 81E
6697	84D	6755	86B	6833 * 82B	6911 * 83E
6698	84F	6756	86B	6834 * 82B	6912 * 82C
6699	82C	6757	86B	6835 * 82B	6913 * 83D
6700	87K	6758	88C	6836 * 83A	6914 * 82D
6701	88B	6759	86B	6837 * 83G	6915 * 82A
6702	88B	6760	86B	6838 * 86A	6916 * 85C
6703	88B	6761	87B	6839 * 84B	6917 * 85B
6704	88B	6762	87C	6840 * 86G	6918 * 87E
6705	88B	6763	87K	6841 * 6C	6919 * 82F
6706	88B	6764	86B	6842 * 82B	6920 * 81F
6707	88B	6765	88B	6843 * 87J	6921 * 83D
6708	88B	6766	86B	6844 * 87F	6922 * 81F
6709	88B	6767	88B	6845 * 83G	6923 * 81D
6710	86B	6768	87K	6846 * 82B	6924 * 81F
6711	86B	6769	88B	6847 * 86A	6925 * 84B
6712	88C	6770	88B	6848 * 83D	6926 * 84B
6713	87K	6771	88B	6849 * 86A	6927 * 81D
6714	87K	6772	86B	6850 * 82C	6928 * 84G
6715	87B	6773	88B	6851 * 85A	6929 * 84C
6716	82C	6774	88B	6852 * 82B	6930 * 85A
6717	87B	6775	88B	6853 * 84E	6931 * 83F
6718	87B	6776	87K	6854 * 81F	6932 * 86C
6719	87C	6777	87K	6855 * 83D	6933 * 83A
6720	87K	6778	88B	6856 * 83B	6934 * 84B
6721	87K	6779	87K	6857 * 84K	6935 * 87G
6722	88C	6800 * 83G	6858 * 83D	6936 * 82A

6937 * 81F	6995 * 83B	7214 86A	7318 87H
6938 * 83A	6996 * 83B	7215 87F	7319 86A
6939 * 86C	6997 * 82A	7216 86J	7320 87F
6940 * 83D	6998 * 86C	7217 87E	7321 85A
6941 * 83D	6999 * 86C	7218 86A	7322 86C
6942 * 84K		7219 86A	7323 82B
6943 * 86C	7000 * 83A	7220 86G	7324 81F
6944 * 84G	7001 * 81A	7221 86J	7329 84B
6945 * 82F	7002 * 87G	7222 86A	7339 84B
6946 * 86C	7003 * 87E	7223 86E	7400 87G
6947 * 85A	7004 * 81A	7224 87D	7401 87G
6948 * 86C	7005 * 85A	7225 87F	7402 87G
6949 * 84A	7006 * 85B	7226 87D	7403 84J
6950 * 85A	7007 * 85A	7227 86A	7404 81F
6951 * 82A	7008 * 81A	7228 87F	7405 89A
6952 * 81E	7009 * 87E	7229 86A	7406 89C
6953 * 81D	7010 * 81A	7230 88C	7407 87G
6954 * 82A	7011 * 82A	7231 86A	7408 87K
6955 * 82D	7012 * 87E	7232 86A	7409 84J
6956 * 84A	7013 * 85A	7233 86G	7410 89A
6957 * 82A	7014 * 82A	7234 86G	7411 81F
6958 * 82A	7015 * 85A	7235 86G	7412 81F
6959 * 81A	7016 * 87E	7236 87E	7413 82C
6960 * 81D	7017 * 81A	7237 86E	7414 84J
6961 * 81A	7018 * 82A	7238 81F	7415 82C
6962 * 81A	7019 * 82A	7239 81F	7416 85C
6963 * 84K	7020 * 81A	7240 87F	7417 89C
6964 * 84A	7021 * 87E	7241 88C	7418 82C
6965 * 83D	7022 * 83D	7242 89A	7419 87G
6966 * 82C	7023 * 86C	7243 86A	7420 84F
6967 * 82C	7024 * 81A	7244 87B	7421 82C
6968 * 81D	7025 * 81A	7245 86A	7422 87G
6969 * 86C	7026 * 84A	7246 86A	7423 86J
6970 * 81F	7027 * 81A	7247 84B	7424 82C
6971 * 84E	7028 * 87G	7248 87E	7425 87G
6972 * 82A	7029 * 83A	7249 87B	7426 86E
6973 * 81A	7030 * 81A	7250 82B	7427 83A
6974 * 81A	7031 * 83D	7251 86A	7428 84F
6975 * 84B	7032 * 81A	7252 88C	7429 84F
6976 * 84C	7033 * 81A	7253 86A	7430 84F
6977 * 82F	7034 * 82A	7300 82D	7431 84J
6978 * 81A	7035 * 82A	7301 85C	7432 84F
6979 * 84C	7036 * 81A	7302 82D	7433 84J
6980 * 84G	7037 * 82C	7303 82B	7434 89A
6981 * 82A	7200 87E	7304 83B	7435 84F
6982 * 82B	7201 86G	7305 84B	7436 81F
6983 * 81E	7202 88A	7306 87H	7437 85C
6984 * 81S	7203 87F	7307 87F	7438 84E
6985 * 85B	7204 86G	7308 85C	7439 87G
6986 * 82A	7205 88A	7309 84G	7440 84J
6987 * 85A	7206 86G	7310 84J	7441 84F
6988 * 83D	7207 87E	7311 83B	7442 84J
6989 * 85A	7208 86E	7312 85B	7443 84J
6990 * 81A	7209 87E	7313 84J	7444 87G
6991 * 81C	7210 86A	7314 87F	7445 88A
6992 * 85C	7211 87F	7315 84C	7446 83E
6993 * 82C	7212 86A	7316 83C	7447 84F
6994 * 82D	7213 86G	7317 84E	7448 84F

7449	84F	7758	84E	7816 *	83E	8402	21C
7700	85B	7759	84B	7817 *	84J	8403	21C
7701	87A	7760	81F	7818 *	84B	8404	21C
7702	84D	7761	83C	7819 *	89A	8405	21C
7703	86H	7762	83D	7820 *	83D	8406	21C
7704	87D	7763	84E	7821 *	84E	8407	87B
7705	84F	7764	86E	7822 *	84K	8408	87D
7706	87B	7765	87F	7823 *	83F	8409	83G
7707	85A	7766	88D	7824 *	83G	8410	87B
7708	81D	7767	87A	7825 *	87G	8411	84A
7709	83E	7768	86A	7826 *	87G	8412	83F
7710	81E	7769	87A	7827 *	84K	8413	81C
7712	86B	7770	86F	7828 *	84G	8414	88B
7713	84E	7771	86A	7829 *	87G	8415	84E
7714	6C	7772	88A	7900 *	81F	8416	88B
7715	83E	7773	86J	7901 *	82A	8417	84E
7716	83C	7774	86H	7902 *	81A	8418	87B
7717	88D	7775	86C	7903 *	81A	8419	88F
7718	87F	7776	87F	7904 *	81A	8420	88F
7719	82B	7777	85A	7905 *	83D	8421	83F
7720	86J	7778	86F	7906 *	81D	8422	83D
7721	86B	7779	88A	7907 *	82A	8423	87B
7722	88B	7780	82F	7908 *	84E	8424	88B
7723	85B	7781	86A	7909 *	83D	8425	83D
7724	86G	7782	82F	7910 *	81C	8426	83D
7725	86F	7783	82B	7911 *	81F	8427	85A
7726	88A	7784	82D	7912 *	84E	8428	84E
7727	82D	7785	87F	7913 *	84E	8429	88B
7728	82B	7786	87A	7914 *	81D	8430	81D
7729	82B	7787	86A	7915 *	84B	8431	87D
7730	81C	7788	81D	7916 *	83A	8432	81F
7731	81C	7789	86E	7917 *	82D	8433	82C
7732	86F	7790	82B	7918 *	84E	8434	81A
7733	88E	7791	81A	7919 *	81D	8435	81E
7734	81A	7792	82C	7920 *	85A	8436	86H
7735	84E	7793	82B	7921 *	84K	8437	88B
7736	86A	7794	82C	7922 *	84K	8438	88B
7737	87A	7795	82B	7923 *	82C	8439	86H
7738	88B	7796	86G	7924 *	82D	8440	86A
7739	87A	7797	84G	7925 *	83G	8441	88B
7740	86G	7798	86F	7926 *	85B	8442	87A
7741	85B	7799	87A	7927 *	81D	8443	87D
7742	87A	7800 *	84K	7928 *	85A	8444	86J
7743	87A	7801 *	84K	7929 *	82B	8445	86J
7744	88E	7802 *	89C			8446	87A
7745	87F	7803 *	89C			8447	86C
7746	86F	7804 *	87G			8448	86F
7747	87J	7805 *	85C	8100	84D	8449	84B
7748	82D	7806 *	89C	8101	85D	8450	88C
7749	82B	7807 *	84K	8102	87H	8451	83A
7750	85A	7808 *	85B	8103	87G	8452	85A
7751	88A	7809 *	83D	8104	87A	8453	86A
7752	86F	7810 *	85B	8105	85A	8454	87B
7753	86F	7811 *	84G	8106	85A	8455	88F
7754	84H	7812 *	83D	8107	87H	8456	83C
7755	86A	7813 *	83A	8108	84E	8457	88B
7756	87D	7814 *	83A	8109	84D	8458	81E
7757	87A	7815 *	85A	8400	21C	8459	88C
				8401	21C		

8460	88F	8718	85D	8776	86C	9315	82C
8461	82C	8719	83D	8777	87G	9316	85A
8462	84A	8720	87C	8778	86H	9318	87H
8463	87E	8721	86F	8779	82C	9319	84B
8464	88B	8722	88B	8780	88A	9400	81A
8465	88C	8723	86C	8781	85C	9401	30A
8466	83A	8724	87C	8782	87A	9402	81D
8467	87F	8725	84E	8783	82C	9403	81F
8468	84E	8726	84A	8784	87A	9404	81D
8469	88A	8727	85B	8785	87F	9405	81C
8470	88A	8728	86C	8786	86H	9406	81B
8471	88A	8729	84K	8787	88B	9407	81E
8472	82C	8730	84K	8788	87E	9408	84B
8473	83G	8731	85B	8789	87E	9409	81C
8474	87F	8732	87A	8790	82B	9410	81A
8475	87D	8733	83E	8791	84J	9411	81A
8476	87D	8734	84A	8792	84F	9412	81A
8477	87F	8735	88C	8793	82C	9413	81C
8478	88A	8736	88D	8794	87E	9414	81A
8479	82B	8737	83A	8795	82A	9415	81B
8480	85A	8738	87H	8796	86H	9416	81A
8481	88A	8739	87H	8797	84F	9417	81C
8482	88A	8740	86F	8798	84A	9418	81A
8483	87D	8741	82B	8799	82F	9419	81A
8484	88A	8742	84F			9420	81A
8485	83F	8743	88B	9004	89C	9421	81B
8486	83F	8744	82D	9005	89A	9422	81A
8487	85B	8745	82E	9008	89C	9423	81A
8488	85B	8746	82B	9009	89C	9424	81B
8489	88A	8747	82B	9010	89A	9425	88F
8490	87B	8748	86F	9011	82C	9426	86C
8491	82A	8749	87F	9012	89C	9427	86A
8492	85A	8750	81C	9013	89C	9428	84A
8493	86A	8751	81A	9014	89C	9429	85A
8494	86H	8752	81C	9015	89C	9430	87A
8495	88F	8753	81A	9016	89C	9431	87B
8496	85A	8754	81A	9017	89C	9432	84E
8497	86F	8755	81A	9018	89A	9433	83D
8498	86F	8756	81A	9020	89C	9434	83F
8499	86A	8757	81A	9021	89C	9435	84A
8700	84E	8758	81C	9022	89C	9436	87E
8701	85C	8759	81A	9023	82C	9437	88B
8702	83E	8760	81A	9024	89C	9438	85B
8703	82B	8761	81A	9025	89C	9439	83C
8704	84F	8762	81A	9026	89A	9440	83A
8705	86H	8763	81A	9027	89A	9441	85B
8706	87K	8764	81A	9028	84J	9442	87B
8707	86G	8765	81A	9303	84K	9443	88B
8708	87F	8766	86A	9304	85C	9444	87B
8709	83D	8767	81A	9305	81C	9445	85B
8710	86A	8768	81A	9306	86C	9446	87A
8711	86A	8769	81A	9308	84G	9447	87B
8712	86F	8770	81A	9309	81D	9448	87A
8713	84E	8771	81A	9310	87G	9449	84C
8714	82B	8772	81A	9311	83F	9450	86H
8715	87A	8773	81A	9312	84K	9451	86F
8716	86G	8774	81C	9313	82B	9452	87A
8717	85B	8775	87A	9314	84B		

23

9453	88C	9495	82B	9637	87E	9679	88B
9454	87B	9496	84A	9638	88D	9680	84E
9455	85A	9497	83C	9639	84H	9681	89A
9456	87B	9498	84E	9640	81F	9682	84E
9457	87B	9499	82B	9641	81C	9700	81A
9458	86H	9600	82C	9642	83E	9701	81A
9459	86C	9601	82B	9643	88D	9702	81A
9460	86H	9602	87J	9644	86A	9703	81A
9461	86C	9603	86C	9645	87D	9704	81A
9462	83A	9604	82C	9646	83B	9705	81A
9463	83G	9605	82C	9647	83B	9706	81A
9464	85B	9606	87C	9648	86C	9707	81A
9465	87F	9607	86J	9649	86F	9708	81A
9466	85A	9608	84E	9650	86G	9709	81A
9467	83D	9609	86F	9651	6C	9710	81A
9468	86A	9610	82B	9652	87H	9711	83D
9469	81C	9611	81F	9653	81F	9712	86J
9470	84G	9612	82D	9654	81F	9713	86C
9471	85B	9613	84F	9655	83E	9714	87H
9472	84G	9614	84E	9656	84G	9715	87E
9473	87A	9615	82D	9657	84G	9716	83D
9474	83C	9616	86A	9658	81A	9717	85C
9475	85B	9617	87B	9659	81A	9718	83B
9476	82C	9618	88D	9660	86F	9719	84F
9477	88B	9619	85C	9661	81A	9720	82C
9478	87A	9620	82F	9662	86A	9721	82C
9479	81C	9621	84A	9663	83B	9722	81B
9480	85A	9622	88C	9664	86A	9723	86C
9481	82B	9623	82A	9665	85C	9724	84E
9482	86A	9624	84F	9666	87G	9725	81A
9483	87B	9625	87D	9667	86A	9726	81C
9484	87E	9626	82F	9668	83A	9727	84E
9485	87D	9627	87A	9669	84J	9728	84K
9486	85A	9628	82D	9670	83B	9729	82A
9487	83A	9629	83C	9671	83B	9730	86G
9488	82A	9630	84H	9672	82C	9731	86J
9489	87D	9631	88C	9673	83E	9732	82E
9490	86A	9632	87G	9674	86A	9733	84E
9491	87D	9633	83A	9675	88D	9734	87A
9492	85B	9634	87B	9676	88C	9735	87B
9493	86C	9635	84E	9677	88B	9736	87B
9494	86C	9636	84F	9678	83A	9737	87B

W.R. Diesel Railcars

4	86A	15	81F	24	82B	33	81D
5	85A	16	81F	25	82F	34	81C
6	85A	17	84D	26	84D	38	81D
7	85A	18	81D	27	81C		
8	84F	19	85A	28	82B		
11	85A	20	85B	29	84D		
12	81D	21	81C	30	81C		
13	86A	22	84D	31	81C		
14	84F	23	82B	32	85A		

9738	87E	9796	86G	11142	32B	11200	
9739	84B	9797	86G	11143	32B	11201	
9740	82C	9798	84E	11144	6C	11202	
9741	85A	9799	87B	11145	6C	11203	
9742	87B			11146	6C	11204	
9743	87F			11147	6C	11205	
9744	87C	10000	1B	11148	6C	11206	
9745	86E	10001	1B	11149	51C	11207	
9746	86A	10100	17A	11150	51C	11208	
9747	88D	10201	1B	11151	51C	11209	
9748	83G	10202	1B	11152	40B	11210	
9749	81D	10203	1B	11153	40B	11211	
9750	87A	10800	2A	11154	40B	11212	50B
9751	81A			11155	34E	11213	50B
9752	84B			11156	35A	11214	50B
9753	84E	11001	75C	11157	35A	11215	50B
9754	81A			11158	35A	11216	50B
9755	83E			11159	35A	11217	52E
9756	87A	11100	30A	11160	35A	11218	52E
9757	83B	11101	31B	11161	32A	11219	52E
9758	81A	11102	31B	11162	32A	11220	
9759	86C	11103	32E	11163	32B	11221	
9760	87J	11104	32E	11164	41A	11222	
9761	87A	11105	51C	11165	41A	11223	
9762	82D	11106	51C	11166		11224	
9763	81D	11107	51C	11167		11225	
9764	82E	11108	40B	11168		11226	
9765	83C	11109	30A	11169		11227	
9766	87B	11110	30A	11170		11228	
9767	84F	11111	32D	11171		11229	
9768	84B	11112	30A	11172		11230	
9769	88B	11113	32B	11173		11231	
9770	82D	11114	34E	11174		11232	
9771	82A	11115	32B	11175		11233	
9772	82C	11116	6C	11176		11234	
9773	82C	11117	6C	11177	40B	11235	
9774	84H	11118	6C	11178	40F	11236	
9775	87E	11119	6C	11179	40F	11500	32B
9776	88B	11120	6C	11180	40B	11501	32B
9777	87E	11121	30A	11181	40A	11502	32B
9778	86C	11122	30A	11182	40A	11503	30A
9779	87A	11123	30A	11183	40A	11504	30A
9780	86D	11124	40B	11184	40A	11505	30A
9781	81B	11125	32A	11185	40A	11506	30A
9782	84F	11126	40B	11186	40A	11507	30A
9783	87A	11127	40B	11187		11508	30A
9784	81A	11128	32B	11188		11700	51C
9785	87B	11129	30A	11189		11701	51C
9786	87A	11130	30A	11190		11702	51C
9787	87F	11131	30A	11191		11703	62B
9788	87F	11132	30A	11192		11704	64A
9789	81C	11133	30A	11193		11705	64A
9790	82C	11134	30A	11194		11706	64A
9791	81D	11135	30A	11195		11707	64E
9792	87A	11136	30F	11196		11708	
9793	84J	11137	30F	11197		11709	
9794	84K	11138	30F	11198		11710	
9795	82C	11139	32A	11199		11711	
		11140	30F				
		11141	32B				

25

SEE NOTE ON PAGE 29

11712		12049	1A	12107	30A	13024	14A
11713		12050	1A	12108	30A	13025	84E
11714		12051	1A	12109	30A	13026	84E
11715		12052	1A	12110	30A	13027	84E
11716		12053	1A	12111	30A	13028	84E
11717		12054	1A	12112	34A	13029	84E
11718		12055	1A	12113	53C	13030	81A
11719		12056	3C	12114	53C	13031	81A
		12057	2A	12115	53C	13032	81A
		12058	14A	12116	53C	13033	81A
12000	5B	12059	21A	12117	53C	13034	84B
12001	5B	12060	21A	12118	53C	13035	84B
12003	8C	12061	21A	12119	53C	13036	84B
12004	5B	12062	21A	12120	53C	13037	84E
12005	5B	12063	14A	12121	53C	13038	84B
12006	18A	12064	14A	12122	53C	13039	84B
12007	8C	12065	14A	12123	30A	13040	70B
12008	8C	12066	21A	12124	30A	13041	70B
12009	5B	12067	14A	12125	30A	13042	70B
12010	5B	12068	14A	12126	30A	13043	74A
12011	8C	12069	14A	12127	30A	13044	74A
12012	5B	12070	6A	12128	30A	13045	74A
12013	5B	12071	6A	12129	34B	13046	71A
12014	8C	12072	14A	12130	30A	13047	75C
12015	8C	12073	18A	12131	34B	13048	75C
12016	8C	12074	21A	12132	30A	13049	75C
12017	8C	12075	21A	12133	30A	13050	1A
12018	8C	12076	21A	12134	30A	13051	1A
12019	5B	12077	17A	12135	30A	13052	1A
12020	5B	12078	1A	12136	30A	13053	2A
12021	5B	12079	68A	12137	34B	13054	2A
12022	5B	12080	68A	12138	34B	13055	2A
12023	5B	12081	8C			13056	15A
12024	8C	12082	6A			13057	15A
12025	8C	12083	12A			13058	15A
12026	8C	12084	68E			13059	15A
12027	8C	12085	68E	13000	82B	13060	36B
12028	8C	12086	68E	13001	82B	13061	36B
12029	8C	12087	68A	13002	82B	13062	36B
12030	5B	12088	3D	13003	82B	13063	36B
12031	5B	12089	3D	13004	84E	13064	36B
12032	5B	12090	3D	13005	67C	13065	31B
12033	1A	12091	3A	13006	67C	13066	38E
12034	1A	12092	3A	13007	67B	13067	38E
12035	1A	12093	3B	13008	67B	13068	38E
12036	1A	12094	3B	13009	67B	13069	38E
12037	1A	12095	3D	13010	71A	13070	53A
12038	18A	12096	16A	13011	71A	13071	53A
12039	21A	12097	16A	13012	71A	13072	53A
12040	21A	12098	16A	13013	71A	13073	53A
12041	21A	12099	16A	13014	71A	13074	53A
12042	21A	12100	16A	13015	1A	13075	53A
12043	21A	12101	16A	13016	1A	13076	53A
12044	21A	12102	16A	13017	1A	13077	53A
12045	2A	12103	30A	13018	1A	13078	53A
12046	2A	12104	30A	13019	1A	13079	53A
12047	2A	12105	30A	13020	3D	13080	53A
12048	2A	12106	30A	13021	3C	13081	53A
				13022	14A		
				13023	14A		

13082	21A	13140	51A	13198	66A	13256	82B
13083	16A	13141	51A	13199	66A	13257	82B
13084	16A	13142	51A	13200	66A	13258	87F
13085	19A	13143	51A	13201	66A	13259	87F
13086	16A	13144	51A	13202	66B	13260	87F
13087	12A	13145	51A	13203	66B	13261	87F
13088	12A	13146	51A	13204	66B	13262	87A
13089	5B	13147	51A	13205	66B	13263	87A
13090	3B	13148	51A	13206	66C	13264	87A
13091	3C	13149	51A	13207	65A	13265	87A
13092	75C	13150	51A	13208	65A	13266	87A
13093	75A	13151	51B	13209	65A	13267	87A
13094	75A	13152	40B	13210	62A	13268	81D
13095	73C	13153	40B	13211	62A	13269	81D
13096	73C	13154	40B	13212	65C	13270	73C
13097	73C	13155	40B	13213	65C	13271	73C
13098	73C	13156	40B	13214	65C	13272	73C
13099	73C	13157	40B	13215	65B	13273	73C
13100	73C	13158	34A	13216	65B	13274	73C
13101	73C	13159	40B	13217	75A	13275	62A
13102	86E	13160	34A	13218	75A	13276	65A
13103	86E	13161	34A	13219	75A	13277	65C
13104	86E	13162	34A	13220	75A	13278	65B
13105	84C	13163	34A	13221	75A	13279	65B
13106	84C	13164	34A	13222	75C	13280	65B
13107	84C	13165	34A	13223	75C	13281	65F
13108	84C	13166	34A	13224	75C	13282	66B
13109	84C	13167	21A	13225	75C	13283	66B
13110	84C	13168	21A	13226	75C	13284	66B
13111	84G	13169	2A	13227	51A	13285	66B
13112	84F	13170	12A	13228	51A	13286	66B
13113	84F	13171	12A	13229	51A	13287	66B
13114	84G	13172	5B	13230	53A	13288	19A
13115	84F	13173	1A	13231	53A	13289	18A
13116	84G	13174	1A	13232	53C	13290	16A
13117	18A	13175	5B	13233	53C	13291	16A
13118	18A	13176	5B	13234	53C	13292	18A
13119	18A	13177	2A	13235	53C	13293	18A
13120	18A	13178	2A	13236	53C	13294	55B
13121	18A	13179	14A	13237	50A	13295	55B
13122	18A	13180	14A	13238	50A	13296	55B
13123	9D	13181	14A	13239	50A	13297	55B
13124	18A	13182	82B	13240	50A	13298	30A
13125		13183	82B	13241	52E	13299	30A
13126		13184	82B	13242	52E	13300	30A
13127	35A	13185	82B	13243	52E	13301	30A
13128	35A	13186	82B	13244	52E	13302	30A
13129	35A	13187	82B	13245	5B	13303	30A
13130	31B	13188	86E	13246	16A	13304	34E
13131	35A	13189	86E	13247	16A	13305	34E
13132	65F	13190	86E	13248	17A	13306	34E
13133	65F	13191	84B	13249	14A	13307	34A
13134	65F	13192	84E	13250	17A	13308	34A
13135	65F	13193	84G	13251	19A	13309	34A
13136	65F	13194	84G	13252	19A	13310	34A
13137	51A	13195	81D	13253	19A	13311	34A
13138	51A	13196	81D	13254	19A	13312	34A
13139	51A	13197	66A	13255	82B	13313	50A

SEE NOTE ON PAGE 29

13314	50A	15220	73C	26030	Reddish	30037	72D
13315	50A	15221	73C	26031	Reddish	30038	70B
13316	52E	15222	73C	26032	Reddish	30039	70F
13317	52E	15223	73C	26033	Reddish	30040	71B
13318	50A	15224	73C	26034	Reddish	30041	70B
13319	50A	15225	73C	26035	Reddish	30042	70B
13320	50A	15226	73C	26036	Reddish	30043	70B
13321	52E	15227	73C	26037	Reddish	30044	72A
13322	52E	15228	73C	26038	Reddish	30045	72A
13323	53A	15229	73C	26039	Reddish	30046	72A
13324	52E	15230	71A	26040	Reddish	30047	75D
13325	34A	15231	71A	26041	Reddish	30048	75D
13326	35A	15232	71A	26042	Reddish	30049	75D
13327	31B	15233	71A	26043	Reddish	30050	75D
13328	36B	15234	71A	26044	Reddish	30051	75D
13329	36B	15235	71A	26045	Reddish	30052	75A
13330	36B	15236	71A	26046	Reddish	30053	75A
13331	41A			26047	Reddish	30054	75A
13332	41A			26048	Reddish	30055	75A
13333	41A	18000	81A	26049	Reddish	30056	75A
13334	41A	18100	81A	26050	Reddish	30057	71B
13335	41A			26051	Reddish	30058	71B
13336	41A			26052	Reddish	30059	71B
13337	62A	20001	Durnsford Rd.	26053	Reddish	30060	71B
13338	62A	20002	Durnsford Rd.	26054	Reddish	30061	71I
13339	62A	20003	Durnsford Rd.	26055	Reddish	30062	71I
13340	62A			26056	Reddish	30063	71I
13341	62A			26057	Reddish	30064	71I
13342	62C	26000 *	Reddish	26500	52B	30065	71I
13343	62C	26001	Reddish	26501	52B	30066	71I
		26002	Reddish	26510	30A	30067	71I
		26003	Reddish			30068	71I
		26004	Reddish			30069	71I
15000	31B	26005	Reddish	27000	Reddish	30070	71I
15001	31B	26006	Reddish	27001	Reddish	30071	71I
15002	31B	26007	Reddish	27002	Reddish	30072	71I
15003	31B	26008	Reddish	27003	Reddish	30073	71I
15004	35A	26009	Reddish	27004	Reddish	30074	71I
15100	82B	26010	Reddish	27005	Reddish	30082	71A
15101	81A	26011	Reddish	27006	Reddish	30083	71A
15102	81A	26012	Reddish			30084	74C
15103	81A	26013	Reddish			30086	70C
15104	81A	26014	Reddish	30021	72A	30087	71B
15105	81A	26015	Reddish	30022	70F	30088	72D
15106	81A	26016	Reddish	30023	72A	30089	72D
15107	82B	26017	Reddish	30024	72A	30093	71B
15201	75C	26018	Reddish	30025	72B	30096	71A
15202	73C	26019	Reddish	30026	70C	30102	72D
15203	75C	26020	Reddish	30027	70C	30104	71B
15211	75C	26021	Reddish	30028	71A	30105	71B
15212	75C	26022	Reddish	30029	71A	30106	71B
15213	75C	26023	Reddish	30030	71A	30107	71B
15214	75C	26024	Reddish	30031	75A	30108	71B
15215	75C	26025	Reddish	30032	71A	30109	70C
15216	73C	26026	Reddish	30033	71A	30110	70C
15217	73C	26027	Reddish	30034	72D	30111	71B
15218	73C	26028	Reddish	30035	72D	30112	71B
15219	73C	26029	Reddish	30036	72D	30117	71A

NEW NUMBERING SYSTEM FOR
B.R. DIESEL LOCOS.

British Railways are to adopt a new system of numbering for all new main line diesel locomotives and for new and existing standard diesel shunting locomotives.

The present system of numbering, which uses numbers from 1 to 99999 and covers steam, diesel and electric locomotives, leaves insufficient scope for allocating consecutive block numbers to all the main line diesel locomotives planned under the railway modernisation and re-equipment programme. To have continued with this series would have meant using six-figure numbers commencing at 100,000 which would have been cumbersome, costly and liable to misquotation.

To overcome this difficulty it has been decided to adopt a scheme of numbering using the letter 'D' as a prefix and starting with D.1. Under this system block numbers are being allocated to the various diesel locomotive power groupings so that a locomotive's number, in addition to identifying it, will also indicate its power range. For example, 1000-1250 h.p. locomotives are to be numbered in the D.5000-6000 series, and the 800-1000 h.p. locomotives in the D.8000 series.

The first locomotives to be numbered under this new scheme are the 174 main line diesel locomotives now being built under the contracts announced in 1955.

The B.R. Standard 350 h.p. diesel shunting locomotives at present included in the 13000 series are being re-numbered in the D.3000 group. The 200 h.p. diesel shunting locomotives at present numbered in the 11000 series will eventually be included in the D.2000 group. It is not intended to re-number the existing eight main line diesel and gas turbine locomotives.

D200	D3347	D3375	D3403
D201	D3348	D3376	D3404
D202	D3349	D3377	D3405
D203	D3350	D3378	D3406
D204	D3351	D3379	D3407
D205	D3352	D3380	
D206	D3353	D3381	
D207	D3354	D3382	
D208	D3355	D3383	D3419
D209	D3356	D3384	D3420
	D3357	D3385	D3421
	D3358	D3386	D3422
D600	D3359	D3387	D3423
D601	D3360	D3388	D3424
D602	D3361	D3389	D3425
D603	D3362	D3390	D3426
D604	D3363	D3391	D3427
	D3364	D3392	D3428
	D3365	D3393	D3439
D800	D3366	D3394	D3440
D801	D3367	D3395	D3441
D802	D3368	D3396	D3442
	D3369	D3397	D3443
	D3370	D3398	D3444
	D3371	D3399	D3445
D3344	D3372	D3400	D3446
D3345	D3373	D3401	D3447
D3346	D3374	D3402	D3448

D3449	D3468		D8006
D3450	D3469		D8007
D3451	D3470	D5500	D8008
D3452	D3471	D5501	D8009
D3453	D3472		D8010
D3454	D3473		D8011
D3455	D3474	D6300	D8012
D3456	D3475	D6301	D8013
D3457	D3476	D6302	D8014
D3458	D3477	D6303	
D3459	D3478	D6304	
D3460	D3479	D6305	D8200
D3461	D3480		D8201
D3462	D3481		D8202
D3463	D3482	D8000	D8203
D3464	D3483	D8001	D8204
D3565	D3484	D8002	D8205
D3466	D3485	D8003	D8206
D3467	D3486	D8004	
	D3487	D8005	D8400

Two New abc's

abc British Electric Trains

abc British Railways Diesels

—— 2/6 each ——

30120	71A	30288	71A	30475	71A	30540	75C
30123	70A	30289	71A	30476	71A	30541	71B
30124	70C	30300	71A	30477	71A	30542	71A
30125	71A	30301	72B	30478	70A	30543	71A
30127	71B	30304	72B	30479	71A	30544	75D
30128	71B	30306	71A	30480	71A	30545	75D
30129	72C	30308	70C	30481	71A	30546	75D
30130	71A	30309	72B	30482	70A	30547	75D
30131	72C	30310	71A	30483	70A	30548	71B
30132	70A	30313	72B	30484	70A	30549	75C
30133	70A	30315	72A	30486	70A	30564	72A
30160	70D	30316	71A	30487	70A	30566	71A
30162	72D	30317	72B	30488	70A	30567	70B
30177	70B	30318	71B	30489	70A	30568	70B
30179	70B	30319	70A	30491	70A	30575	70C
30182	72C	30320	70A	30492	70B	30578	70C
30183	72A	30321	70A	30493	70B	30580	70C
30192	72D	30322	70A	30494	70B	30582	72A
30193	72A	30323	72A	30495	70B	30583	72A
30199	72A	30324	71B	30496	70B	30584	72A
30200	72F	30325	70C	30497	70B	30585	72F
30207	70F	30326	70C	30498	70B	30586	72F
30212	71A	30327	72B	30499	70B	30587	72F
30216	72D	30328	71A	30500	70B	30588	71A
30223	71A	30330	72B	30501	70B	30589	71A
30224	70A	30331	72B	30502	70B	30667	72A
30225	72D	30333	72B	30503	70B	30668	72A
30229	71A	30334	72B	30504	70B	30669	72A
30232	72A	30335	72B	30505	70B	30670	72A
30233	71A	30337	70C	30506	70B	30671	72E
30236	72F	30338	70A	30507	70B	30673	72B
30238	70C	30339	70B	30508	70B	30674	72B
30241	70A	30346	70B	30509	70B	30675	70C
30242	70A	30349	70C	30510	70B	30676	72A
30243	70A	30350	70C	30511	70B	30687	70B
30244	70A	30352	70B	30512	70B	30688	70B
30245	70A	30355	70B	30513	70B	30689	70B
30246	70C	30356	71A	30514	70B	30690	71B
30247	72E	30357	70F	30515	70B	30691	72A
30248	70A	30368	70D	30516	70B	30692	70A
30249	70A	30374	72B	30517	70B	30693	70C
30250	72E	30375	71A	30518	70B	30694	70A
30251	72E	30376	71A	30519	70B	30695	71B
30252	72E	30377	71A	30520	70B	30696	70B
30253	72E	30378	71A	30521	70A	30697	70C
30254	72E	30379	71A	30522	70A	30698	70C
30255	72E	30448 * 72B		30523	70A	30699	70A
30256	72E	30449 * 72B		30524	70A	30700	70C
30258	70D	30450 * 72B		30530	71A	30701	70A
30260	71B	30451 * 72B		30531	71A	30702	72B
30266	72B	30452 * 72B		30532	71A	30705	70C
30270	72B	30453 * 72B		30533	75C	30706	71B
30274	71H	30454 * 72B		30534	75C	30707	71A
30277	70E	30455 * 70A		30535	71A	30708	72A
30283	71A	30456 * 70D		30536	71A	30709	72A
30284	71A	30457 * 70A		30537	75C	30710	72A
30285	71A	30473	71A	30538	75C	30711	72A
30287	71A	30474	71A	30539	71B	30712	72A

30715	72A	30801 * 73B	30910 * 74E	31069	74C
30717	72A	30802 * 74A	30911 * 74B	31071	73B
30718	70A	30803 * 74A	30912 * 74B	31086	73B
30719	70A	30804 * 74A	30913 * 74B	31102	73B
30721	72B	30805 * 74A	30914 * 74B	31107	74C
30724	70D	30806 * 73C	30915 * 73A	31112	73D
30726	70F	30823 72B	30916 * 74B	31113	74C
30727	71B	30824 72B	30917 * 74B	31128	74C
30729	70F	30825 72B	30918 * 74B	31145	70C
30730	70F	30826 72B	30919 * 74C	31147	74C
30732	70F	30827 72B	30920 * 74E	31150	74C
30738 * 71B	30828 72B	30921 * 74C	31161	73D
30739 * 71B	30829 72B	30922 * 74B	31162	74E
30748 * 71A	30830 72B	30923 * 74E	31164	74D
30749 * 70D	30831 72B	30924 * 73B	31165	73B
30750 * 70A	30832 72B	30925 * 73B	31174	74E
30751 * 70D	30833 70B	30926 * 73B	31177	74D
30755 * 70D	30834 70B	30927 * 73B	31178	74C
30757 * 71A	30835 75B	30928 * 73B	31184	74D
30763 * 71A	30836 75B	30929 * 73B	31191	74C
30764 * 71B	30837 75B	30930 * 74E	31193	74D
30765 * 71B	30838 70B	30931 * 73B	31218	74A
30766 * 73A	30839 70B	30932 * 73B	31219	74A
30767 * 73A	30840 70B	30933 * 73B	31221	74A
30768 * 73A	30841 72A	30934 * 73B	31223	74A
30769 * 73A	30842 72A	30935 * 73B	31227	73D
30770 * 71A	30843 72A	30936 * 73B	31229	73D
30771 * 71B	30844 72A	30937 * 73B	31239	74D
30772 * 73C	30845 72A	30938 * 73B	31242	73E
30773 * 70A	30846 72A	30939 * 73B	31243	74C
30774 * 70A	30847 72B	30950 72A	31244	74D
30775 * 74C	30850 * 71A	30951 74A	31245	74B
30776 * 74C	30851 * 71A	30952 74A	31246	74A
30777 * 74C	30852 * 71A	30953 72B	31247	70C
30778 * 70A	30853 * 71A	30954 71H	31252	74B
30779 * 70A	30854 * 71A	30955 74A	31253	73A
30780 * 71B	30855 * 71A	30956 72A	31255	73E
30781 * 71B	30856 * 71A	30957 72B	31256	73E
30782 * 71B	30857 * 71A		31258	74C
30783 * 71B	30858 * 70A		31259	74D
30784 * 71A	30859 * 70A		31261	73A
30785 * 71A	30860 * 70A	31004 74B	31263	74A
30786 * 71A	30861 * 71A	31005 74A	31265	73A
30787 * 71A	30862 * 71A	31010 74E	31266	73A
30788 * 71A	30863 * 71A	31018 73C	31267	73B
30789 * 71A	30864 * 71B	31019 73A	31268	73E
30790 * 71A	30865 * 71B	31027 74C	31269	74E
30791 * 71A	30900 * 74E	31033 73C	31270	74D
30792 * 73A	30901 * 74E	31037 74A	31271	74B
30793 * 73A	30902 * 74E	31047 74A	31272	74D
30794 * 73A	30903 * 74E	31048 74A	31274	74E
30795 * 73B	30904 * 74E	31054 73C	31276	74A
30796 * 74C	30905 * 74E	31059 73C	31278	75F
30797 * 74C	30906 * 74E	31061 73C	31279	74E
30798 * 74C	30907 * 74E	31064 74A	31280	74D
30799 * 73B	30908 * 74E	31065 74C	31287	73C
30800 * 73B	30909 * 74E	31067 73A	31293	73B
		31068 73B	31295	74E

31297	73B	31509	73E	31626	72C	31767	73E
31298	74B	31510	73D	31627	70C	31768	73E
31305	73B	31512	73D	31628	70C	31770	74D
31306	73B	31517	74D	31629	71A	31771	74D
31307	74A	31518	73D	31630	70C	31772	74A
31308	73D	31519	74E	31631	70C	31773	74D
31310	75F	31520	74E	31632	71B	31774	74A
31317	74C	31521	75E	31633	70D	31775	74A
31319	74A	31522	74A	31634	70A	31776	75A
31321	73A	31523	74D	31635	70C	31777	75A
31322	73D	31530	75E	31636	70C	31778	75A
31323	74C	31533	73B	31637	70F	31779	74B
31324	74B	31540	73B	31638	70F	31780	74B
31325	75A	31542	74C	31639	71A	31781	74B
31326	74B	31543	74D	31681	73D	31782	74A
31327	75F	31544	75F	31682	73D	31783	73B
31328	74C	31545	73A	31683	73D	31784	73B
31329	75F	31548	74D	31684	73D	31785	73D
31337	74C	31550	73A	31686	73C	31786	73D
31339	74C	31551	73A	31688	73C	31787	73D
31340	74C	31552	73A	31689	73C	31789	74C
31370	74A	31553	73B	31690	73C	31789	74C
31400	74A	31554	75F	31691	73C	31790	72C
31401	74A	31556	75A	31692	73C	31791	72C
31402	74A	31557	73A	31693	73C	31792	72C
31403	74A	31558	73A	31694	73C	31793	72C
31404	74A	31573	73A	31695	73C	31794	72C
31405	74A	31575	73A	31714	73E	31795	72C
31406	74A	31576	73A	31715	73E	31796	72C
31407	74A	31578	73A	31716	74D	31797	70C
31408	73A	31579	73A	31717	73B	31798	70C
31409	73A	31581	73A	31719	73A	31799	70C
31410	73A	31582	73A	31720	73D	31800	70C
31411	73A	31583	73A	31721	73C	31801	71A
31412	73A	31584	73A	31722	70C	31802	71A
31413	73A	31585	74D	31723	70C	31803	71A
31414	73A	31588	74D	31724	75A	31804	70F
31425	74C	31589	74A	31725	75A	31805	70F
31430	74C	31590	74D	31727	74A	31806	70D
31434	74C	31592	74B	31735	73B	31807	70F
31461	73B	31593	74A	31739	73B	31808	70F
31470	74D	31610	72C	31741	73B	31809	70F
31480	73B	31611	70D	31743	73A	31810	73A
31481	73E	31612	70D	31749	73A	31811	73A
31487	74D	31613	71A	31753	74C	31812	73A
31489	74D	31614	71B	31754	74C	31813	72B
31492	74D	31615	71B	31755	74C	31814	72B
31494	73E	31616	70C	31756	74A	31815	73D
31495	73D	31617	70A	31757	74A	31816	73D
31497	73B	31618	71A	31758	74A	31817	75B
31498	74E	31619	71A	31759	74A	31818	74C
31500	74B	31620	71A	31760	74D	31819	74C
31503	73E	31621	70A	31762	74D	31820	74C
31504	73A	31622	70C	31763	74D	31821	74C
31505	73E	31623	72C	31764	74B	31822	73C
31506	73A	31624	70A	31765	73E	31823	73B
31507	73B	31625	70C	31766	73E		
31508	73D						

31824	73B	31869	75B	31922	73C	32353	75E
31825	73B	31870	73B	31923	73C	32407	75C
31826	73B	31871	73B	31924	73C	32408	73B
31827	73B	31872	73B	31925	73C	32409	73B
31828	73B	31873	73B			32410	73B
31829	73B	31874	73B			32411	75C
31830	72A	31875	73B			32412	73B
31831	72A	31876	73C			32413	75C
31832	72A	31877	73C			32414	75C
31833	72A	31878	73C	32100	73A	32415	73B
31834	72A	31879	73C	32101	711	32416	75C
31835	72A	31880	73C	32102	73A	32417	75C
31836	72A	31890	73B	32103	73A	32418	75C
31837	72A	31891	73B	32104	73A	32424	*75A
31838	72A	31892	73E	32105	73A	32437	75A
31839	72A	31893	73E	32106	73A	32438	75E
31840	72A	31894	74D	32107	71A	32440	75A
31841	72A	31895	73A	32108	711	32441	75A
31842	72A	31896	74D	32109	711	32442	75A
31843	72A	31897	73A	32113	711	32443	74D
31844	72A	31898	73A	32124	72A	32444	75C
31845	72A	31899	73B	32135	72A	32445	75C
31846	72A	31900	73B	32139	70F	32446	75C
31847	72A	31901	73B	32151	711	32447	75C
31848	74A	31902	73B	32165	75A	32448	75C
31849	72A	31903	73E	32166	75A	32449	75A
31850	73E	31904	73A	32170	73B	32450	75B
31851	73B	31905	73A	32331	*70D	32451	75B
31852	73E	31906	73A	32337	70F	32454	73B
31853	73B	31907	73A	32338	75A	32455	73A
31854	73C	31908	74D	32339	75A	32456	74D
31855	73C	31909	74D	32340	75A	32462	73B
31856	73C	31910	74D	32341	75A	32463	75D
31857	73C	31911	73C	32342	75A	32466	75C
31858	73C	31912	73C	32343	75A	32467	75A
31859	73C	31913	73C	32344	75E	32468	75A
31860	73C	31914	73A	32345	75E	32469	75D
31861	73C	31915	73A	32346	75E	32470	75D
31862	75B	31916	73C	32347	75E	32471	73B
31863	75B	31917	75C	32348	75E	32472	73B
31864	75B	31918	75C	32349	70F	32473	73B
31865	75B	31919	75C	32350	75E	32474	73B
31866	75B	31920	75C	32351	75E	32475	75A
31867	75B	31921	73A	32352	75E		
31868	75B						

Isle of Wight Locomotives

W 3	*70G	W20	*70H	W27	*70G	W33	*70G
W 4	*70G	W21	*70H	W28	*70G	W35	*70G
W14	*70H	W22	*70H	W29	*70G	W36	*70G
W16	*70H	W24	*70H	W30	*70G		
W17	*70H	W25	*70H	W31	*70G		
W18	*70H	W26	*70G	W32	*70G		

32476	70A	32551	73B	33024	74D	34039 * 75A
32477	75C	32552	73B	33025	70C	34040 * 71B
32479	70F	32553	73B	33026	70B	34041 * 71B
32480	75D	32554	73B	33027	70B	34042 * 71B
32481	75A	32556	71A	33028	74D	34043 * 71B
32484	75A	32557	71A	33029	74D	34044 * 71B
32485	75A	32559	71A	33030	74D	34045 * 75A
32486	70A	32560	75B	33031	74D	34046 * 75A
32487	70C	32562	75A	33032	74D	34047 * 75A
32488	74D	32563	70A	33033	74D	34048 * 75A
32491	71A	32564	73B	33034	74D	34049 * 72B
32492	70A	32565	73B	33035	74D	34050 * 72B
32493	70A	32566	75A	33036	74D	34051 * 72B
32494	75A	32577	75A	33037	73C	34052 * 72B
32495	70F	32578	74D	33038	70A	34053 * 72B
32497	70A	32579	71A	33039	74E	34054 * 72B
32498	70A	32580	74D	33040	74E	34055 * 72B
32499	70A	32581	75F			34056 * 72A
32500	70A	32608	72E			34057 * 72A
32502	75A	32636	74E			34058 * 72A
32503	75A	32640	70F	34001 * 72A		34059 * 72B
32504	75A	32646	70F	34002 * 72A		34060 * 72A
32505	70C	32650	70F	34003 * 72A		34061 * 72A
32506	70C	32655	75A	34004 * 72A		34062 * 72A
32507	75B	32661	70F	34005 * 70A		34063 * 70A
32508	75A	32662	75A	34006 * 70A		34064 * 70A
32509	70F	32670	74E	34007 * 70A		34065 * 70A
32510	71A	32677	70F	34008 * 70A		34066 * 73A
32512	75A	32678	74E	34009 * 70A		34067 * 73A
32515	75A	32689	711	34010 * 70A		34068 * 73A
32517	75F	32694	70F	34011 * 70A		34069 * 72A
32519	75E	32697	72A	34012 * 70A		34070 * 74C
32521	75A			34013 * 72A		34071 * 74C
32522	75D			34014 * 72A		34072 * 74C
32523	75E			34015 * 72A		34073 * 74C
32524	73B	33001	70C	34016 * 72A		34074 * 74C
32525	73B	33002	70C	34017 * 73A		34075 * 74B
32526	75D	33003	70C	34018 * 70A		34076 * 74B
32527	75E	33004	70C	34019 * 70A		34077 * 74B
32528	75E	33005	70C	34020 * 70A		34078 * 74B
32529	75E	33006	70B	34021 * 72A		34079 * 74B
32532	75E	33007	70B	34022 * 72A		34080 * 74B
32534	75E	33008	70B	34023 * 72A		34081 * 74B
32535	75E	33009	70B	34024 * 72A		34082 * 74B
32536	75E	33010	70B	34025 * 72A		34083 * 74B
32537	73B	33011	70B	34026 * 72A		34084 * 74B
32538	73B	33012	70B	34027 * 72A		34085 * 74B
32539	73B	33013	70B	34028 * 72A		34086 * 74B
32540	75A	33014	73C	34029 * 72A		34087 * 73A
32541	75D	33015	70A	34030 * 72A		34088 * 73A
32543	75C	33016	70A	34031 * 72A		34089 * 73A
32544	75C	33017	70A	34032 * 72A		34090 * 73A
32545	75C	33018	70B	34033 * 72A		34091 * 73A
32546	75C	33019	70C	34034 * 72A		34092 * 73A
32547	75C	33020	71A	34035 * 72D		34093 * 71B
32548	70F	33021	71A	34036 * 72D		34094 * 71B
32549	70F	33022	70C	34037 * 72D		34095 * 70A
32550	70F	33023	71A	34038 * 72D		34096 * 74B

34097 * 74B		40005	84G	40063	26A	40121	6C
34098 * 74B		40006	1A	40064	1A	40122	2C
34099 * 74B		40007	1A	40065	26A	40123	6G
34100 * 74B		40008	84G	40066	1A	40124	17E
34101 * 73A		40009	17F	40067	17E	40125	1A
34102 * 73A		40010	1C	40068	1A	40126	6E
34103 * 74C		40011	11A	40069	6D	40127	8E
34104 * 74C		40012	2A	40070	6D	40128	6E
34105 * 71B		40013	26A	40071	9B	40129	3C
34106 * 71B		40014	26A	40072	24E	40130	6G
34107 * 71B		40015	26A	40073	6E	40131	6C
34108 * 71B		40016	1A	40074	55F	40132	6H
34109 * 71B		40017	2A	40075	55E	40133	6G
34110 * 71B		40018	9E	40076	2C	40134	8D
		40019	1A	40077	9A	40135	6C
		40020	1C	40078	2C	40136	2B
		40021	14A	40079	16C	40137	8D
		40022	14C	40080	3C	40138	2B
		40023	14A	40081	9B	40139	55F
35001 * 73A		40024	14C	40082	55D	40140	55A
35002 * 72A		40025	14A	40083	6G	40141	17F
35003 * 72A		40026	14C	40084	9A	40142	14B
35004 * 72B		40027	14B	40085	6E	40143	8D
35005 * 70A		40028	14B	40086	6E	40144	21B
35006 * 72B		40029	14B	40087	2B	40145	86G
35007 * 72B		40030	14A	40088	17F	40146	16C
35008 * 72A		40031	14B	40089	17E	40147	55F
35009 * 72A		40032	14B	40090	27C	40148	19B
35010 * 71B		40033	14B	40091	86G	40149	21A
35011 * 70A		40034	14B	40092	14B	40150	60D
35012 * 70A		40035	14B	40093	9A	40151	60B
35013 * 72A		40036	14B	40094	17E	40152	65D
35014 * 70A		40037	14C	40095	6G	40153	65D
35015 * 73A		40038	14B	40096	16C	40154	65D
35016 * 70A		40039	14C	40097	17F	40155	55F
35017 * 70A		40040	14B	40098	86K	40156	1A
35018 * 70A		40041	11A	40099	24E	40157	2B
35019 * 70A		40042	1A	40100	14B	40158	65D
35020 * 70A		40043	1C	40101	6C	40159	65D
35021 * 70A		40044	1A	40102	6C	40160	14B
35022 * 71B		40045	2A	40103	24E	40161	86K
35023 * 72A		40046	1A	40104	2B	40162	24H
35024 * 72A		40047	1A	40105	17F	40163	24H
35025 * 71B		40048	84G	40106	6E	40164	24E
35026 * 72A		40049	2B	40107	9A	40165	15D
35027 * 71B		40050	1A	40108	3E	40166	27A
35028 * 73A		40051	1A	40109	24E	40167	14B
35029 * 70A		40052	17F	40110	6E	40168	16C
35030 * 70A		40053	1A	40111	14B	40169	55A
		40054	1A	40112	55F	40170	68B
		40055	17F	40113	17E	40171	86K
		40056	2A	40114	55F	40172	14B
		40057	2A	40115	21A	40173	3C
		40058	84G	40116	22A	40174	24E
40001	17E	40059	2A	40117	55F	40175	16C
40002	6D	40060	6K	40118	3E	40176	65D
40003	6H	40061	1C	40119	14B	40177	65D
40004	2A	40062	26A	40120	24H	40178	55F

Part	Code	Part	Code	Part	Code	Part	Code
40179	55E	40482	19B	40589	6K	40647	67A
40180	3D	40485	15C	40590	67C	40648	61A
40181	55D	40487	16A	40592	67B	40649	67A
40182	15C	40489	22B	40593	67B	40650	61A
40183	24H	40491	55A	40594	67A	40651	68A
40184	16C	40493	16A	40595	67A	40652	5A
40185	68A	40495	21B	40596	67A	40653	5A
40186	65D	40501	3C	40597	67B	40654	11B
40187	65D	40502	18C	40598	67A	40655	5A
40188	65D	40504	16A	40599	67A	40656	12A
40189	65D	40509	71G	40600	61C	40657	12A
40190	27C	40511	21A	40601	71G	40658	6A
40191	27C	40513	17A	40602	68A	40659	5A
40192	27C	40519	17B	40603	61A	40660	6A
40193	55A	40520	55D	40604	61A	40661	67B
40194	27C	40525	17B	40605	67B	40663	61A
40195	27C	40534	14B	40606	67D	40664	67C
40196	27C	40536	17A	40607	67D	40665	67B
40197	27C	40537	16A	40608	67D	40666	67D
40198	27C	40538	19B	40609	67D	40667	67D
40199	27C	40540	22B	40610	67C	40668	67D
40200	65D	40541	21B	40611	68C	40669	67D
40201	8D	40542	16A	40612	67B	40670	67C
40202	6D	40543	15C	40613	68A	40671	10C
40203	8E	40548	14B	40614	68B	40672	1C
40204	2B	40550	18C	40615	68A	40673	5A
40205	6E	40552	55A	40616	68C	40674	9A
40206	3D	40553	16A	40617	61B	40675	6A
40207	2B	40557	16A	40618	61B	40676	10C
40208	9E	40559	6A	40619	67B	40677	2E
40209	6C	40563	71H	40620	67A	40678	5C
40332	21A	40564	71H	40621	67A	40679	6A
40337	18C	40565	10B	40622	61C	40680	27D
40356	17B	40566	67B	40623	68C	40681	26C
40396	17B	40567	5A	40624	67D	40682	17A
40402	15C	40569	71H	40625	67D	40683	2E
40404	17A	40569	71H	40626	67D	40684	27A
40407	17A	40570	67B	40627	67A	40685	24H
40409	24G	40571	67B	40628	12A	40686	67B
40411	16A	40572	67B	40629	12A	40687	67B
40412	17A	40573	67B	40630	55E	40688	67B
40413	21A	40574	67C	40631	10C	40689	67B
40416	17A	40575	67C	40632	16A	40690	55A
40420	6K	40576	68B	40633	17B	40691	18C
40421	3C	40577	68B	40634	71H	40692	5A
40426	22A	40578	67D	40635	10C	40693	9A
40433	19B	40579	67D	40636	67A	40694	10B
40439	21B	40580	6A	40637	67A	40695	12A
40443	21A	40581	55C	40638	67D	40696	71G
40447	16A	40582	12A	40640	67C	40697	71G
40452	15C	40583	5C	40641	67A	40698	71G
40453	17B	40584	55C	40642	67A	40699	12A
40454	16A	40585	15C	40643	67B	40700	71G
40461	16A	40586	26C	40644	67B	40907	19B
40464	15C	40587	27D	40645	67B	40920	68C
		40588	27A	40646	5C	40925	6G

40926	5A	41158	6A	41233	6H	41289	10D
40927	17A	41159	9A	41234	6H	41290	73A
40928	21A	41162	2A	41235	6E	41291	73A
40931	17D	41163	17F	41236	6G	41292	73A
40933	3E	41164	6A	41237	6E	41293	71A
40935	16A	41165	2A	41238	6G	41294	74A
40936	3E	41167	5A	41239	6H	41295	72E
40937	27A	41168	9A	41240	22A	41296	71J
		41172	2A	41241	71G	41297	72E
		41173	17F	41242	71G	41298	72E
		41179	68B	41243	71G	41299	73B
		41181	22B	41244	6E	41300	73B
41045	24J	41185	17D	41245	19B	41301	74B
41048	15A	41186	27C	41246	19B	41302	72D
41049	22B	41189	24E	41247	55F	41303	74A
41060	24J	41190	19B	41248	71H	41304	71J
41062	19B	41192	17A	41249	71H	41305	71A
41063	55F	41193	24E	41250	56F	41306	72A
41066	17F	41194	21B	41251	56A	41307	72A
41068	55A	41195	22B	41252	56A	41308	73E
41071	55A	41196	24J	41253	56A	41309	73E
41073	21B	41197	24J	41254	55C	41310	73E
41078	15C	41199	19B	41255	55C	41311	73E
41083	17A	41200	6H	41256	55C	41312	73E
41086	6J	41201	86K	41257	55F	41313	73E
41089	21B	41202	82A	41258	55C	41314	73B
41090	3E	41203	82A	41259	55C	41315	72D
41093	6G	41204	86K	41260	24F	41316	72D
41094	55A	41205	24G	41261	24F	41317	74A
41095	15C	41206	24H	41262	56F	41318	74B
41098	24J	41207	22A	41263	56F	41319	74B
41100	55A	41208	22A	41264	56F	41320	1C
41101	27A	41209	19B	41265	55F	41321	2C
41102	24E	41210	8B	41266	55F	41322	2B
41103	17A	41211	10D	41267	55A	41323	2B
41105	2A	41212	8B	41268	15C	41324	1E
41106	6A	41213	3C	41269	15D	41325	24G
41111	6G	41214	2A	41270	15D	41326	24G
41112	24J	41215	6D	41271	15D	41327	24G
41113	2A	41216	6K	41272	15D	41328	15A
41114	17F	41217	11B	41273	55F	41329	15D
41116	17F	41218	2E	41274	55D	41518	18D
41118	17F	41219	2E	41275	1C	41528	18D
41119	6G	41220	6H	41276	6K	41529	18D
41120	6A	41221	11B	41277	15A	41530	22B
41121	24J	41222	1E	41278	2A	41531	18D
41122	2A	41223	3C	41279	3C	41532	17B
41123	17F	41224	3C	41280	26E	41533	18D
41140	21A	41225	3B	41281	55D	41534	17A
41143	16A	41226	2B	41282	55D	41535	17A
41144	16A	41227	2C	41283	27B	41536	17B
41150	17F	41228	2C	41284	27A	41537	22B
41152	24J	41229	5A	41285	2C	41661	55B
41153	6A	41230	6H	41286	10D	41702	39A
41156	21B	41231	6E	41287	10C	41708	18D
41157	6A	41232	6E	41288	10D	41710	17A

41712	16A	41988	33A	42091	73A	42149	56E
41724	17A	41989	33A	42092	74A	42150	56E
41726	17A	41990	33A	42093	52A	42151	56E
41734	6C	41991	33A	42094	52A	42152	56D
41739	18D	41992	33A	42095	74A	42153	24A
41748	22B	41993	33A	42096	74A	42154	24D
41752	18D			42097	74A	42155	8A
41754	17A			42098	74A	42156	14B
41763	18D			42099	74A	42157	14B
41769	87K			42100	74A	42158	24C
41773	17A			42101	75F	42159	14C
41779	36A			42102	75F	42160	15C
41795	19A			42103	75F	42161	16A
41797	55B			42104	75F	42162	64D
41803	18D			42105	75F	42163	64D
41804	18D			42106	73A	42164	66C
41835	19C			42107	56F	42165	66C
41844	16C	42050	17A	42108	56F	42166	66C
41847	17A	42051	24H	42109	56F	42167	66C
41855	24G	42052	55F	42110	24A	42168	63A
41857	19A	42053	21A	42111	27E	42169	63A
41875	19C	42054	21A	42112	27E	42170	66A
41878	17B	42055	66A	42113	27E	42171	66A
41879	22A	42056	66A	42114	26E	42172	66A
41900	9A	42057	66A	42115	26E	42173	64D
41901	5A	42058	66A	42116	56F	42174	17A
41902	2C	42059	66A	42117	1A	42175	66D
41903	24J	42060	66A	42118	1A	42176	66D
41904	24J	42061	2A	42119	10A	42177	64D
41905	9D	42062	2A	42120	10A	42178	14B
41906	9D	42063	26A	42121	8A	42179	11B
41907	9A	42064	17F	42122	67A	42180	27D
41908	9A	42065	17F	42123	67A	42181	17A
41909	2C	42066	75E	42124	67A	42182	15C
41928	33A	42067	75E	42125	66B	42183	15C
41936	30E	42068	75E	42126	66B	42184	17A
41939	33A	42069	75E	42127	66B	42185	16A
41941	33A	42070	75E	42128	66C	42186	21B
41945	33A	42071	75E	42129	66C	42187	24B
41946	33A	42072	52A	42130	68D	42188	56F
41947	18A	42073	52A	42131	67C	42189	56F
41948	33A	42074	74B	42132	24H	42190	67A
41949	30E	42075	74C	42133	14C	42191	67A
41950	33A	42076	74C	42134	14C	42192	68D
41969	33C	42077	74C	42135	24J	42193	67A
41975	30E	42078	74C	42136	24J	42194	67C
41977	33A	42079	74C	42137	15C	42195	67C
41978	33A	42080	73B	42138	55F	42196	67C
41980	33A	42081	73B	42139	55F	42197	67C
41981	33A	42082	73B	42140	16A	42198	63B
41982	33A	42083	50G	42141	55F	42199	63B
41983	33A	42084	50E	42142	64D	42200	66B
41984	33A	42085	50E	42143	66A	42201	67C
41985	33A	42086	73A	42144	66A	42202	67C
41986	33A	42087	75F	42145	64D	42203	66B
41987	33A	42088	73A	42146	17A	42204	64D
		42089	73A	42147	24D	42205	68D
		42090	73A	42148	24E	42206	65B

42207	65B	42265	66D	42323	5C	42381	9A
42208	66B	42266	66D	42324	53E	42382	9C
42209	67D	42267	3E	42325	14B	42383	21A
42210	67D	42268	64C	42326	21A	42384	55G
42211	67D	42269	64C	42327	21A	42385	87K
42212	67D	42270	64C	42328	34D	42386	9C
42213	68D	42271	64C	42329	14B	42387	87K
42214	68D	42272	64C	42330	15C	42388	87K
42215	68D	42273	64C	42331	15C	42389	5C
42216	64D	42274	66A	42332	11B	42390	87K
42217	64D	42275	66A	42333	16A	42391	9B
42218	33A	42276	66A	42334	21B	42392	11B
42219	33A	42277	66A	42335	14C	42393	11D
42220	33A	42278	26A	42336	16A	42394	87K
42221	33A	42279	26A	42337	21A	42395	11B
42222	34E	42280	26A	42338	21B	42396	11D
42223	33A	42281	26A	42339	16A	42397	9A
42224	33A	42282	26A	42340	21B	42398	9A
42225	34E	42283	26A	42341	14C	42399	9A
42226	33A	42284	26A	42342	16A	42400	5D
42227	33A	42285	56D	42343	12A	42401	11B
42228	17A	42286	26A	42344	5D	42402	11B
42229	67A	42287	26A	42345	5C	42403	11D
42230	34E	42288	26A	42346	5C	42404	11D
42231	34E	42289	26C	42347	5C	42405	56D
42232	34E	42290	26A	42348	9A	42406	56D
42233	5D	42291	27C	42349	8E	42407	53E
42234	5D	42292	27C	42350	9A	42408	55G
42235	10A	42293	27C	42351	9A	42409	55G
42236	66D	42294	24A	42352	8E	42410	55G
42237	14B	42295	24A	42353	9B	42411	53E
42238	66D	42296	24C	42354	9B	42412	55G
42239	66D	42297	27D	42355	9C	42413	55G
42240	66D	42298	24C	42356	9C	42414	55G
42241	66D	42299	27D	42357	9C	42415	6H
42242	66A	42300	14C	42358	5D	42416	6H
42243	66A	42301	11C	42359	11B	42417	6D
42244	66A	42302	14C	42360	5D	42418	5D
42245	66A	42303	6A	42361	16A	42419	17F
42246	66A	42304	9A	42362	9C	42420	5D
42247	66D	42305	87K	42363	9C	42421	5D
42248	34E	42306	9D	42364	11B	42422	3E
42249	34E	42307	87K	42365	9D	42423	10C
42250	34E	42308	6A	42366	5D	42424	11D
42251	34E	42309	5C	42367	5D	42425	5C
42252	34E	42310	55G	42368	9D	42426	8A
42253	34E	42311	53E	42369	9C	42427	11B
42254	33A	42312	55G	42370	9D	42428	3B
42255	33A	42313	11C	42371	9D	42429	3B
42256	34E	42314	11C	42372	11B	42430	9A
42257	33A	42315	6A	42373	16A	42431	5D
42258	66D	42316	2C	42374	34D	42432	11A
42259	66D	42317	11C	42375	5D	42433	24A
42260	66D	42318	9C	42376	11B	42434	24C
42261	66D	42319	9A	42377	55A	42435	24C
42262	66D	42320	11B	42378	5D	42436	53E
42263	66D	42321	5A	42379	9B	42437	24A
42264	66D	42322	9A	42380	55F	42438	24B

42439	24B	42502	33C	42560	10C	42618	26C
42440	5D	42503	33C	42561	10C	42619	24A
42441	3C	42504	33C	42562	5C	42620	24A
42442	10C	42505	33C	42563	10C	42621	26A
42443	5D	42506	33C	42564	8A	42622	56F
42444	26D	42507	33C	42565	26C	42623	24A
42445	8E	42508	33C	42566	5A	42624	26A
42446	2F	42509	33C	42567	5D	42625	24E
42447	6C	42510	33C	42568	26A	42626	26C
42448	8E	42511	33C	42569	27D	42627	3C
42449	5D	42512	33C	42570	8A	42628	8E
42450	26A	42513	33C	42571	10A	42629	26C
42451	26A	42514	33C	42572	10A	42630	26C
42452	17F	42515	33C	42573	2A	42631	27D
42453	14B	42516	33C	42574	10C	42632	27D
42454	5D	42517	33C	42575	5A	42633	26C
42455	26D	42518	33C	42576	2A	42634	24A
42456	10A	42519	33C	42577	2A	42635	26C
42457	11C	42520	33C	42578	5C	42636	24E
42458	5D	42521	33C	42579	3E	42637	24E
42459	8A	42522	33C	42580	8E	42638	24E
42460	26D	42523	33C	42581	11B	42639	56E
42461	26A	42524	33C	42582	5D	42640	27D
42462	10A	42525	33C	42583	8A	42641	27D
42463	10A	42526	33C	42584	8E	42642	27D
42464	11C	42527	33C	42585	2A	42643	24A
42465	10A	42528	33C	42586	3C	42644	27D
42466	8E	42529	33C	42587	14B	42645	26B
42467	9G	42530	33C	42588	26D	42646	26B
42468	5F	42531	33C	42589	24J	42647	26B
42469	17F	42532	33C	42590	5D	42648	26B
42470	3D	42533	33C	42591	11A	42649	56F
42471	5E	42534	33C	42592	27D	42650	56F
42472	26C	42535	33C	42593	5D	42651	26A
42473	27D	42536	33C	42594	9A	42652	26D
42474	24B	42537	27C	42595	14B	42653	26C
42475	24B	42538	5C	42596	8E	42654	26C
42476	24C	42539	9B	42597	6C	42655	26C
42477	56D	42540	14B	42598	8E	42656	26C
42478	9A	42541	2A	42599	6C	42657	3E
42479	8E	42542	9A	42600	5D	42658	3E
42480	24C	42543	5D	42601	3E	42659	5D
42481	24C	42544	12A	42602	8A	42660	26A
42482	3C	42545	26C	42603	5D	42661	24A
42483	24D	42546	24B	42604	3C	42662	10C
42484	24D	42547	24B	42605	5F	42663	5D
42485	24D	42548	24A	42606	8B	42664	8A
42486	26A	42549	24A	42607	8B	42665	5F
42487	1A	42550	26C	42608	6C	42666	10A
42488	3C	42551	26E	42609	5D	42667	5D
42489	2A	42552	3E	42610	14B	42668	5D
42490	24D	42553	56D	42611	5E	42669	2A
42491	24C	42554	27D	42612	8E	42670	5D
42492	24C	42555	24B	42613	11C	42671	5D
42493	6C	42556	24C	42614	27D	42672	5D
42494	5D	42557	27D	42615	2A	42673	2A
42500	33C	42558	24D	42616	3D	42674	3E
42501	33C	42559	24D	42617	14B	42675	17F

42676	17F	42734	26B	42792	17D	42850	66C
42677	5A	42735	66C	42793	68A	42851	24J
42678	33C	42736	65F	42794	19A	42852	1A
42679	33C	42737	65F	42795	55A	42853	3D
42680	14C	42738	63C	42796	24D	42854	2B
42681	33C	42739	67C	42797	19A	42855	14A
42682	14B	42740	66D	42798	55A	42856	5B
42683	17F	42741	66C	42799	17B	42857	21A
42684	33C	42742	67D	42800	63C	42858	9A
42685	14B	42743	67B	42801	63C	42859	9B
42686	14C	42744	67B	42802	65F	42860	26B
42687	33C	42745	67C	42803	65F	42861	56A
42688	68D	42746	65B	42804	68A	42862	56A
42689	66B	42747	1A	42805	67C	42863	56A
42690	62B	42748	68A	42806	67D	42864	26B
42691	62B	42749	68C	42807	64C	42865	55C
42692	62B	42750	26A	42808	67C	42866	55C
42693	62B	42751	68A	42809	67C	42867	24F
42694	65B	42752	68A	42810	24J	42868	26B
42695	64C	42753	26B	42811	5B	42869	24B
42696	66B	42754	21A	42812	1A	42870	1A
42697	67D	42755	26B	42813	5B	42871	26A
42698	66D	42756	17B	42814	9A	42872	17A
42699	66B	42757	68A	42815	5B	42873	17D
42700	26D	42758	21A	42816	21A	42874	17D
42701	26A	42759	14A	42817	2B	42875	68A
42702	55C	42760	17D	42818	17B	42876	68A
42703	26A	42761	21A	42819	26B	42877	68A
42704	26A	42762	55F	42820	26D	42878	27B
42705	26A	42763	17B	42821	24D	42879	67C
42706	24B	42764	15B	42822	17B	42880	66C
42707	26A	42765	24F	42823	21A	42881	68A
42708	26A	42766	55C	42824	17B	42882	68A
42709	26A	42767	17B	42825	17B	42883	68A
42710	26A	42768	17D	42826	17B	42884	68A
42711	27B	42769	16A	42827	21A	42885	1A
42712	26D	42770	55F	42828	24B	42886	9A
42713	55C	42771	55A	42829	17B	42887	9A
42714	26A	42772	9A	42830	68A	42888	6C
42715	26A	42773	9B	42831	68A	42889	9A
42716	24B	42774	55A	42832	68A	42890	21A
42717	24B	42775	17E	42833	68A	42891	2B
42718	24D	42776	5B	42834	68A	42892	8C
42719	26D	42777	5B	42835	68A	42893	24J
42720	68A	42778	6C	42836	68A	42894	5B
42721	27B	42779	3A	42837	68A	42895	24J
42722	26B	42780	65F	42838	26B	42896	17B
42723	26B	42781	2B	42839	14A	42897	17A
42724	26B	42782	3A	42840	24F	42898	24B
42725	26B	42783	2B	42841	24F	42899	68A
42726	26A	42784	16A	42842	24F	42900	21A
42727	27B	42785	5B	42843	24F	42901	26A
42728	26A	42786	9A	42844	24F	42902	17D
42729	24D	42787	1A	42845	26B	42903	21A
42730	26B	42788	17E	42846	21A	42904	19A
42731	26D	42789	55C	42847	17A	42905	68A
42732	24F	42790	21A	42848	9A	42906	68A
42733	26A	42791	21A	42849	8C	42907	68A

42908	68B	42966	5B	43029	11D	43087	35A
42909	68B	42967	6C	43030	52B	43088	35A
42910	67C	42968	5B	43031	14A	43089	31A
42911	67D	42969	6C	43032	19B	43090	31D
42912	67D	42970	6C	43033	16A	43091	31D
42913	68A	42971	6B	43034	2B	43092	31D
42914	67C	42972	5B	43035	11D	43093	31D
42915	68A	42973	6B	43036	21A	43094	31D
42916	67C	42974	3D	43037	19C	43095	31D
42917	67C	42975	6B	43038	51D	43096	50C
42918	68B	42976	6B	43039	55A	43097	50C
42919	68B	42977	6C	43040	16A	43098	50C
42920	5B	42978	6C	43041	17A	43099	53A
42921	3A	42979	3D	43042	19A	43100	53A
42922	17B	42980	5B	43043	52B	43101	52B
42923	9A	42981	6C	43044	55B	43102	51D
42924	9A	42982	6B	43045	15C	43103	53A
42925	9A	42983	5B	43046	21A	43104	31D
42926	5B	42984	5B	43047	21A	43105	31D
42927	67C			43048	17A	43106	38E
42928	24J			43049	21A	43107	31D
42929	3D			43050	51A	43108	35A
42930	9A			43051	51D	43109	31D
42931	1A			43052	50C	43110	31D
42932	5B			43053	53A	43111	31D
42933	5B			43054	51K	43112	24G
42934	9B			43055	52B	43113	24G
42935	9A			43056	52B	43114	55E
42936	9A			43057	52D	43115	19A
42937	5B	43000	1D	43058	35A	43116	55E
42938	9A	43001	1D	43059	35A	43117	55A
42939	5B	43002	2B	43060	35A	43118	14A
42940	5B	43003	2B	43061	35A	43119	14C
42941	6C	43004	12C	43062	35A	43120	14A
42942	9D	43005	12C	43063	38E	43121	14A
42943	9D	43006	12C	43064	35A	43122	53A
42944	5B	43007	12C	43065	35A	43123	50C
42945	6B	43008	12C	43066	35A	43124	51A
42946	3D	43009	12C	43067	35A	43125	50C
42947	3D	43010	21A	43068	31D	43126	52B
42948	5B	43011	2B	43069	53A	43127	35C
42949	8E	43012	19A	43070	52B	43128	51C
42950	5B	43013	21A	43071	51D	43129	52B
42951	3D	43014	55B	43072	51D	43130	51A
42952	5B	43015	51C	43073	51D	43131	53A
42953	5B	43016	52B	43074	51D	43132	65E
42954	3D	43017	21A	43075	52B	43133	65E
42955	5A	43018	15C	43076	53A	43134	65E
42956	5B	43019	14A	43077	53A	43135	65A
42957	3D	43020	1D	43078	53A	43136	65A
42958	3D	43021	1D	43079	53A	43137	65A
42959	5B	43022	1D	43080	35A	43138	64F
42960	9A	43023	2B	43081	35A	43139	68E
42961	5A	43024	1D	43082	35A	43140	64E
42962	5B	43025	12C	43083	35A	43141	64E
42963	5A	43026	12C	43084	35A	43142	31D
42964	5B	43027	17A	43085	35A	43143	31D
		43028	11D	43086	35A	43144	31D

43145	32G	43247	17B	43357	9B	43502	24J
43146	32G	43248	71H	43359	21B	43506	22B
43147	32G	43249	16A	43361	17B	43507	21A
43148	32G	43250	55D	43367	15B	43509	55E
43149	32G	43251	18A	43368	17A	43510	17A
43150	32G	43253	18B	43369	19C	43514	68A
43151	32G	43254	19A	43370	17D	43515	18D
43152	32G	43256	17B	43371	19C	43520	22B
43153	32G	43257	24G	43373	22B	43521	21B
43154	32G	43258	22B	43374	21A	43522	16C
43155	32G	43261	14A	43378	16A	43523	21A
43156	32G	43263	21B	43379	17A	43529	15D
43157	32F	43266	18B	43381	21A	43531	15D
43158	32F	43267	55D	43386	18D	43538	9G
43159	32F	43268	9D	43387	9D	43548	17A
43160	32F	43271	24J	43388	19A	43553	55F
43161	32F	43274	9D	43389	3D	43558	16A
43174	15D	43277	84G	43392	55B	43562	5B
43178	24G	43278	9D	43394	84G	43565	14C
43180	19C	43282	8B	43395	17B	43570	84G
43183	55E	43284	21A	43396	6K	43572	17A
43185	17A	43286	17B	43398	8B	43574	17B
43186	21C	43287	16B	43399	2E	43575	18D
43187	3E	43290	17D	43400	17D	43578	17A
43188	17B	43292	17A	43401	16A	43579	55B
43189	5B	43294	17A	43405	18A	43580	18B
43192	9B	43295	24G	43406	17B	43583	21B
43193	18B	43300	9D	43410	3C	43584	17A
43194	71H	43301	68A	43411	15C	43585	24H
43200	17A	43305	16B	43419	71H	43586	55F
43203	21B	43306	17B	43427	22A	43587	17B
43205	15C	43307	14A	43428	15D	43593	22A
43207	5B	43308	8B	43429	17D	43594	21A
43208	19C	43309	18A	43431	16C	43596	16B
43210	21A	43312	17A	43433	21A	43599	21A
43211	18C	43314	8B	43435	21A	43605	18D
43212	18C	43315	17A	43436	71H	43603	17B
43213	22B	43318	17A	43440	14A	43612	39A
43214	21A	43321	55E	43441	21A	43615	2B
43216	71H	43323	17D	43443	21A	43618	2B
43218	71H	43324	17A	43444	22A	43619	8B
43219	21A	43325	9A	43446	55D	43620	21A
43222	15D	43326	15C	43449	55E	43621	84G
43223	21A	43327	17B	43453	18A	43622	68A
43224	18D	43329	8B	43456	55B	43623	17B
43225	19C	43330	5B	43457	9A	43624	15A
43231	3E	43332	19A	43459	17A	43627	21A
43233	55D	43333	15C	43464	22A	43629	15C
43234	18D	43335	19A	43468	16B	43630	39A
43235	18B	43337	22B	43474	15D	43631	18D
43237	8B	43339	21A	43476	55D	43634	18C
43239	16C	43340	17B	43482	21A	43637	19A
43240	16A	43341	19A	43484	21A	43638	39A
43241	68A	43342	17D	43490	21A	43639	55E
43242	16B	43344	22A	43491	84G	43644	21A
43243	19A	43355	21B	43496	17D	43645	22B
43244	15C	43356	71H	43499	18A	43650	18A
43245	14C						

43651	9G	43785	15D	43880	18B	43946	18A
43652	17B	43786	2B	43881	17A	43947	14A
43656	55E	43787	8B	43882	19A	43948	17B
43657	8B	43789	55D	43883	66B	43949	21A
43658	17A	43793	18A	43884	63B	43950	17D
43660	19C	43798	21A	43885	17C	43951	21A
43664	19C	43799	15C	43886	18D	43952	27D
43665	15D	43800	19A	43887	22B	43953	17B
43668	21B	43806	15C	43888	16A	43954	16A
43669	19A	43808	15D	43890	24J	43955	17A
43673	21A	43809	17B	43892	17B	43957	35C
43674	21A	43812	21A	43893	24G	43958	16A
43675	21B	43814	19C	43896	12A	43960	24G
43678	68A	43815	17B	43897	24D	43961	18A
43679	84G	43822	84G	43898	15D	43962	16A
43680	21A	43823	18A	43899	67A	43963	21A
43681	55B	43825	18B	43900	18D	43964	14B
43682	71J	43826	18A	43901	14A	43965	17B
43684	21A	43828	18A	43902	68A	43966	18B
43687	21B	43829	15D	43903	16B	43967	15D
43690	21A	43832	18A	43904	11B	43968	55A
43693	21A	43836	9D	43905	14A	43969	17A
43705	55D	43837	21B	43906	55D	43970	16B
43709	17B	43839	17B	43907	16B	43971	15D
43710	15C	43840	17A	43908	6B	43972	16A
43711	18D	43841	1E	43910	8E	43973	68A
43712	22A	43842	9D	43911	21A	43975	14B
43714	55E	43843	15C	43913	24G	43976	17B
43715	19A	43844	19A	43914	55D	43977	15A
43717	9A	43845	18A	43915	8E	43978	19C
43721	15D	43846	17F	43916	24G	43979	15A
43727	16C	43847	17A	43917	16A	43980	11D
43728	15C	43848	65B	43918	16A	43981	6G
43729	16A	43849	65B	43919	14B	43982	17D
43731	19A	43850	18B	43920	18D	43983	55D
43734	22A	43851	55B	43921	17F	43984	24J
43735	17A	43853	22B	43922	68A	43985	21A
43737	55B	43854	17E	43923	17C	43986	21A
43742	55F	43855	21B	43924	22B	43987	55B
43745	19A	43856	16A	43925	17A	43988	18A
43749	19A	43858	21A	43926	22A	43989	21B
43750	17D	43859	16B	43927	39A	43990	18A
43751	18A	43860	18B	43928	39A	43991	17A
43753	15C	43861	15A	43929	15A	43993	18D
43754	22B	43863	18D	43930	15C	43994	18A
43756	26A	43864	5D	43931	55B	43995	15A
43757	84G	43865	18A	43932	21B	43996	67A
43759	17D	43866	18B	43933	17C	43997	16B
43760	84G	43868	68A	43934	14A	43998	18B
43762	21C	43869	18D	43935	14A	43999	24G
43763	17A	43870	15C	43937	15C	44000	24G
43766	15D	43871	55B	43938	21A	44001	67A
43771	21A	43872	19C	43939	21A	44002	19C
43773	16B	43873	15D	43940	21A	44003	55D
43776	17D	43876	15D	43941	18A	44004	21A
43778	17B	43877	6E	43942	55D	44005	16B
43784	55F	43878	21A	43944	55F	44007	24G
		43879	17A	43945	17E	44008	68A

44009	68A	44068	5D	44126	12A	44183	68A
44010	18D	44069	9A	44127	8E	44184	15C
44011	63B	44070	18D	44128	19C	44185	21A
44012	18A	44071	19C	44129	18D	44186	5B
44013	17D	44072	1E	44130	18B	44187	21A
44014	27E	44073	6B	44131	16A	44188	27E
44015	8E	44074	5D	44132	16A	44189	67A
44016	18A	44075	9B	44133	18C	44190	17C
44017	17A	44076	2E	44134	17D	44191	18B
44018	16A	44077	5D	44135	22A	44192	11A
44019	56A	44078	3C	44136	18C	44193	63A
44020	17A	44079	5E	44137	21A	44194	65B
44021	16A	44080	17F	44138	21A	44195	16A
44022	26A	44081	12A	44139	16A	44196	66C
44023	16B	44082	19C	44140	18A	44197	24G
44025	39A	44083	11D	44141	55D	44198	67A
44026	21A	44084	21A	44142	17A	44199	65B
44027	3B	44085	17C	44143	14B	44200	18A
44028	55B	44086	11B	44144	17E	44201	21A
44029	14A	44087	19A	44145	18A	44202	16B
44030	16A	44088	16B	44146	71H	44203	21A
44031	17A	44089	19C	44147	18D	44204	18B
44032	5D	44090	17E	44148	17C	44205	18D
44033	16A	44091	18A	44149	24H	44206	19C
44034	15C	44092	21A	44150	18B	44207	55A
44035	22B	44093	5D	44151	16A	44208	1A
44036	19C	44094	55B	44152	35C	44209	22B
44037	19C	44095	16A	44153	55B	44210	14B
44038	27E	44096	71H	44154	18A	44211	21A
44039	19A	44097	35C	44155	9G	44212	19A
44040	27E	44098	55E	44156	17C	44213	21A
44041	24G	44099	55E	44157	2B	44214	17A
44042	17A	44100	17B	44158	16A	44215	16A
44043	15D	44101	17D	44159	67B	44216	55F
44044	55A	44102	71H	44160	21A	44217	18C
44045	22B	44103	17C	44161	18A	44218	27E
44046	17D	44104	18D	44162	18C	44219	2E
44047	17B	44105	27D	44163	17D	44220	27D
44048	17A	44106	18A	44164	17A	44221	27D
44049	17A	44107	55D	44165	21A	44222	24G
44050	17D	44108	21A	44166	17C	44223	16A
44051	14A	44109	17C	44167	22B	44224	18A
44052	14B	44110	35C	44168	17D	44225	27D
44053	18C	44111	19C	44169	17A	44226	21A
44054	18C	44112	17A	44170	55E	44227	21A
44055	55A	44113	17C	44171	21A	44228	14A
44056	56D	44114	39A	44172	17D	44229	18B
44057	3E	44115	3C	44173	18B	44230	21A
44058	6E	44116	1A	44174	19A	44231	15C
44059	9B	44117	6B	44175	15A	44232	8E
44060	12A	44118	16B	44176	17A	44233	18B
44061	9A	44119	26A	44177	17A	44234	65B
44062	56D	44120	3D	44178	17E	44235	21A
44063	5E	44121	12A	44179	21A	44236	17E
44064	2A	44122	15B	44180	17C	44237	8B
44065	6B	44123	22B	44181	68A	44238	55B
44066	18D	44124	17B	44182	15A	44239	35C
44067	5F	44125	5E			44240	27D

44241	17D	44298	14B	44355	22A	44412	16A
44242	2E	44299	27E	44356	8B	44413	21A
44243	14B	44300	10D	44357	5F	44414	16A
44244	18C	44301	5B	44358	5D	44415	16C
44245	19C	44302	3D	44359	5B	44416	16C
44246	5D	44303	10D	44360	11D	44417	71H
44247	35C	44304	17A	44361	17E	44418	15B
44248	21A	44305	6H	44362	18A	44419	17A
44249	18D	44306	11A	44363	1C	44420	17A
44250	17E	44307	6E	44364	1E	44421	17E
44251	63A	44308	5D	44365	12C	44422	71G
44252	15C	44309	5D	44366	11B	44423	15C
44253	63A	44310	5D	44367	6K	44424	22A
44254	63A	44311	26A	44368	11B	44425	17A
44255	65B	44312	67B	44369	17A	44426	19A
44256	65B	44313	16A	44370	1A	44427	18A
44257	63A	44314	63C	44371	18D	44428	17A
44258	63A	44315	68A	44372	1A	44429	17D
44259	14A	44316	17B	44373	5D	44430	18B
44260	17C	44317	15D	44374	5D	44431	24G
44261	17E	44318	63B	44375	5D	44432	5D
44262	17D	44319	67B	44376	18A	44433	17B
44263	21A	44320	65F	44377	5D	44434	17B
44264	22B	44321	18B	44378	17A	44435	17B
44265	19A	44322	63B	44379	17E	44436	17B
44266	15D	44323	67C	44380	17A	44437	19A
44267	18D	44324	68A	44381	1D	44438	10D
44268	16B	44325	67B	44382	9B	44439	3B
44269	22A	44326	68A	44383	5D	44440	1A
44270	14B	44327	17D	44384	8B	44441	1D
44271	9B	44328	63A	44385	5B	44442	1C
44272	22B	44329	67A	44386	5E	44443	11B
44273	35C	44330	67C	44387	17E	44444	3C
44274	55D	44331	67C	44388	2F	44445	6H
44275	17F	44332	17B	44389	6G	44446	55D
44276	24H	44333	21A	44390	12C	44447	1E
44277	24G	44334	17A	44391	2E	44448	3C
44278	15B	44335	55B	44392	17F	44449	12C
44279	17C	44336	55E	44393	5D	44450	5E
44280	10D	44337	55E	44394	16C	44451	1A
44281	67B	44338	55E	44395	2A	44452	5E
44282	24H	44339	9D	44396	8E	44453	5E
44283	66A	44340	9B	44397	1A	44454	11A
44284	18B	44341	9G	44398	24D	44455	5D
44285	18B	44342	5E	44399	11A	44456	9G
44286	17E	44343	1C	44400	55F	44457	19A
44287	19A	44344	5B	44401	16A	44458	55E
44288	18C	44345	3C	44402	17A	44459	5D
44289	18A	44346	12A	44403	15C	44460	24D
44290	55D	44347	11B	44404	18D	44461	12C
44291	27E	44348	1D	44405	5D	44462	27E
44292	2B	44349	9A	44406	21A	44463	21A
44293	8E	44350	10D	44407	17E	44464	27D
44294	18C	44351	11B	44408	55E	44465	15B
44295	17A	44352	1E	44409	17A	44466	22A
44296	22A	44353	5D	44410	18C	44467	55B
44297	14A	44354	5E	44411	22A	44468	24G

44469	11D	44526	17B	44583	21A	44691	27A
44470	16B	44527	17B	44584	55B	44692	24A
44471	27E	44528	17B	44585	16A	44693	56F
44472	16A	44529	14A	44586	55B	44694	56F
44473	1A	44530	14A	44587	8E	44695	56F
44474	56D	44531	14B	44588	17D	44696	26A
44475	18D	44532	14B	44589	17A	44697	26A
44476	35C	44533	16A	44590	18D	44698	63A
44477	19A	44534	22A	44591	17A	44699	63A
44478	5D	44535	15B	44592	5B	44700	64D
44479	24D	44536	22A	44593	1E	44701	64D
44480	16A	44537	22A	44594	11B	44702	65A
44481	27E	44538	17B	44595	5B	44703	61B
44482	18B	44539	17C	44596	12A	44704	63A
44483	24D	44540	17A	44597	17B	44705	63A
44484	5D	44541	27E	44598	18B	44706	67A
44485	56D	44542	17B	44599	17B	44707	65A
44486	27D	44543	26A	44600	17B	44708	10C
44487	11B	44544	27D	44601	17A	44709	11A
44488	3B	44545	17A	44602	17D	44710	6A
44489	8E	44546	16A	44603	18C	44711	2A
44490	3E	44547	19A	44604	55E	44712	2A
44491	2E	44548	5D	44605	27E	44713	1A
44492	3D	44549	12C	44606	18D	44714	12A
44493	6B	44550	55D	44658	14B	44715	2A
44494	8E	44551	17B	44659	21A	44716	2A
44495	12C	44552	17B	44660	21A	44717	17F
44496	5D	44553	22A	44661	19B	44718	60A
44497	1A	44554	17C	44662	55A	44719	60A
44498	5D	44555	16A	44663	14A	44720	63A
44499	5D	44556	17D	44664	21A	44721	63A
44500	5D	44557	71G	44665	17F	44722	60A
44501	17E	44558	71G	44666	21A	44723	60A
44502	5D	44559	71G	44667	17A	44724	60A
44503	5E	44560	71G	44668	68A	44725	68A
44504	5F	44561	71G	44669	68A	44726	68A
44505	12C	44562	17B	44670	68A	44727	68A
44506	3E	44563	14B	44671	68A	44728	27C
44507	5D	44564	17D	44672	68A	44729	27C
44508	5D	44565	17D	44673	68A	44730	24E
44509	35C	44566	17D	44674	68A	44731	24E
44510	11A	44567	22B	44675	68A	44732	24E
44511	11B	44568	19A	44676	68A	44733	24E
44512	3C	44569	22A	44677	65B	44734	26A
44513	5D	44570	55B	44678	12A	44735	26A
44514	3E	44571	21A	44679	5A	44736	26A
44515	21A	44572	17C	44680	5A	44737	24E
44516	21A	44573	19A	44681	6J	44738	6G
44517	3D	44574	15A	44682	5A	44739	6G
44518	35C	44575	15A	44683	5A	44740	6G
44519	35C	44576	19C	44684	5A	44741	9A
44520	21A	44577	16A	44685	5A	44742	9A
44521	35C	44578	16A	44686	9A	44743	22A
44522	35C	44579	24H	44687	9A	44744	22A
44523	71G	44590	21A	44638	27A	44745	22A
44524	2E	44581	14A	44689	24A	44746	22A
44525	6G	44582	55D	44690	27A	44747	22A

44748	9A	44806	14B	44864	6G	44922	65B
44749	9A	44807	5A	44865	6G	44923	65B
44750	9A	44808	10C	44866	2A	44924	63A
44751	9A	44809	17A	44867	2A	44925	63A
44752	9A	44810	21A	44868	5B	44926	24E
44753	55A	44811	17B	44869	1A	44927	24E
44754	55A	44812	14B	44870	2A	44928	27A
44755	55A	44813	21A	44871	5D	44929	26B
44756	55A	44814	21A	44872	3D	44930	24E
44757	55A	44815	17A	44873	3C	44931	63A
44758	5A	44816	14B	44874	11A	44932	26B
44759	5A	44817	14B	44875	1A	44933	26A
44760	9A	44818	17A	44876	3D	44934	26A
44761	5A	44819	17A	44877	68A	44935	9A
44762	5A	44820	63A	44878	68A	44936	12A
44763	5A	44821	21A	44879	63A	44937	9A
44764	5A	44822	14B	44880	65B	44938	9A
44765	5A	44823	26B	44881	65B	44939	12A
44766	5A	44824	56A	44882	68A	44940	24B
44767	27A	44825	14B	44883	68A	44941	9A
44768	8A	44826	55A	44884	68A	44942	3D
44769	8A	44827	5B	44885	63A	44943	55A
44770	12A	44828	55A	44886	68A	44944	19A
44771	1A	44829	3B	44887	27C	44945	21A
44772	8A	44830	19B	44888	21A	44946	56F
44773	8A	44831	2A	44889	24A	44947	24E
44774	14A	44832	5B	44890	26A	44948	24B
44775	21A	44833	2A	44891	26A	44949	24B
44776	21A	44834	5B	44892	11A	44950	24E
44777	14A	44835	84G	44893	26A	44951	56F
44778	24E	44836	2A	44894	26A	44952	64D
44779	24E	44837	2A	44895	26A	44953	64D
44780	24B	44838	1A	44896	55C	44954	62B
44781	26B	44839	17A	44897	3D	44955	64D
44782	26B	44840	9A	44898	68A	44956	65A
44783	60A	44841	21A	44899	68A	44957	65A
44784	60A	44842	21A	44900	68A	44958	68A
44785	60A	44843	17B	44901	68A	44959	63A
44786	65B	44844	3D	44902	68A	44960	63A
44787	65A	44845	26A	44903	68A	44961	63A
44788	60A	44846	14B	44904	11A	44962	21A
44789	60A	44847	19B	44905	11A	44963	21A
44790	68A	44848	17A	44906	8A	44964	21A
44791	67A	44849	55A	44907	8A	44965	21A
44792	68A	44850	66B	44908	65A	44966	21A
44793	64D	44851	17A	44909	2A	44967	65A
44794	61B	44852	55A	44910	6A	44968	65A
44795	68A	44853	55A	44911	34A	44969	66B
44796	63A	44854	55A	44912	56F	44970	65B
44797	63A	44855	14B	44913	6H	44971	6B
44798	60A	44856	17A	44914	3A	44972	65J
44799	60A	44857	55A	44915	2A	44973	65J
44800	6B	44858	19A	44916	1A	44974	65J
44801	63A	44859	21A	44917	71G	44975	65J
44802	19A	44860	2A	44918	16A	44976	65J
44803	26A	44861	16A	44919	21A	44977	65J
44804	21A	44862	2A	44920	21A	44978	63A
44805	21A	44863	2A	44921	63A	44979	63A

44980	63A	45036	64C	45094	3D	45152	66B
44981	21B	45037	11A	45095	10C	45153	65B
44982	24E	45038	3D	45096	10B	45154 *	26A
44983	55A	45039	8A	45097	11A	45155	65B
44984	15D	45040	21A	45098	60A	45156 *	26A
44985	14B	45041	12A	45099	66B	45157 *	65B
44986	19B	45042	10C	45100	68A	45158 *	65B
44987	26B	45043	6B	45101	26A	45159	65B
44988	24E	45044	5B	45102	26A	45160	67A
44989	27C	45045	5B	45103	26A	45161	64C
44990	56F	45046	11A	45104	26A	45162	61B
44991	60A	45047	63A	45105	26A	45163	68A
44992	60A	45048	5B	45106	12A	45164	62B
44993	68A	45049	63B	45107	24F	45165	63A
44994	64C	45050	2E	45108	5B	45166	64D
44995	68B	45051	3A	45109	9A	45167	61B
44996	65A	45052	3D	45110	6J	45168	63A
44997	63A	45053	63A	45111	5B	45169	68B
44998	63A	45054	11A	45112	68A	45170	63A
44999	63A	45055	6B	45113	5A	45171	63A
		45056	19B	45114	3A	45172	63A
		45057	10A	45115	65B	45173	64D
45000	12A	45058	3D	45116	26B	45174	64D
45001	6B	45059	14A	45117	63A	45175	64D
45002	5B	45060	5B	45118	68A	45176	66B
45003	5A	45061	27C	45119	65B	45177	65B
45004	1E	45062	19A	45120	12A	45178	65B
45005	8A	45063	55C	45121	66B	45179	60A
45006	17F	45064	1A	45122	68A	45180	5B
45007	68A	45065	3D	45123	60A	45181	8A
45008	66B	45066	60A	45124	60A	45182	10C
45009	66B	45067	5B	45125	63A	45183	64C
45010	67B	45068	24A	45126	68A	45184	12A
45011	64D	45069	8A	45127	64C	45185	12A
45012	68A	45070	10C	45128	5B	45186	21A
45013	68A	45071	12A	45129	10C	45187	1A
45014	11A	45072	11A	45130	6B	45188	5B
45015	3B	45073	12A	45131	5B	45189	5D
45016	63B	45074	5B	45132	3D	45190	84G
45017	11A	45075	55C	45133	6G	45191	2E
45018	68A	45076	26A	45134	5B	45192	60A
45019	11A	45077	24E	45135	10A	45193	11A
45020	1E	45078	24A	45136	60B	45194	67A
45021	2E	45079	55C	45137	15D	45195	1E
45022	64C	45080	55C	45138	68A	45196	8B
45023	64C	45081	68A	45139	15D	45197	12A
45024	1A	45082	68A	45140	12A	45198	5B
45025	1A	45083	68A	45141	11B	45199	10C
45026	10A	45084	63B	45142	6B	45200	24E
45027	1A	45085	66B	45143	84G	45201	27A
45028	6B	45086	64C	45144	6H	45202	26A
45029	66B	45087	64D	45145	84G	45203	26A
45030	64C	45088	16A	45146	9A	45204	55C
45031	26A	45089	1A	45147	1A	45205	24B
45032	8B	45090	60A	45148	5A	45206	24F
45033	5A	45091	2E	45149	5D	45207	56F
45034	3E	45092	11A	45150	5A	45208	56F
45035	8B	45093	5B	45151	66B	45209	24B

45210	27A	45268	21A	45326	11A	45384	62B
45211	55C	45269	21A	45327	11A	45385	3A
45212	24F	45270	5B	45328	8B	45386	11B
45213	63B	45271	8B	45329	12A	45387	1A
45214	63B	45272	21A	45330	68A	45388	1E
45215	55G	45273	55A	45331	1E	45389	63A
45216	27A	45274	14A	45332	10B	45390	5A
45217	8E	45275	6B	45333	8E	45391	5B
45218	27C	45276	8A	45334	68A	45392	2E
45219	56F	45277	14B	45335	14A	45393	1E
45220	26A	45278	1A	45336	26A	45394	12A
45221	15D	45279	14B	45337	26B	45395	3C
45222	55G	45280	21A	45338	26B	45396	63B
45223	26B	45281	68A	45339	55G	45397	3D
45224	26A	45282	5A	45340	55G	45398	8A
45225	26A	45283	84G	45341	26A	45399	8A
45226	24A	45284	26A	45342	15D	45400	63B
45227	24A	45285	14B	45343	8A	45401	8A
45228	27C	45286	12A	45344	3C	45402	12A
45229	24B	45287	3B	45345	6B	45403	3B
45230	11A	45288	1A	45346	8E	45404	1A
45231	3D	45289	5A	45347	10A	45405	3B
45232	26A	45290	26A	45348	12A	45406	84G
45233	26A	45291	11A	45349	3D	45407	14B
45234	26B	45292	2E	45350	1A	45408	10A
45235	5A	45293	12A	45351	12A	45409	12A
45236	11B	45294	10C	45352	10C	45410	8A
45237	55G	45295	12A	45353	1A	45411	10C
45238	14B	45296	12A	45354	8B	45412	12A
45239	17F	45297	19B	45355	65B	45413	8A
45240	5A	45298	84G	45356	65B	45414	12A
45241	11A	45299	9A	45357	63B	45415	24A
45242	8A	45300	5A	45358	65B	45416	3D
45243	8A	45301	5B	45359	63B	45417	6H
45244	12A	45302	5A	45360	60A	45418	3D
45245	63A	45303	8A	45361	60A	45419	2A
45246	12A	45304	10C	45362	67A	45420	10C
45247	6B	45305	5B	45363	68A	45421	8A
45248	12A	45306	11A	45364	68A	45422	84G
45249	8A	45307	1E	45365	63A	45423	63B
45250	8A	45308	3E	45366	63A	45424	10C
45251	67A	45309	66B	45367	63A	45425	10A
45252	8B	45310	3B	45368	12A	45426	5B
45253	14B	45311	5B	45369	5A	45427	11A
45254	5A	45312	6A	45370	3D	45428	55A
45255	8B	45313	10A	45371	12A	45429	3E
45256	8A	45314	10A	45372	1A	45430	1A
45257	3E	45315	12A	45373	5A	45431	12A
45258	12A	45316	12A	45374	1A	45432	68B
45259	12A	45317	11B	45375	1A	45433	66C
45260	17A	45318	24E	45376	8A	45434	5A
45261	26B	45319	60A	45377	10C	45435	26A
45262	17B	45320	60A	45378	10C	45436	24E
45263	17A	45321	8B	45379	5A	45437	6G
45264	17B	45322	3D	45380	8A	45438	12A
45265	21A	45323	12A	45381	1A	45439	3B
45266	67B	45324	1A	45382	6J	45440	71G
45267	15D	45325	6B	45383	11B	45441	6G

45442 10C	45500 * 12A	45558 * 10C	45616 * 14B
45443 65B	45501 * 9A	45559 * 10C	45617 * 5A
45444 14B	45502 * 12A	45560 * 16A	45618 * 17F
45445 12A	45503 * 5A	45561 * 17F	45619 * 55A
45446 5A	45504 * 12A	45562 * 55A	45620 * 16A
45447 14B	45505 * 9A	45563 * 10C	45621 * 67A
45448 3D	45506 * 12A	45564 * 55A	45622 * 17F
45449 10A	45507 * 5A	45565 * 55A	45623 * 8A
45450 26B	45508 12A	45566 * 55A	45624 * 9A
45451 12A	45509 * 17A	45567 * 8A	45625 * 5A
45452 63A	45510 1A	45568 * 55A	45626 * 17A
45453 60A	45511 * 1A	45569 * 55A	45627 * 14B
45454 10A	45512 * 12A	45570 * 17A	45628 * 17F
45455 68A	45513 12A	45571 * 24E	45629 * 9A
45456 63A	45514 * 1B	45572 * 22A	45630 * 5A
45457 63A	45515 * 8A	45573 * 55A	45631 * 9A
45458 63A	45516 * 8A	45574 * 24E	45632 * 9A
45459 63A	45517 1A	45575 * 14B	45633 * 10B
45460 63A	45518 * 8A	45576 * 19B	45634 * 5A
45461 60A	45519 * 9A	45577 * 22A	45635 * 26A
45462 66B	45520 * 9A	45578 * 9A	45636 * 16A
45463 63A	45521 * 8A	45579 * 14B	45638 * 9A
45464 24E	45522 * 1B	45590 * 24E	45639 * 55A
45465 63A	45523 * 1B	45581 * 55C	45640 * 68A
45466 68A	45524 * 12A	45582 * 10B	45641 * 14B
45467 63A	45525 * 8A	45583 * 8A	45642 * 26A
45468 65B	45526 * 12A	45584 * 24E	45643 * 5A
45469 61B	45527 * 8A	45585 * 17A	45644 * 9A
45470 63A	45528 5A	45586 * 5A	45645 * 10C
45471 65B	45529 * 5A	45587 * 9A	45646 * 55C
45472 63A	45530 * 9A	45588 * 24E	45647 * 3B
45473 63A	45531 * 8A	45589 * 55A	45648 * 14B
45474 63A	45532 * 1B	45590 * 19B	45649 * 14B
45475 63A	45533 * 8A	45591 * 5A	45650 * 14B
45476 60A	45534 * 8A	45592 * 1B	45651 * 22A
45477 60A	45535 * 8A	45593 * 12A	45652 * 9E
45478 60A	45536 * 9A	45594 * 19B	45653 * 24E
45479 60A	45537 * 12A	45595 * 9A	45654 * 19B
45480 68B	45538 * 8A	45596 * 8A	45655 * 9A
45481 68A	45539 * 8A	45597 * 55A	45656 * 19B
45482 65B	45540 * 9A	45598 * 14B	45657 * 68A
45483 63A	45541 * 12A	45599 * 12A	45658 * 55A
45484 66B	45542 12A	45600 * 10C	45659 * 55A
45485 66B	45543 * 12A	45601 * 1B	45660 * 22A
45486 62B	45544 8A	45602 * 17A	45661 * 26A
45487 63A	45545 * 1B	45603 * 1A	45662 * 22A
45488 63A	45546 * 5A	45604 * 5A	45663 * 22A
45489 67A	45547 1A	45605 * 55A	45664 * 19B
45490 67A	45548 * 5A	45606 * 1B	45665 * 67A
45491 68A	45549 12A	45607 * 19B	45666 * 12A
45492 63A	45550 8A	45608 * 55A	45667 * 16A
45493 2A	45551 12A	45609 * 19B	45668 * 10C
45494 12A	45552 * 8A	45610 * 17A	45669 * 1B
45495 8B	45553 * 5A	45611 * 16A	45670 * 8A
45496 63A	45554 * 16A	45612 * 14B	45671 * 26A
45497 63A	45555 * 3B	45613 * 12A	45672 * 1B
45498 66B	45556 * 5A	45614 * 14B	45673 * 63A
45499 65B	45557 * 14B	45615 * 14B	45674 * 5A

45675 * 55A	45733 * 3B	46146 * 1B	46241 * 1B
45676 * 1B	45734 * 3B	46147 * 6J	46242 * 1B
45677 * 67A	45735 * 1B	46148 * 6J	46243 * 5A
45678 * 5A	45736 * 5A	46149 * 6J	46244 * 1B
45679 * 68A	45737 * 3B	46150 * 5A	46245 * 1B
45690 * 9A	45738 * 3B	46151 * 5A	46246 * 5A
45681 * 8A	45739 * 55A	46152 * 8A	46247 * 1B
45682 * 22A	45740 * 1A	46153 * 9A	46248 * 5A
45683 * 19B	45741 * 3B	46154 * 1B	46249 * 5A
45684 * 5A	45742 * 3B	46155 * 5A	46250 * 1B
45685 * 22A		46156 * 5A	46251 * 5A
45686 * 1B		46157 * 8A	46252 * 5A
45687 * 67A	46100 * 1B	46158 * 9A	46253 * 1B
45688 * 3B	46101 * 5A	46159 * 5A	46254 * 1B
45689 * 9A	46102 * 66A	46160 * 9A	46255 * 12A
45690 * 22A	46103 * 55A	46161 * 1B	46256 * 1B
45691 * 68A	46104 * 66A	46162 * 1B	46257 * 1B
45692 * 63A	46105 * 66A	46163 * 5A	46400 19B
45693 * 67A	46106 * 5A	46164 * 8A	46401 22B
45694 * 55A	46107 * 66A	46165 * 12A	46402 15C
45695 * 55C	46108 * 55A	46166 * 5A	46403 15B
45696 * 68A	46109 * 55A	46167 * 12A	46404 15B
45697 * 68A	46110 * 5A	46168 * 1B	46405 27B
45698 * 27A	46111 * 9A	46169 * 9A	46406 26D
45699 * 22A	46112 * 55A	46170 * 1B	46407 53E
45700 * 26A	46113 * 55A	46200 * 8A	46408 53E
45701 * 26A	46114 * 8A	46201 * 5A	46409 53E
45702 * 26A	46115 * 9A	46203 * 8A	46410 26A
45703 * 5A	46116 * 12A	46204 * 8A	46411 26A
45704 * 68A	46117 * 55A	46205 * 8A	46412 27B
45705 * 24E	46118 * 5A	46206 * 5A	46413 56A
45706 * 26A	46119 * 5A	46207 * 8A	46414 26D
45707 * 67A	46120 * 5A	46208 * 8A	46415 56A
45708 * 55C	46121 * 66A	46209 * 5A	46416 26D
45709 * 3B	46122 * 9A	46210 * 8A	46417 26D
45710 * 26A	46123 * 8A	46211 * 5A	46418 26A
45711 * 67A	46124 * 8A	46212 * 5A	46419 26A
45712 * 17F	46125 * 5A	46220 * 66A	46420 2D
45713 * 63A	46126 * 12A	46221 * 66A	46421 3A
45714 * 68A	46127 * 5A	46222 * 66A	46422 10A
45715 * 68A	46128 * 5A	46223 * 66A	46423 6K
45716 * 68A	46129 * 5A	46224 * 66A	46424 1A
45717 * 27A	46130 * 12A	46225 * 5A	46425 3A
45718 * 68A	46131 * 9A	46226 * 12A	46426 24J
45719 * 27A	46132 * 8A	46227 * 66A	46427 3D
45720 * 67A	46133 * 55A	46228 * 12A	46428 10A
45721 * 5A	46134 * 5A	46229 * 1B	46429 5D
45722 * 12A	46135 * 5A	46230 * 66A	46430 5D
45723 * 9A	46136 * 12A	46231 * 66A	46431 1A
45724 * 68A	46137 * 5A	46232 * 66A	46432 12C
45725 * 19B	46138 * 5A	46233 * 5A	46433 6K
45726 * 5A	46139 * 1B	46234 * 5A	46434 10A
45727 * 63A	46140 * 9A	46235 * 5A	46435 56A
45728 * 68A	46141 * 12A	46236 * 1B	46436 26D
45729 * 68A	46142 * 8A	46237 * 1B	46437 26A
45730 * 68A	46143 * 9A	46238 * 12A	46438 56A
45731 * 68A	46144 * 1B	46239 * 1B	46439 27B
45732 * 68A	46145 * 55A	46240 * 1B	46440 17A

46441	24J	46499	18C	47203	14A	47272	18C
46442	24G	46500	18C	47204	14B	47273	15A
46443	17A	46501	16C	47205	14B	47274	15C
46444	15B	46502	16A	47206	14A	47275	71G
46445	6K	46503	89A	47207	14A	47276	21C
46446	2D	46504	89A	47208	15A	47277	16A
46447	12C	46505	89A	47209	14B	47278	18C
46448	10A	46506	82B	47210	14A	47279	15A
46449	12A	46507	89A	47211	14A	47280	5B
46450	19A	46508	89B	47212	14B	47281	5D
46451	19A	46509	89A	47213	14A	47282	35A
46452	24G	46510	89A	47214	14A	47283	14B
46453	55A	46511	89A	47216	14A	47284	6E
46454	17A	46512	89A	47217	14A	47285	2B
46455	12C	46513	89A	47218	18C	47286	1D
46456	12C	46514	89A	47219	14A	47287	11B
46457	12C	46515	89A	47221	18D	47288	10D
46458	1A	46516	89B	47222	55F	47289	9B
46459	3A	46517	85C	47223	18A	47290	12C
46460	61A	46518	89B	47224	14A	47291	10B
46461	64A	46519	89B	47225	21A	47292	12A
46462	64A	46520	89B	47226	14A	47293	10B
46463	62B	46521	89B	47227	15C	47294	3A
46464	62B	46522	89B	47228	19A	47295	12A
46465	31A	46523	89A	47229	14B	47296	3C
46466	31A	46524	89B	47230	27A	47297	6A
46467	31A	46525	82B	47231	17B	47298	10D
46468	30E	46526	89A	47234	18A	47299	56E
46469	30E	46527	82B	47235	19A	47300	35B
46470	51H			47236	17B	47301	27A
46471	51F			47238	19C	47302	1D
46472	51H			47239	55E	47303	27A
46473	51A			47241	14B	47304	1D
46474	51A	47000	17D	47242	14B	47305	27B
46475	51A	47001	27A	47243	14B	47306	35A
46476	51A	47002	27A	47246	14B	47307	1D
46477	51A	47003	18C	47247	18A	47308	21C
46478	51E	47004	18C	47248	14A	47309	1CC
46479	51A	47005	6C	47249	55B	47310	1D
46480	51F	47006	6C	47250	17A	47311	35A
46481	51F	47007	1D	47251	14A	47312	33A
46482	51F	47008	10B	47254	55A	47313	21A
46483	56A	47009	6C	47255	55F	47314	1D
46484	26A	47160	6E	47257	17B	47315	1D
46485	26B	47161	24F	47258	27B	47316	71G
46486	26B	47162	64A	47259	87K	47317	11A
46487	26A	47163	64C	47260	14B	47318	2E
46488	12C	47164	1D	47261	14C	47319	10B
46489	12C	47165	24F	47262	33A	47320	8E
46490	3A	47166	6F	47263	18D	47321	6J
46491	12C	47167	66D	47264	15D	47322	11B
46492	3D	47168	66D	47265	15A	47323	11B
46493	55A	47169	66D	47266	56E	47324	6C
46494	19B	47190	71G	47267	9A	47325	8E
46495	15B	47191	71G	47268	8B	47326	12A
46496	15B	47200	14B	47269	2A	47327	8E
46497	18C	47201	24J	47270	5D	47328	33A
46498	55A	47202	14B	47271	55B	47329	67A

47330	5B	47388	8C	47446	55E	47505	1A
47331	66C	47389	6A	47447	17D	47506	22B
47332	68A	47390	12C	47448	55D	47507	6C
47333	22A	47391	12A	47449	17C	47508	56E
47334	55E	47392	8A	47450	5B	47509	56E
47335	55E	47393	10D	47451	5D	47510	56A
47336	39A	47394	6G	47452	10D	47511	1D
47337	12C	47395	9A	47453	10D	47512	33A
47338	2D	47396	3A	47454	24G	47513	19A
47339	11A	47397	3B	47455	18D	47514	1D
47340	12A	47398	3B	47456	17D	47515	1D
47341	9A	47399	10C	47457	17D	47516	5B
47342	1A	47400	9A	47458	35B	47517	1D
47343	9A	47401	10C	47459	17D	47518	1D
47344	5D	47402	8A	47460	17D	47519	8A
47345	9A	47403	55G	47461	17D	47520	1A
47346	9B	47404	8A	47462	55D	47521	1E
47347	9A	47405	55E	47463	55B	47522	1B
47348	1D	47406	11A	47464	17B	47523	5B
47349	1D	47407	8A	47465	71G	47524	5B
47350	6K	47408	12A	47466	18B	47525	12C
47351	33A	47409	11A	47467	1B	47526	5B
47352	8B	47410	11A	47468	24J	47527	1B
47353	8A	47411	8A	47469	24J	47528	9A
47354	1B	47412	1A	47470	24J	47529	1B
47355	1C	47413	10B	47471	24J	47530	8E
47356	1B	47414	5B	47472	10B	47531	1A
47357	8A	47415	12A	47473	3B	47532	24J
47358	1B	47416	8A	47474	1A	47533	15C
47359	5C	47417	22B	47475	1A	47534	15C
47360	10B	47418	55A	47476	6J	47535	18C
47361	1A	47419	55F	47477	87K	47536	66D
47362	8B	47420	55A	47478	87K	47537	68A
47363	3B	47421	55D	47479	87K	47538	55B
47364	10C	47422	22B	47480	27E	47539	22B
47365	10C	47423	18C	47481	87K	47540	68A
47366	10D	47424	18D	47482	1D	47541	66A
47367	8E	47425	27B	47483	1D	47542	71G
47368	6J	47426	18D	47484	33A	47543	15A
47369	9A	47427	24G	47485	17B	47544	22A
47370	5D	47428	24G	47486	1D	47545	18D
47371	6B	47429	35B	47487	8A	47546	19C
47372	6B	47430	10C	47488	1D	47547	19C
47373	11A	47431	5B	47489	8A	47548	19A
47374	6A	47432	19A	47490	8D	47549	15D
47375	6A	47433	14A	47491	6E	47550	22A
47376	8B	47434	14A	47492	2B	47551	18A
47377	12A	47435	14A	47493	8C	47552	22A
47378	1A	47436	55A	47494	1D	47554	14C
47379	56E	47437	14B	47495	1D	47555	33A
47380	5D	47438	55D	47496	71G	47556	55G
47381	24J	47439	6J	47497	1D	47557	71G
47382	3A	47440	26A	47498	8A	47558	1D
47383	6A	47441	15C	47499	1D	47559	1D
47384	5B	47442	15C	47500	1E	47560	1D
47385	8A	47443	55B	47501	1D	47561	1D
47386	24B	47444	10D	47502	21C	47562	24G
47387	8B	47445	5E	47503	11C	47563	17A
				47504	6A		

47564	1D	47624	19A	47967	18C	48069	15B
47565	21C	47625	18D	47968	18C	48070	55D
47566	8A	47626	18D	47969	18C	48073	16B
47567	55C	47627	6C	47982	18C	48074	1A
47568	55C	47628	6F	47986	18C	48075	19C
47569	55C	47629	17A	47987	18C	48076	55E
47570	55C	47630	18D	47994	18C	48077	2B
47571	55C	47631	16A	47995	18C	48078	55D
47572	56A	47632	55B			48079	17A
47573	56A	47633	5E			48080	55D
47574	26B	47634	55D			48081	16B
47575	24B	47635	55E			48082	18C
47576	24B	47636	19A			48083	17A
47577	24B	47637	18D			48084	55E
47578	26B	47638	21A			48085	2A
47579	26B	47639	24J			48088	16C
47580	56A	47640	55B			48089	17E
47581	55D	47641	17B	48000	16B	48090	2E
47582	56A	47642	14B	48001	16C	48092	16B
47583	26B	47643	17B	48002	17B	48093	55D
47584	26D	47644	14B	48003	16B	48094	8B
47585	26B	47645	14B	48004	16B	48095	18C
47586	24B	47646	6B	48005	17A	48096	16B
47587	5D	47647	5D	48006	16B	48097	16B
47588	5C	47648	5D	48007	15C	48098	16B
47589	55B	47649	5C	48008	16B	48099	17E
47590	5C	47650	6B	48009	16B	48100	16B
47591	8B	47651	8C	48010	15C	48101	16B
47592	CW	47652	8B	48011	19C	48102	16B
47593	12C	47653	5C	48012	2C	48103	18D
47594	2B	47654	8B	48016	2B	48104	55A
47595	5E	47655	87K	48017	8D	48105	24H
47596	5D	47656	6B	48018	2C	48106	6C
47597	8A	47657	8B	48020	2B	48107	15C
47598	5E	47658	5F	48024	16C	48108	16A
47599	5D	47659	10B	48026	19C	48109	14A
47600	6A	47660	17A	48027	15C	48110	84G
47601	9B	47661	5B	48029	16B	48111	16A
47602	12A	47662	5E	48033	18D	48112	18B
47603	8B	47664	12A	48035	21A	48113	55D
47604	12C	47665	5C	48036	1A	48114	16B
47605	11B	47666	12A	48037	18D	48115	18B
47606	5E	47667	1B	48039	8C	48116	19A
47607	55E	47668	1B	48045	9G	48117	16A
47608	5B	47669	1B	48046	9G	48118	18B
47609	5D	47670	5B	48050	15B	48119	16C
47610	5D	47671	1B	48053	16A	48120	6C
47611	17B	47672	10C	48054	8C	48121	17A
47612	2E	47673	9A	48055	55E	48122	1A
47614	12A	47674	6F	48056	17D	48123	55E
47615	6B	47675	1A	48057	18B	48124	15B
47616	8D	47676	1A	48060	18B	48125	18A
47618	12A	47677	2A	48061	15C	48126	55B
47619	18D	47678	22A	48062	14A	48127	17E
47620	18D	47679	17D	48063	17D	48128	18A
47621	10C	47680	5B	48064	16A	48129	1A
47622	6F	47681	87K	48065	18C	48130	55E
47623	22B			48067	55A	48131	15B

48132	14A	48190	17E	48268	9D	48329	17E
48133	15C	48191	17E	48269	21A	48330	87K
48134	1A	48192	17D	48270	16B	48331	18D
48135	9G	48193	16B	48271	18A	48332	18A
48136	16A	48194	18A	48272	16C	48333	18A
48137	16B	48195	18A	48273	18A	48334	16B
48138	19C	48196	18A	48274	55E	48335	1A
48139	18B	48197	18A	48275	9A	48336	21A
48140	19C	48198	17E	48276	55B	48337	55D
48141	15B	48199	18D	48277	16C	48338	21A
48142	15B	48200	18A	48278	9D	48339	21A
48143	15B	48201	18A	48279	16A	48340	9G
48144	19A	48202	55E	48280	21A	48341	18D
48145	18A	48203	18A	48281	55D	48342	24J
48146	55D	48204	18A	48282	16A	48343	2B
48147	2E	48205	18A	48283	55A	48344	84G
48148	17E	48206	16A	48284	18A	48345	2B
48149	15C	48207	1E	48285	15B	48346	18D
48150	19C	48208	17E	48286	24J	48347	84G
48151	19C	48209	19C	48287	5B	48348	8B
48152	21A	48210	18D	48288	17F	48349	8B
48153	17A	48211	15C	48289	5B	48350	18A
48154	2B	48212	18C	48290	1A	48351	21A
48155	9G	48213	18D	48291	5B	48352	55E
48156	16C	48214	16B	48292	5B	48353	18B
48157	55A	48215	16B	48293	17A	48354	84G
48158	55A	48216	19C	48294	5B	48355	15B
48159	55A	48217	16A	48295	5B	48356	15B
48160	55E	48218	16A	48296	9G	48357	55E
48161	17E	48219	18A	48297	3A	48358	55B
48162	55D	48220	17E	48301	15B	48359	15A
48163	14A	48221	18A	48302	17A	48360	2E
48164	18D	48222	55D	48303	18A	48361	18A
48165	9D	48223	16B	48304	18A	48362	18A
48166	9D	48224	16B	48305	2E	48363	15A
48167	18D	48225	16B	48306	15C	48364	15A
48168	17A	48246	6B	48307	84G	48365	15A
48169	55D	48247	8B	48308	84G	48366	3A
48170	16A	48248	5B	48309	87K	48367	18A
48171	1A	48249	6C	48310	3A	48368	9G
48172	84G	48250	3A	48311	55B	48369	84G
48173	2A	48251	5B	48312	2B	48370	18A
48174	6B	48252	5B	48313	15B	48371	18C
48175	3A	48253	6F	48314	18A	48372	2B
48176	19C	48254	9G	48315	17E	48373	8C
48177	15D	48255	5B	48316	17E	48374	15A
48178	18A	48256	5B	48317	17F	48375	3A
48179	19A	48257	5B	48318	3A	48376	15A
48180	14A	48258	2B	48319	18A	48377	16A
48181	19C	48259	6B	48320	2B	48378	15A
48182	18A	48260	8A	48321	68A	48379	16B
48183	18A	48261	24J	48322	9D	48380	15B
48184	18A	48262	5B	48323	8C	48381	14A
48185	18A	48263	5B	48324	18A	48382	16B
48186	18A	48264	15A	48325	1A	48383	16B
48187	18A	48265	55D	48326	9D	48384	18A
48188	8B	48266	15C	48327	17E	48385	15A
48189	19A	48267	16B	48328	84G	48386	15A

48387	18A	48445	2E	48517	15C	48615	18A
48388	21A	48446	1E	48518	1A	48616	24H
48389	9A	48447	16C	48519	9D	48617	15A
48390	17A	48448	6C	48520	8B	48618	18A
48391	19C	48449	2B	48521	9G	48619	15C
48392	16B	48450	82B	48522	8C	48620	18B
48393	16B	48451	9D	48523	21B	48621	16C
48394	55E	48452	85C	48524	87K	48622	55B
48395	18A	48453	3A	48525	87K	48623	15C
48396	19C	48454	55A	48526	2B	48624	1A
48397	19C	48455	6C	48527	17E	48625	15A
48398	2B	48456	2B	48528	17E	48626	5B
48399	55A	48457	8A	48529	5B	48627	15A
48400	87K	48458	6B	48530	18A	48628	1A
48401	17B	48459	82B	48531	8B	48629	1A
48402	84C	48460	86G	48532	55D	48630	5B
48403	17A	48461	82B	48533	18D	48631	8C
48404	82B	48462	8D	48534	2E	48632	1A
48405	16C	48463	85C	48535	1E	48633	9A
48406	17E	48464	68A	48536	68A	48634	17E
48407	19C	48465	9D	48537	55B	48635	16A
48408	82B	48466	55D	48538	18A	48636	18A
48409	85C	48467	15B	48539	18D	48637	18A
48410	82B	48468	84G	48540	55D	48638	18A
48411	5B	48469	55D	48541	16C	48639	16A
48412	84C	48470	86G	48542	55D	48640	18D
48413	16B	48471	84C	48543	18A	48641	55B
48414	14A	48472	68A	48544	1E	48642	19A
48415	86G	48473	55D	48545	18D	48643	16C
48416	1A	48474	84G	48546	18D	48644	15A
48417	86G	48475	82B	48547	17B	48645	15B
48418	86G	48476	1A	48548	19C	48646	19C
48419	84C	48477	3A	48549	1E	48647	21A
48420	82B	48478	84G	48550	1E	48648	1A
48421	9D	48479	9D	48551	1A	48649	1A
48422	2E	48490	18A	48552	16B	48650	18B
48423	2E	48491	8B	48553	15A	48651	15A
48424	86G	48492	15A	48554	8D	48652	55B
48425	9A	48493	2E	48555	9G	48653	16A
48426	9G	48494	18B	48556	3A	48654	17D
48427	2A	48495	18B	48557	17E	48655	18A
48428	9A	48500	9A	48558	8D	48656	1A
48429	17E	48501	17E	48559	2A	48657	1A
48430	82B	48502	8C	48600	1A	48658	2B
48431	82B	48503	17E	48601	1A	48659	1A
48432	17D	48504	8C	48602	3A	48660	84G
48433	8A	48505	5B	48603	1A	48661	18B
48434	82B	48506	9G	48604	18D	48662	18A
48435	2B	48507	15C	48605	9G	48663	18D
48436	82B	48508	19C	48606	18A	48664	55D
48437	2A	48509	8A	48607	18A	48665	1A
48438	84G	48510	17A	48608	55D	48666	16A
48439	55D	48511	8C	48609	15B	48667	6F
48440	1A	48512	8A	48610	1A	48668	21A
48441	8B	48513	8A	48611	15B	48669	21A
48442	16C	48514	3A	48612	68A	48670	55D
48443	55B	48515	18D	48613	9G	48671	15A
48444	86G	48516	9A	48614	16A	48672	18A

48673	18A	48731	17E	48944	8C	49109	8C
48674	3A	48732	87K	48945	84G	49112	2B
48675	16A	48733	3A	48950	3A	49113	86G
48676	17E	48734	5B	48951	1E	49114	2A
48677	17E	48735	87K	48952	1E	49115	5C
48678	15A	48736	5B	48953	1E	49116	8D
48679	9D	48737	87K	48964	3A	49117	87K
48680	9A	48738	84G			49119	8B
48681	18A	48739	84G			49120	2B
48682	17E	48740	9D			49121	86K
48683	8B	48741	17F			49122	1A
48684	6C	48742	9G			49125	3A
48685	18A	48743	5B			49126	8D
48686	2B	48744	9A			49129	10A
48687	21A	48745	9D			49130	11A
48688	1E	48746	9D			49132	9D
48689	55D	48747	8C			49134	8C
48690	15B	48748	16A	49002	2B	49137	8A
48691	6C	48749	6B	49005	1E	49139	1A
48692	2E	48750	14A	49007	10A	49141	10B
48693	9G	48751	2B	49008	8B	49142	2B
48694	18A	48752	3A	49009	3A	49143	8C
48695	15A	48753	8D	49010	9B	49144	10A
48696	16A	48754	1E	49018	10A	49145	10A
48697	9G	48755	3A	49020	3C	49146	87K
48698	17F	48756	68A	49021	3A	49147	10C
48699	15A	48757	2A	49023	10A	49148	87K
48700	21A	48758	68A	49025	10A	49149	10C
48701	16C	48759	15B	49027	10C	49150	10B
48702	55E	48760	84G	49033	87K	49153	8C
48703	55B	48761	87K	49034	10C	49154	10A
48704	15B	48762	3A	49037	3B	49155	10A
48705	3A	48763	16A	49044	3B	49157	84G
48706	87K	48764	6C	49045	3D	49158	5C
48707	84G	48765	19A	49047	5C	49160	10A
48708	68A	48766	3A	49048	5C	49164	1A
48709	16A	48767	3A	49049	2A	49167	3B
48710	55D	48768	87K	49057	9D	49168	86G
48711	9G	48769	3A	49061	1E	49172	2B
48712	9D	48770	16B	49063	3D	49173	8A
48713	3A	48771	8D	49064	86K	49174	86G
48714	8B	48772	18A	49066	3C	49177	87K
48715	8B	48895	10A	49070	1A	49180	1A
48716	2B	48898	1E	49073	10A	49181	2B
48717	9G	48905	3C	49077	3A	49186	3D
48718	6C	48907	3C	49078	1A	49191	10B
48719	6C	48914	2A	49079	8D	49196	10B
48720	8D	48915	10A	49081	8D	49198	5C
48721	55B	48917	3C	49082	86K	49199	10C
48722	3A	48921	86K	49087	10C	49200	8A
48723	2B	48922	5C	49088	1A	49202	3A
48724	84G	48926	10C	49093	10A	49203	10A
48725	3A	48927	2B	49094	1E	49209	10C
48726	6C	48930	3A	49099	3A	49210	9D
48727	3A	48932	9D	49104	10B	49214	8C
48728	15C	48940	3B	49105	2E	49216	3A
48729	1A	48942	8C	49106	3A	49224	8A
48730	87K	48943	3C	49108	3C	49226	87K

49228	10A	49366	8D	49433	2A	50646	15D
49229	5C	49367	3A	49434	8A	50647	26C
49230	5B	49368	8C	49435	2A	50660	26C
49234	10C	49373	3C	49436	10A	50705	8B
49239	10D	49375	8A	49437	8A	50712	27C
49240	3B	49376	87K	49438	11A	50721	27C
49243	84G	49377	2C	49439	9A	50725	55G
49245	2A	49378	10A	49440	85C	50746	27C
49246	3A	49381	10A	49441	2D	50752	56E
49247	3B	49382	10B	49442	2D	50757	56F
49249	2A	49385	10A	49443	1E	50777	56E
49252	11A	49386	10C	49444	2F	50781	27C
49260	84G	49387	3C	49445	8A	50795	55F
49262	10D	49390	10B	49446	2F	50818	56E
49266	2C	49391	10B	49447	2F	50829	26C
49267	10A	49392	8A	49448	5B	50831	56F
49268	10A	49393	10A	49449	11A	50850	26C
49270	2E	49394	8A	49450	1E	50855	56F
49271	3C	49395	9D	49451	8C	50665	55G
49275	3D	49396	10B	49452	2A	50887	26C
49276	84G	49397	2A	49453	9B		
49277	1A	49398	8C	49454	5B		
49278	3D	49399	8A	49505	26E		
49281	10D	49400	10C	49508	26A		
49287	1E	49401	10A	49509	26E		
49288	10D	49402	10A	49511	26A		
49289	1E	49403	86G	49515	26A		
49293	2B	49404	8A	49536	26E		
49301	3C	49405	2A	49538	26C		
49304	2A	49406	8C	49544	26C	51202	22A
49306	10A	49407	5B	49545	27B	51204	8D
49308	3A	49408	10A	49547	27B	51206	27A
49310	1E	49409	86K	49560	26A	51207	26B
49311	10A	49410	5C	49566	27B	51212	22A
49313	3A	49411	2D	49578	26E	51217	17A
49314	2B	49412	8A	49582	27B	51218	5B
49315	10A	49413	2A	49586	27B	51221	6H
49318	10D	49414	2B	49592	56E	51222	53E
49321	2E	49415	2D	49598	27D	51227	27A
49323	8B	49416	8D	49618	26E	51229	27A
49327	3A	49417	2A	49624	26A	51230	26B
49328	3A	49418	9B	49627	26B	51231	27A
49330	1E	49419	8A	49637	27D	51232	27A
49335	10C	49420	8C	49640	27B	51234	27A
49340	10C	49421	10C	49648	26B	51235	50A
49342	2B	49422	86G	49662	26E	51237	27A
49343	8D	49423	8A	49667	26A	51241	26B
49344	1A	49424	84G	49668	26E	51244	53E
49345	84G	49425	2D	49674	26C	51246	27A
49348	9D	49426	10C			51253	27A
49350	2B	49427	8A			51307	26A
49352	10A	49428	9A			51316	10D
49355	8A	49429	8A			51319	10D
49357	2E	49430	2B			51321	24F
49358	87K	49431	2F	50636	55F	51336	26A
49361	3A	49432	2B	50643	8B	51338	26A
				50644	8B	51343	26A

51353	8A	52143	10A	52368	24C	53807	71G
51358	56D	52154	53E	52378	27B	53808	71G
51371	27A	52159	26A	52387	26D	53809	71G
51381	26A	52160	27B	52388	26E	53810	71G
51397	10D	52161	27C	52389	26C		
51404	56F	52162	6K	52393	10D		
51408	26C	52163	8C	52399	56E		
51412	CW	52171	27B	52400	56E		
51413	27B	52172	6K	52410	26E		
51415	24D	52175	8C	52411	56E		
51419	24F	52179	24B	52413	24D		
51423	24C	52182	24C	52415	24E		
51424	56D	52183	27C	52427	26E		
51429	HW	52186	56A	52429	10D		
51432	53E	52201	2B	52431	26A		
51441	10D	52207	CW	52432	8B	54439	60D
51444	CW	52212	CW	52438	8C	54441	66D
51445	8A	52216	24C	52441	CW	54452	64C
51446	CW	52217	56E	52443	26D	54453	66D
51453	56D	52218	CW	52445	24C	54458	60A
51457	26A	52225	8B	52449	10A	54461	64D
51458	26A	52230	6H	52452	56E	54462	66B
51474	24A	52232	8C	52455	26A	54463	60A
51481	26A	52235	56F	52456	24C	54464	66B
51486	39A	52236	56D	52458	24C	54465	66B
51486	26C	52237	26C	52459	CW	54466	60B
51496	26A	52240	24E	52461	26C	54467	63C
51497	24A	52244	53E	52464	CW	54468	66D
51498	24D	52248	26E	52466	24E	54469	63A
51499	26B	52252	53E	52501	11A	54470	60C
51506	24D	52260	24D	52510	12C	54471	60E
51512	39A	52268	26D	52515	56F	54472	60E
51524	24F	52269	6H	52517	CW	54473	60E
51526	24C	52270	26A	52521	56F	54474	65B
51537	27B	52271	26A	52523	24E	54475	65B
51544	27A	52275	26A	52526	24B	54476	63A
51546	27A	52278	26A	52527	24E	54477	64D
52044	56A	52289	26D			54478	64C
52089	56F	52290	24C			54479	66D
52093	CW	52293	26E			54480	60C
52094	26D	52305	53E			54482	60B
52095	24B	52311	27B			54483	65B
52108	26A	52312	CW			54484	60A
52119	6H	52319	53E			54485	63A
52120	56F	52322	10D			54486	63C
52121	56D	52328	26A			54487	60A
52123	27C	52338	10D			54488	60B
52125	10D	52341	26A			54489	63A
52129	26D	52345	CW			54490	64D
52133	56A	52348	26C	53800	71G	54491	60D
52135	27B	52350	26C	53801	71G	54492	68C
52136	27B	52351	56E	53802	71G	54493	60A
52139	56D	52355	56F	53803	71G	54494	63A
52140	8A	52356	6K	53804	71G	54495	60C
52141	26A	52360	26C	53805	71G	54496	60A
		52366	10D	53806	71G	54497	66D
						54498	66D
						54499	63A

54500	63A	55228	66A	56168	65G	56300	65D
54501	65B	55229	64C	56169	65B	56301	60E
54502	68B	55230	63C	56170	65G	56302	65D
54503	63A	55231	67C	56171	65D	56304	66A
54504	63B	55232	68D	56172	65E	56305	60A
54505	64D	55233	64C	56173	66D	56306	66A
54506	66D	55234	68D	56232	63B	56308	66A
54507	68B	55235	67A	56234	68C	56309	66C
54508	68C	55236	60C	56235	68A	56310	68B
		55237	66A	56236	67B	56311	67D
		55238	65F	56238	65G	56312	64C
		55239	66A	56239	66A	56313	64C
		55240	68C	56240	61B	56314	66A
55124	68B	55260	68D	56241	66B	56315	65G
55126	63B	55261	64D	56242	66C	56316	68A
55141	66A	55262	67C	56244	66A	56318	66A
55160	60A	55263	63D	56245	66B	56320	66C
55164	68B	55264	67B	56246	63A	56321	66C
55165	64C	55265	66A	56247	66B	56322	66A
55167	66A	55266	67A	56251	61B	56323	62B
55168	65B	55267	66D	56252	65B	56324	66A
55169	66A	55268	66A	56253	64C	56325	62B
55173	60B	55269	67A	56254	63B	56326	61B
55176	63B			56255	66C	56327	68B
55178	60E			56256	66C	56328	63A
55182	66C			56259	67D	56329	67A
55185	61C			56260	66A	56330	67C
55189	66A			56262	60A	56331	63A
55195	63B			56264	66B	56332	68A
55198	63C			56265	66B	56333	68A
55199	60A	56011	60A	56266	66A	56334	66B
55200	63C	56025	RW	56267	67A	56335	66B
55201	66A	56027	CW	56269	66B	56336	65F
55202	64C	56028	66D	56272	67C	56337	66B
55203	67B	56029	65D	56274	67C	56338	66B
55204	63B	56030	65G	56275	65D	56340	68A
55206	67A	56031	66D	56277	66B	56341	60A
55207	66A	56032	CW	56278	61B	56343	63B
55208	63D	56035	64A	56279	67D	56344	65D
55209	63A	56038	60A	56280	66A	56345	66B
55210	64C	56039	65G	56281	63B	56346	66A
55211	67B	56151	65B	56282	67D	56347	63A
55212	63A	56152	65A	56283	64C	56348	61B
55213	63A	56153	66A	55284	66C	56349	66A
55214	65F	56154	66A	56285	66B	56350	67A
55215	63D	56155	66A	56286	66C	56352	63A
55216	60A	56156	66D	56287	66C	56353	63A
55217	62A	56157	66D	56288	66D	56354	66B
55218	63A	56158	65G	56289	65B	56356	66B
55219	67A	56159	66A	56290	63C	56357	66B
55220	63D	56160	66A	56291	60A	56359	63A
55221	61C	56161	65G	56292	66A	56360	66C
55222	63B	56162	66A	56293	60A	56361	67A
55223	66A	56163	66D	56294	66C	56362	66C
55224	66A	56164	65F	56295	66A	56363	67C
55225	67A	56165	66D	56296	66C	56364	67A
55226	63A	56166	66D	56297	65G	56365	63B
55227	62B	56167	65D	56298	66A	56367	66B

56368	67B	57288	66A	57385	64D	57569	67C
56369	67A	57291	66B	57386	64D	57570	67B
56370	65B	57292	66A	57389	66A	57571	67B
56371	66C	57295	67C	57392	67C	57572	67B
56372	68C	57296	65D	57396	63B	57573	67B
56373	63A	57299	66B	57398	66C	57575	67A
56374	68A	57300	67A	57404	66B	57576	64C
56375	63B	57302	68B	57405	66B	57577	67D
56376	65F	57303	66B	57407	66C	57579	67A
		57307	66C	57411	65B	57580	67A
		57309	67D	57413	66C	57581	66A
		57311	65B	57414	66B	57582	66B
		57314	65D	57416	66B	57583	64D
		57317	66A	57417	66B	57585	60D
57232	63B	57319	66A	57418	66B	57586	60B
57233	63B	57321	66A	57419	66B	57587	60C
57236	67B	57324	63B	57424	63C	57588	66B
57237	66B	57325	66B	57426	65B	57590	67D
57238	68C	57326	66B	57429	65D	57591	61C
57239	66A	57328	66B	57430	66C	57592	65D
57240	65B	57329	68B	57431	66C	57593	66B
57241	67A	57331	67B	57432	66A	57594	67A
57242	66C	57335	66C	57434	65B	57595	66B
57243	63B	57336	65D	57435	66B	57596	67A
57244	66C	57338	65F	57436	66B	57597	60A
57245	65D	57339	63B	57437	66B	57599	66B
57246	63B	57340	68C	57441	63B	57600	68B
57247	66B	57341	65D	57443	66A	57601	68B
57249	67A	57345	63A	57444	66A	57602	68B
57250	66C	57346	65D	57445	68C	57603	66A
57251	65B	57347	66A	57446	66A	57604	64D
57252	63B	57348	67D	57447	66A	57605	65D
57253	65B	57349	68B	57448	66A	57607	65D
57254	67D	57350	65B	57451	64D	57608	64D
57256	66B	57353	67B	57461	66B	57609	66C
57257	63B	57354	67C	57462	66B	57611	67C
57258	65B	57355	67D	57463	66A	57612	65D
57259	65G	57356	67D	57465	66A	57613	64D
57261	65B	57357	67D	57470	65D	57614	67C
57262	67C	57359	67A	57472	65D	57615	67C
57263	67D	57360	66A	57473	63A	57617	65B
57264	63B	57361	66A	57550	64C	57618	64D
57265	65F	57362	68B	57552	66D	57619	66A
57266	67D	57363	66B	57553	66A	57620	60E
57267	66B	57364	67C	57554	65D	57621	68B
57268	66A	57365	66A	57555	66A	57622	66A
57269	65B	57366	65F	57556	66D	57623	68B
57270	66B	57367	66A	57557	65B	57625	66A
57271	66A	57368	63C	57558	65B	57626	64D
57273	65D	57369	66A	57559	66C	57627	67D
57274	67D	57370	66A	57560	67A	57628	67C
57275	66A	57373	65B	57562	67A	57630	66C
57276	63D	57375	68C	57563	66A	57631	65B
57278	66B	57377	66B	57564	66A	57632	60B
57279	67C	57378	68B	57565	64C	57633	67C
57284	67C	57383	67B	57566	67A	57634	61C
57285	65F	57384	66C	57568	68D	57635	64D
57297	65F						

57637	67B	58130	17B	58228	17D	60026 * 34A
57638	66B	58131	14B	58238	19C	60027 * 64B
57640	67C	58132	17A	58246	17A	60028 * 34A
57642	60A	58135	3A	58247	17C	60029 * 34A
57643	67B	58136	55B	58260	55D	60030 * 35B
57644	67C	58137	16A	58261	21A	60031 * 64B
57645	64C	58138	21B	58271	5B	60032 * 34A
57650	67B	58140	19A	58279	10C	60033 * 34A
57651	67B	58143	21B	58281	2B	60034 * 34A
57652	65D	58144	17A	58283	3C	60035 * 64B
57653	68A	58146	18A	58287	11B	60036 * 50B
57654	64C	58148	17B	58288	3D	60037 * 64B
57655	64D	58153	18A	58291	11B	60038 * 52A
57658	67C	58157	2A	58293	11B	60039 * 34A
57659	66B	58158	17A	58295	3D	60040 * 52A
57661	60A	58160	17B	58298	15C	60041 * 64B
57663	66C	58163	17C	58305	15C	60042 * 51A
57665	66C	58165	18A	58308	2A	60043 * 64B
57666	66B	58166	18A	58850	17D	60044 * 34A
57667	63D	58167	21B	58856	17D	60045 * 52A
57668	66B	58168	21A	58857	2A	60046 * 36A
57669	67D	58169	3C	58859	1D	60047 * 35B
57670	64D	58170	19C	58860	17D	60048 * 36A
57671	67B	58171	18A	58926	84G	60049 * 38C
57672	67B	58173	18A			60050 * 35B
57673	67D	58174	3C			60051 * 56C
57674	66A	58175	16A			60052 * 56C
57679	64C	58177	11B			60053 * 56C
57681	66B	58178	3E			60054 * 34A
57682	66D	58181	2A			60055 * 34A
57684	67C	58182	3D			60056 * 35B
57686	65B	58183	3B			60057 * 64B
57688	67B	58185	3E	60001 * 52A	60058 * 56C
57689	67F	58186	17B	60002 * 52A	60059 * 34A
57690	66D	58187	11B	60003 * 35B	60060 * 52A
57691	65F	58189	17D	60004 * 64B	60061 * 35B
		58190	19A	60005 * 52A	60062 * 34A
		58191	55D	60006 * 34A	60063 * 35B
		58192	19A	60007 * 34A	60064 * 36A
		58196	5B	60008 * 35B	60065 * 35B
		58197	55D	60009 * 64B	60066 * 36A
		58198	19C	60010 * 35B	60067 * 36A
58065	36E	58199	11B	60011 * 64B	60068 * 68E
58066	55D	58203	3C	60012 * 64B	60069 * 52B
58083	9D	58204	3B	60013 * 34A	60070 * 52A
58085	36E	58206	22B	60014 * 34A	60071 * 51A
58086	71J	58209	17C	60015 * 34A	60072 * 52B
58114	19C	58213	84G	60016 * 52A	60073 * 52B
58115	11B	58214	15B	60017 * 34A	60074 * 50B
58116	11B	58215	15D	60018 * 52A	60075 * 52A
58118	2B	58216	36A	60019 * 52A	60076 * 52A
58119	3B	58217	11B	60020 * 52B	60077 * 52B
58120	11B	58218	2A	60021 * 34A	60078 * 52A
58121	11B	58219	17A	60022 * 34A	60079 * 68E
58122	3C	58220	3E	60023 * 52A	60080 * 52B
58123	11B	58221	11B	60024 * 64B	60081 * 50B
58124	3E	58225	19A	60025 * 34A	60082 * 52B
58128	17B				60083 * 52B

60084 * 50B	60142 * 52A	60537 * 64B	60854 35A
60085 * 52B	60143 * 52A	60538 * 52A	60855 34A
60086 * 50B	60144 * 35B	60539 * 52B	60856 50A
60087 * 64B	60145 * 52A	60700 36A	60857 36A
60088 * 52B	60146 * 50A	60800 * 34A	60858 31B
60089 * 64B	60147 * 52A	60801 52B	60859 56C
60090 * 64B	60148 * 56C	60802 52B	60860 * 52D
60091 * 52B	60149 * 34A	60803 31B	60861 56B
60092 * 52B	60150 * 52A	60804 62B	60862 34A
60093 * 68E	60151 * 52A	60805 52D	60863 38C
60094 * 64B	60152 * 64B	60806 52B	60864 50A
60095 * 68E	60153 * 50A	60807 52A	60865 56C
60096 * 64B	60154 * 52A	60808 52D	60866 35A
60097 * 64B	60155 * 52A	60809 * 52B	60867 35A
60098 * 64B	60156 * 34A	60810 52B	60868 52A
60099 * 64B	60157 * 34A	60811 52B	60869 35A
60100 * 64B	60158 * 35B	60312 52B	60870 36A
60101 * 64B	60159 * 64B	60813 64A	60871 34A
60102 * 38C	60160 * 64B	60814 34A	60872 * 36A
60103 * 34A	60161 * 64B	60815 38E	60873 * 64A
60104 * 38C	60162 * 64B	60816 64B	60874 35A
60105 * 35B	60500 * 35A	60817 36A	60875 35A
60106 * 38C	60501 * 50A	60818 64A	60876 34A
60107 * 38C	60502 * 50A	60819 61B	60877 34A
60108 * 34A	60503 * 50A	60820 34E	60878 38C
60109 * 36A	60504 * 35A	60821 35A	60879 38E
60110 * 35B	60505 * 35A	60822 62B	60880 36A
60111 * 38C	60506 * 35A	60823 64A	60881 36A
60112 * 36A	60507 * 64B	60824 61B	60882 64A
60113 * 35B	60508 * 35A	60825 64A	60883 64A
60114 * 35B	60509 * 64B	60826 35A	60884 56B
60115 * 52A	60510 * 64B	60827 61B	60885 56C
60116 * 52B	60511 * 52B	60828 34A	60886 52B
60117 * 56C	60512 * 50A	60829 35A	60887 52A
60118 * 56C	60513 * 35A	60830 31B	60888 61B
60119 * 35B	60514 * 35A	60831 38E	60889 36A
60120 * 56C	60515 * 50A	60832 35A	60890 38E
60121 * 50A	60516 * 52A	60833 52A	60891 52B
60122 * 35B	60517 * 52B	60834 62B	60892 64A
60123 * 56B	60518 * 52A	60835 * 52B	60893 35A
60124 * 52A	60519 * 64B	60836 64A	60894 64A
60125 * 35B	60520 * 35A	60837 50A	60895 50A
60126 * 52B	60521 * 52A	60838 62B	60896 36A
60127 * 52B	60522 * 50A	60839 50A	60897 35A
60128 * 35B	60523 * 35A	60840 64A	60898 61B
60129 * 52A	60524 * 50A	60841 36A	60899 31B
60130 * 56B	60525 * 61B	60842 35A	60900 64A
60131 * 56C	60526 * 50A	60843 50A	60901 52B
60132 * 52A	60527 * 62B	60844 62B	60902 34A
60133 * 56C	60528 * 62B	60845 35A	60903 34A
60134 * 56C	60529 * 64B	60846 56B	60904 50A
60135 * 52A	60530 * 64B	60847 * 50A	60905 36A
60136 * 34A	60531 * 61B	60848 52A	60906 35A
60137 * 52A	60532 * 61B	60849 36A	60907 50A
60138 * 50B	60533 * 35A	60850 35A	60908 35A
60139 * 34A	60534 * 64B	60851 61B	60909 36A
60140 * 50A	60535 * 64B	60852 36A	60910 52B
60141 * 56C	60536 * 64B	60853 35A	60911 35A

60912	35A	60970	61B	61042	32A	61101	62C
60913	56C	60971	62B	61043	32A	61102	62B
60914	34A	60972	61B	61044	41A	61103	62A
60915	38E	60973	61B	61045	32A	61104	30A
60916	56B	60974	50A	61046	32A	61105	34D
60917	36A	60975	50A	61047	35C	61106	38A
60918	50A	60976	50A	61048	32A	61107	36A
60919	61B	60977	50A	61049	51A	61108	64A
60920	62B	60978	52B	61050	41A	61109	30A
60921	36A	60979	52B	61051	41A	61110	56B
60922	52B	60980	64A	61052	32B	61111	30A
60923	52A	60981	50A	61053	50A	61112	36B
60924	35A	60982	50A	61054	32B	61113	35A
60925	50A	60983	34A	61055	32B	61114	36A
60926	52D			61056	38A	61115	50A
60927	64B			61057	32A	61116	34E
60928	36A	61000 *	30E	61058	32B	61117	65C
60929	50A	61001 *	32B	61059	32B	61118	62A
60930	36A	61002 *	50A	61060	35B	61119	30A
60931	62B	61003 *	30F	61061	51A	61120	36A
60932	52D	61004 *	30F	61062	50B	61121	36A
60933	64A	61005 *	35C	61063	38C	61122	36A
60934	50A	61006 *	35C	61064	68E	61123	56B
60935	36A	61007 *	64B	61065	50B	61124	36A
60936	35A	61008 *	38C	61066	38A	61125	36A
60937	62B	61009 *	41A	61067	65C	61126	36E
60938	31B	61010 *	53B	61068	53B	61127	36A
60939	52B	61011 *	56B	61069	50B	61128	36A
60940	52A	61012 *	52A	61070	35A	61129	56C
60941	50A	61013 *	56B	61071	50A	61130	40B
60942	52B	61014 *	52D	61072	62A	61131	56B
60943	34A	61015 *	51A	61073	35A	61132	62B
60944	52B	61016 *	50A	61074	35B	61133	62A
60945	52B	61017 *	50A	61075	34A	61134	62A
60946	50A	61018 *	51E	61076	64B	61135	30F
60947	52A	61019 *	52C	61077	34E	61136	34E
60948	31B	61020 *	51A	61078	38E	61137	36A
60949	52A	61021 *	51A	61079	40B	61138	41A
60950	34A	61022 *	52A	61080	53A	61139	34A
60951	64B	61023 *	51A	61081	64B	61140	65A
60952	52B	61024 *	51A	61082	40B	61141	38A
60953	64A	61025 *	52D	61093	35C	61142	40B
60954	50A	61026 *	36A	61084	50A	61143	40A
60955	61B	61027 *	34D	61085	40A	61144	40B
60956	36A	61028 *	34E	61086	50B	61145	36A
60957	64B	61029 *	64A	61087	36A	61146	62A
60958	62B	61030 *	51E	61088	38A	61147	62A
60959	64B	61031 *	56G	61089	30E	61148	62A
60960	50A	61032 *	51E	61090	34D	61149	30F
60961	50A	61033 *	41A	61091	34D	61150	41A
60962	52B	61034 *	51E	61092	38A	61151	41A
60963	50A	61035 *	50B	61093	34D	61152	41A
60964	52A	61036 *	36A	61094	34D	61153	41A
60965	64A	61037 *	51E	61095	35C	61154	41A
60966	35A	61038 *	50A	61096	41A	61155	36A
60967	52A	61039 *	51A	61097	34D	61156	41A
60968	50A	61040 *	51A	61098	40B	61157	36A
60969	62B	61041	41A	61099	64A	61158	36A
				61100	52C		

61159	40B	61217	68E	61275	51C	61333	61A
61160	38A	61218	50B	61276	51A	61334	41A
61161	39A	61219	68E	61277	65A	61335	30A
61162	36A	61220	51E	61278	62B	61336	30E
61163	38A	61221 *	64B	61279	30A	61337	50A
61164	30A	61222	68E	61280	30A	61338	51A
61165	36B	61223	32A	61281	40B	61339	50A
61166	36B	61224	51A	61282	35A	61340	65A
61167	36B	61225	36A	61283	34A	61341	64A
61168	40B	61226	30F	61284	40B	61342	65A
61169	41A	61227	30F	61285	36A	61343	61A
61170	36A	61228	32B	61286	31A	61344	65A
61171	36A	61229	56G	61287	31A	61345	61A
61172	62B	61230	56G	61288	50A	61346	61A
61173	51E	61231	36E	61289	53B	61347	61A
61174	41A	61232	30F	61290	68E	61348	35C
61175	40B	61233	30A	61291	51A	61349	61A
61176	51A	61234	30A	61292	62B	61350	61A
61177	38A	61235	30A	61293	62B	61351	61A
61178	64B	61236	30A	61294	61A	61352	61A
61179	41A	61237 *	50B	61295	56B	61353	51A
61180	62B	61238 *	52C	61296	56G	61354	64A
61181	41A	61239	68E	61297	56B	61355	64B
61182	30A	61240 *	50B	61298	38C	61356	64A
61183	41A	61241 *	52D	61299	38C	61357	64A
61184	64A	61242 *	61A	61300	31A	61358	64A
61185	38A	61243 *	65A	61301	31A	61359	64A
61186	38A	61244 *	64B	61302	35A	61360	30E
61187	34E	61245 *	64B	61303	51E	61361	30E
61188	38A	61246 *	64C	61304	53B	61362	30A
61189 *	56B	61247 *	36A	61305	53B	61363	30E
61190	40B	61248 *	40A	61306	53B	61364	34A
61191	64A	61249 *	30A	61307	61A	61365	36A
61192	38E	61250 *	36A	61308	61A	61366	40B
61193	36A	61251 *	34D	61309	56C	61367	34A
61194	36B	61252	32B	61310	56B	61368	38E
61195	40B	61253	32B	61311	30A	61369	38C
61196	36A	61254	32B	61312	32A	61370	30E
61197	65A	61255	51A	61313	41A	61371	31A
61198	51A	61256	50B	61314	41A	61372	30A
61199	52D	61257	50B	61315	41A	61373	30E
61200	34A	61258	40A	61316	41A	61374	40B
61201	38A	61259	50B	61317	32A	61375	30A
61202	40A	61260	64A	61318	40B	61376	38C
61203	34A	61261	64A	61319	54C	61377	36A
61204	35A	61262	62A	61320	56G	61378	30A
61205	35A	61263	62B	61321	54C	61379 *	40B
61206	34E	61264	30F	61322	52D	61380	38C
61207	35A	61265	39A	61323	35C	61381	38C
61208	36E	61266	36A	61324	61A	61382	56B
61209	38A	61267	56G	61325	40B	61383	56B
61210	35A	61268	56G	61326	36A	61384	30F
61211	36E	61269	38C	61327	41A	61385	56B
61212	36E	61270	32A	61328	40B	61386	56C
61213	36E	61271	38A	61329	30A	61387	56C
61214	56C	61272	38B	61330	64A	61388	56C
61215 *	53B	61273	51A	61331	34A	61389	35A
61216	50B	61274	51A	61332	64A	61390	40B

61391	35A	61447	50B	61572	32B	61653 *	31A
61392	35A	61448	50A	61573	31A	61654 *	30A
61393	34A	61449	50A	61575	31C	61655 *	30A
61394	34E	61450	50A	61576	31A	61656 *	32D
61395	68E	61451	52B	61577	32B	61657 *	31B
61396	65A	61452	50A	61580	31A	61658 *	30E
61397	64A	61453	50A	61600 *	31A	61659 *	32D
61398	64A	61454	50A	61601 *	31A	61660 *	30A
61399	30A	61455	50A	61602 *	32D	61661 *	30A
61400	61A	61456	52B	61603 *	31A	61662 *	30E
61401	62A	61457	50A	61605 *	30A	61663 *	30A
61402	62B	61458	52B	61606 *	30A	61664 *	32D
61403	62A	61459	50A	61607 *	31A	61665 *	32D
61404	64B	61460	50A	61608 *	30A	61666 *	30E
61405	40A	61461	50A	61609 *	30A	61667 *	30E
61406	40B	61462	50A	61610 *	30A	61668 *	30A
61407	62C	61463	50A	61611 *	32B	61669 *	32B
61408	40B	61464	50A	61612 *	30A	61670 *	32D
61409	40B	61465	50A	61613 *	30A	61671 *	31A
61410	52B	61466	50A	61614 *	31A	61672 *	30A
61411	50B	61467	50A	61615 *	31A	61701	61B
61412	50B	61468	50A	61616 *	31A	61721	62C
61413	52B	61469	52B	61617 *	31A	61723	38A
61414	50B	61470	50B	61618 *	32B	61724	41A
61415	50B	61471	50B	61619 *	31B	61725	40F
61416	50A	61472	50A	61620 *	31B	61726	38A
61417	50A	61473	50A	61621 *	31B	61728	41A
61418	50A	61474	50C	61622 *	32D	61729	38A
61419	50A	61475	50A	61623 *	31A	61730	40B
61420	50A	61476	50A	61625 *	32B	61731	40F
61421	50A	61477	50A	61626 *	31B	61733	65C
61422	50A	61478	50D	61627 *	31B	61736	40B
61423	50A	61514	32A	61629 *	32B	61738	38A
61424	50A	61516	31C	61630 *	30A	61739	41A
61425	50B	61519	32A	61631 *	32B	61740	40B
61426	50A	61520	32A	61632 *	31A	61741	61A
61427	50B	61530	32F	61633 *	31B	61742	40F
61428	50B	61533	32B	61634 *	31A	61743	40F
61429	50B	61535	32B	61635 *	31B	61745	40F
61430	50A	61540	32F	61636 *	31A	61746	40A
61431	50B	61542	32A	61637 *	32B	61747	41A
61432	50B	61546	31A	61638 *	31B	61748	40F
61433	50C	61547	32A	61639 *	31A	61749	41A
61434	50A	61549	31A	61640 *	31A	61750	40F
61435	50A	61553	31A	61641 *	31B	61751	40A
61436	50A	61554	31A	61642 *	31A	61752	38A
61437	50A	61555	31A	61643 *	31B	61753	38A
61438	50A	61556	32A	61644 *	31A	61754	38A
61439	50A	61558	31C	61645 *	31B	61755	61C
61440	52B	61561	32B	61646 *	31A	61756	40F
61441	50B	61564	32B	61647 *	32B	61757	40F
61442	50B	61566	32B	61648 *	30A	61758	62C
61443	50A	61567	31A	61649 *	32B	61759	40A
61444	50A	61568	32A	61650 *	30E	61760	41A
61445	50E	61570	32B	61651 *	30E	61761	41A
61446	50B	61571	32B	61652 *	31A	61762	40F

61763	38A	61824	38A	61880	30A	61936	68E
61764 *	65A	61825	40B	61881	64A	61937	68E
61765	40F	61826	31B	61882	68E	61938	41A
61766	40F	61827	31B	61883	53A	61939	32A
61767	40F	61828	40A	61884	53A	61940	36A
61768	38A	61829	36A	61885	64A	61941	53A
61769	65C	61830	35A	61886	31B	61942	30A
61770	62C	61831	31B	61887	36A	61943	40F
61771	38A	61832	39A	61888	38A	61944	40A
61772 *	65C	61833	38A	61889	40A	61945	53A
61773	38A	61834	30A	61890	31B	61946	31B
61774 *	65A	61835	31B	61891	40B	61947	38A
61775 *	65A	61836	40B	61892	53A	61948	31B
61776	65A	61837	40B	61893	53A	61949	32C
61777	38A	61838	38A	61894	40A	61950	40B
61778	40A	61839	40B	61895	36A	61951	30A
61779	61C	61840	30A	61896	38A	61952	52D
61780	38A	61841	38E	61897	53A	61953	32A
61781 *	65A	61842	38E	61898	68E	61954	41A
61782 *	61C	61843	38E	61899	53A	61955	64A
61783 *	61C	61844	52B	61900	64A	61956	40B
61784	65A	61845	31B	61901	52D	61957	32A
61785	65A	61846	53A	61902	53A	61958	32C
61786	65A	61847	53A	61903	53A	61959	32C
61787 *	65A	61848	40A	61904	53A	61960	40A
61788 *	65A	61849	30A	61905	40B	61961	36A
61789 *	65A	61850	36B	61906	52B	61962	52D
61790 *	61A	61851	68E	61907	41A	61963	30A
61791 *	65J	61852	40B	61908	32A	61964	40A
61792	61C	61853	38E	61909	64A	61965	53A
61793	61C	61854	53A	61910	39A	61966	39A
61794 *	65A	61855	64A	61911	64A	61967	41A
61800	40B	61856	38B	61912	40B	61968	64A
61801	31B	61857	53A	61913	39A	61969	52D
61802	40A	61858	68E	61914	38A	61970	32A
61803	40B	61859	40A	61915	31B	61971	32A
61804	38A	61860	31B	61916	68E	61972	31B
61805	35A	61861	31B	61917	52D	61973	32C
61806	40B	61862	30A	61918	32A	61974	38A
61807	40A	61863	30A	61919	40A	61975	38B
61808	39A	61864	35A	61920	53A	61976	31B
61809	38A	61865	39A	61921	30A	61977	30A
61810	30A	61866	38E	61922	53A	61978	35A
61811	31B	61867	36B	61923	53A	61979	35A
61812	36A	61868	36B	61924	64A	61980	38B
61813	53A	61869	52B	61925	40A	61981	32A
61814	53A	61870	38A	61926	32C	61982	38A
61815	30A	61871	53A	61927	52B	61983	64A
61816	31B	61872	53A	61928	64A	61984	52B
61817	30A	61873	38A	61929	31B	61985	52D
61818	52B	61974	53A	61930	52D	61986	52B
61819	53A	61875	52B	61931	64A	61987	52B
61820	30A	61876	64A	61932	53A	61988	64A
61821	38A	61877	32A	61933	64A	61989	32A
61822	31B	61878	64A	61934	53A	61990	64A
61823	64A	61879	64A	61935	53A	61991	64A

61992	64A	62046	50A	62441 *	62C	62555	32A
61993 *	65A	62047	50A	62442 *	62A	62561	32G
61994 *	65A	62048	50A	62467 *	62A	62562	31B
61995 *	65A	62049	50A	62468 *	62A	62564	40A
61996 *	65A	62050	50A	62469 *	61C	62566	31E
61997 *	65J	62051	31B	62470 *	63A	62568	40A
61998 *	65A	62052	65J	62471 *	64A	62570	31A
62001	51A	62053	31B	62472 *	65A	62571	40A
62002	52C	62054	31B	62474 *	65A	62572	31B
62003	51A	62055	31B	62475 *	62A	62575	31C
62004	51A	62056	50A	62477 *	65A	62576	31E
62005	51A	62057	50A	62478 *	62A	62578	32G
62006	52C	62058	51G	62479 *	61A	62580	32E
62007	51A	62059	51G	62480 *	61A	62582	31C
62008	51A	62060	51E	62482 *	61A	62584	31C
62009	51A	62061	50A	62483 *	64A	62586	32E
62010	52C	62062	50A	62484 *	63A	62588	31E
62011	65J	62063	50A	62485 *	62B	62589	31B
62012	65J	62064	51E	62487 *	64A	62592	31C
62013	31B	62065	51E	62488 *	64A	62593	32A
62014	31B	62066	31B	62489 *	61A	62596	32A
62015	31B	62067	31B	62490 *	64A	62597	32G
62016	31B	62068	31B	62492 *	62A	62599	40A
62017	31B	62069	31B	62493 *	61A	62604	32D
62018	31B	62070	31B	62494 *	64A	62605	31B
62019	31B	62277 *	61C	62495 *	64F	62606	31C
62020	31B	62375	52D	62496 *	65A	62610	31A
62021	52C	62381	53B	62497 *	61A	62612	32B
62022	52C	62387	50C	62498 *	61A	62613	32E
62023	52C	62395	50A	62510	31C	62614	31C
62024	52C	62396	53B	62511	32E	62615	31E
62025	52C	62418 *	62A	62513	31E	62617	32G
62026	52C	62419 *	62A	62515	32G	62618	31A
62027	52C	62420 *	64G	62516	31C	62619	32A
62028	52C	62421 *	64A	62517	32F	62660 *	41A
62029	52C	62422 *	64G	62518	31C	62661 *	9G
62030	52C	62423 *	64G	62521	31A	62662 *	9G
62031	65J	62424 *	64A	62522	31C	62663 *	41A
62032	31B	62425 *	64G	62524	32E	62664 *	9G
62033	31B	62426 *	63B	62526	31B	62665 *	9G
62034	65J	62427 *	62C	62529	31B	62666 *	41A
62035	31B	62428 *	64G	62530	31A	62667 *	41A
62036	31B	62429 *	62A	62533	32G	62668 *	17F
62037	31B	62431 *	62A	62534	31A	62669 *	9G
62038	31B	62432 *	64G	62535	40A	62670 *	41A
62039	31B	62434 *	62B	62539	31A	62671 *	65A
62040	31B	62435 *	64G	62540	32A	62672 *	65A
62041	51E	62436 *	62C	62543	31E	62673 *	65A
62042	51E	62437 *	64A	62544	32D	62674 *	65A
62043	51E	62438 *	62B	62545	31A	62675 *	65A
62044	51J	62439 *	64F	62546 *	32D	62676 *	65A
62045	51A	62440 *	64G	62548	31B	62677 *	64B
						62678 *	64B

70

62679 * 64B	62742 * 50B	63357 54D	63415 51C
62680 * 65A	62743 * 64B	63358 54C	63416 51G
62681 * 65A	62744 * 62A	63359 54D	63417 51D
62682 * 65A	62745 * 50A	63360 51B	63418 54D
62683 * 64B	62746 * 50D	63361 54D	63419 51C
62684 * 65A	62747 * 50A	63362 54B	63420 51D
62685 * 64B	62748 * 50B	63363 52C	63421 51C
62686 * 65A	62749 * 50B	63364 51D	63422 51C
62687 * 65A	62750 * 53D	63365 54D	63423 50C
62688 * 65A	62751 * 50E	63366 54D	63424 51D
62689 * 65A	62752 * 50D	63367 51G	63425 50C
62690 * 64B	62753 * 50D	63368 51D	63426 51B
62691 * 64B	62754 * 53B	63369 51D	63427 54D
62692 * 64B	62755 * 50C	63370 51B	63428 52F
62693 * 64B	62756 * 50E	63371 51B	63429 50C
62694 * 64B	62757 * 53B	63372 54D	63430 51B
62700 * 53D	62758 * 50D	63373 51D	63431 54C
62701 * 53D	62759 * 50D	63374 51G	63432 52C
62702 * 50A	62760 * 50A	63375 51D	63433 54D
62703 * 53D	62761 * 50C	63376 52C	63434 54C
62704 * 62A	62762 * 50D	63377 54C	63435 51D
62705 * 64B	62763 * 50D	63378 50C	63436 50B
62706 * 64B	62764 * 50B	63379 54D	63437 54B
62707 * 53D	62765 * 50D	63380 52C	63438 51C
62708 * 62A	62766 * 53B	63381 52C	63439 54D
62709 * 64B	62767 * 53B	63382 50C	63440 50C
62710 * 53B	62769 * 50E	63383 51C	63441 52C
62711 * 64A	62770 * 50E	63384 54C	63442 51D
62712 * 64A	62771 * 50A	63385 52C	63443 51G
62713 * 62A	62772 * 50C	63386 54C	63444 54C
62714 * 63B	62773 * 50D	63387 54B	63445 51B
62715 * 64A	62774 * 50D	63388 51B	63446 51G
62716 * 62A	62775 * 50C	63389 51B	63447 51B
62717 * 53B	62785 31A	63390 52C	63448 50C
62718 * 64A	62788 31A	63391 52F	63449 50C
62719 * 64B	62789 31A	63392 51C	63450 50C
62720 * 53B	62796 31A	63393 51D	63451 50C
62721 * 64A	62797 32C	63394 52C	63452 51D
62722 * 53B		63395 50C	63453 54B
62723 * 53B		63396 51C	63454 51C
62724 * 53B		63397 51C	63455 54D
62725 * 63B	63340 51D	63398 52F	63456 54C
62726 * 50E	63341 51G	63399 51C	63457 51C
62727 * 50D	63342 54C	63400 54C	63458 54C
62728 * 62A	63343 51G	63401 51D	63459 51F
62729 * 62A	63344 51G	63402 54C	63460 54B
62730 * 50A	63345 51G	63403 52F	63461 52C
62731 * 50A	63346 54C	63404 54D	63462 52C
62732 * 68E	63347 51G	63405 51D	63463 54B
62733 * 64B	63348 50B	63406 50C	63464 52C
62734 * 63E	63349 51D	63407 51G	63465 54B
62735 * 50E	63350 54C	63408 51D	63466 54A
62736 * 50D	63351 51F	63409 51D	63467 54A
62737 * 53B	63352 54B	63410 51D	63468 52C
62738 * 50D	63353 52F	63411 51D	63469 54B
62739 * 50E	63354 54C	63412 52C	63470 52C
62740 * 50B	63355 51D	63413 52C	63471 52C
62741 * 53B	63356 52C	63414 51C	63472 52C

63473	54B	63628	36B	63686	39A	63744	36C
63474	54A	63629	41A	63687	31B	63745	36B
63570	56B	63630	31B	63688	36E	63746	31B
63571	31B	63631	39A	63689	38B	63747	36C
63572	36C	63632	40E	63690	36C	63748	41A
63573	39A	63633	56B	63691	40D	63749	38D
63574	41A	63634	40E	63692	40B	63750	40B
63575	39A	63635	40D	63693	36B	63751	36B
63576	36C	63636	40E	63694	38A	63752	38B
63577	40E	63637	36E	63695	41A	63753	36B
63578	38B	63638	38A	63696	36C	63754	38A
63579	38B	63639	39A	63697	36D	63755	54B
63581	41A	63640	41A	63698	36B	63756	36B
63582	39A	63641	39A	63699	38A	63757	36B
63583	41A	63642	36C	63700	39A	63758	40D
63584	56B	63643	40D	63701	36B	63759	40B
63585	40E	63644	40B	63702	38D	63760	54B
63586	36B	63645	41A	63703	40E	63761	36C
63587	38A	63646	31B	63704	36D	63762	38D
63588	36B	63647	38A	63705	38D	63763	36D
63589	38B	63648	38D	63706	38D	63764	36B
63590	31B	63649	39A	63707	40E	63765	40E
63591	38B	63650	31B	63708	40B	63766	39A
63592	38B	63651	40B	63709	39A	63767	39A
63593	36B	63652	31B	63710	41A	63768	38B
63594	38B	63653	36C	63711	38B	63769	36A
63595	36C	63654	36E	63712	54B	63770	40B
63596	31B	63655	36E	63713	39A	63771	41A
63597	40D	63656	36D	63714	41A	63772	38D
63598	39A	63657	38A	63715	40E	63773	31B
63599	41A	63658	41A	63716	39A	63774	36B
63600	39A	63659	36D	63717	40E	63775	39A
63601	36C	63660	36C	63718	36D	63776	40E
63602	38A	63661	41A	63719	39A	63777	38B
63603	39A	63662	36C	63720	38D	63779	36B
63604	41A	63663	31B	63721	39A	63780	31B
63605	56B	63664	40E	63722	40D	63781	36B
63606	36C	63665	40D	63723	36B	63782	36E
63607	40D	63666	36B	63724	56B	63783	41A
63608	36E	63667	40E	63725	31B	63784	38B
63609	41A	63668	36B	63726	36D	63785	36E
63610	38B	63669	36D	63727	36D	63786	31B
63611	36B	63670	31B	63728	36C	63787	38D
63612	36D	63671	36C	63729	38A	63788	36C
63613	36A	63672	36B	63730	36B	63789	38B
63614	38A	63673	36B	63731	36D	63790	41A
63615	40B	63674	38A	63732	40E	63791	36B
63616	40B	63675	38A	63733	41A	63792	38B
63617	36C	63676	38B	63734	41A	63793	36C
63618	36B	63677	36B	63735	38D	63794	39A
63619	31B	63678	31B	63736	36E	63795	31B
63620	41A	63679	40E	63737	41A	63796	38B
63621	41A	63680	41A	63738	40B	63797	41A
63622	40D	63681	39A	63739	40E	63798	36B
63623	36D	63682	41A	63740	38B	63799	36C
63624	41A	63683	40D	63741	36C	63800	40E
63625	36D	63684	36B	63742	41A	63801	38D
63626	36C	63685	41A	63743	39A	63802	40B

63803	31B	63877	38D	63944	36E	64182	56B
63804	38D	63878	40B	63945	36E	64183	38A
63805	39A	63879	31B	63946	35B	64184	35A
63806	38B	63880	36C	63947	36A	64185	36A
63807	36C	63881	41A	63948	35B	64186	34D
63808	38B	63882	41A	63949	36E	64187	35B
63812	36B	63883	36D	63950	35B	64188	36E
63813	36B	63884	38D	63951	36A	64189	35A
63816	38A	63885	56B	63952	36A	64190	40F
63817	38B	63886	38B	63953	36A	64191	35A
63818	36C	63887	31B	63954	36A	64192	35A
63819	40B	63888	41A	63955	36A	64193	36A
63821	41A	63889	41A	63956	36A	64195	38A
63822	41A	63890	31B	63957	36A	64196	34B
63823	56B	63891	36B	63958	36A	64197	34D
63824	36D	63893	40D	63959	36A	64198	35A
63827	38D	63894	36B	63960	35B	64199	38A
63828	36B	63895	39A	63961	36E	64200	38A
63829	36B	63897	36B	63962	36A	64201	40F
63832	36B	63898	36B	63963	36A	64202	38A
63833	40E	63899	38D	63964	36A	64203	56G
63835	36B	63900	40B	63965	36E	64204	40F
63836	40B	63901	38B	63966	35B	64205	56B
63837	40B	63902	40E	63967	36A	64206	34D
63838	38B	63904	36D	63968	36A	64207	35A
63839	38A	63905	36E	63969	36A	64208	56B
63840	40E	63906	36C	63970	36E	64209	36A
63841	36B	63907	36D	63971	36A	64210	35A
63842	40E	63908	36B	63972	36E	64211	35A
63843	36B	63911	36D	63973	36A	64213	38A
63845	38D	63912	40D	63974	36A	64214	40F
63846	41A	63913	36D	63975	36A	64215	38A
63847	38D	63914	36E	63976	36E	64216	40F
63848	39A	63915	39A	63977	36A	64217	35A
63850	41A	63917	36C	63978	36A	64218	38A
63851	36B	63920	56G	63979	36E	64219	35A
63852	41A	63922	36A	63980	36E	64220	35A
63853	36C	63923	35B	63981	36E	64221	38A
63854	38B	63924	36E	63982	36E	64222	56B
63855	36A	63925	36E	63983	36A	64223	34B
63856	54B	63926	36E	63984	36A	64224	35A
63857	56B	63927	36E	63985	36A	64225	38A
63858	36A	63928	36A	63986	36E	64226	56G
63859	38A	63929	35B	63987	36E	64227	35B
63860	40B	63930	35B			64228	35A
63861	40E	63931	35B			64229	40F
63862	39A	63932	35B			64230	38A
63863	38B	63933	35B	64170	56G	64231	35A
63864	56B	63934	36A	64171	35A	64232	36A
63865	38B	63935	36A	64172	35A	64233	34B
63867	38B	63936	35B	64173	56C	64234	36E
63868	31B	63937	36E	64174	36E	64235	38A
63869	38B	63938	35B	64175	34D	64236	36E
63870	40E	63939	36A	64176	35A	64237	34D
63872	38B	63940	35B	64177	35A	64238	38A
63873	38A	63941	36A	64178	35B	64239	38A
63874	54B	63942	36A	64179	36A	64240	34D
63876	36B	63943	36A	64180	40F	64241	36E
				64181	35A		

64243	36A	64305	40B	64383	39A	64451	36E
64244	40F	64306	39A	64384	38D	64452	36D
64245	36E	64308	36C	64385	36E	64453	38C
64246	35A	64310	40E	64386	38B	64460	65E
64247	40F	64311	38A	64387	41A	64461	65C
64248	38A	64313	38D	64388	38A	64462	64A
64249	38A	64314	40E	64389	40E	64463	64G
64250	40F	64315	40A	64392	40D	64464	66A
64251	34D	64316	39A	64393	36B	64466	62A
64252	36E	64317	39A	64394	41A	64468	64F
64253	34B	64318	40A	64395	36E	64470	65E
64254	35A	64319	36C	64396	38D	64471	66A
64255	36E	64320	40B	64397	38A	64472	65E
64256	38A	64321	36E	64399	36D	64473	65E
64257	38A	64322	39A	64401	39A	64474	62A
64258	36A	64324	38B	64402	36B	64475	62C
64259	36E	64325	40B	64403	36E	64476	62C
64260	40F	64328	40B	64404	36D	64477	66A
64261	41A	64329	41A	64405	40D	64478	68E
64262	36A	64331	38E	64406	36B	64479	64A
64263	36A	64332	39A	64407	36C	64480	62C
64264	36A	64333	39A	64409	39A	64482	61B
64265	35A	64336	38D	64411	40B	64483	61B
64266	34B	64337	40E	64412	41A	64484	64F
64267	38A	64338	38A	64414	40E	64485	61B
64268	56B	64340	36E	64416	36E	64486	64A
64269	38A	64341	36E	64417	36D	64487	62C
64270	36A	64343	36D	64418	38E	64488	62A
64271	56B	64344	40D	64419	41A	64489	64A
64272	35A	64345	38A	64420	38B	64490	64E
64273	38A	64346	39A	64421	36E	64491	64F
64274	56B	64348	36E	64422	36E	64492	64A
64275	35A	64349	39A	64423	36E	64493	62C
64276	56C	64351	40A	64424	40D	64494	64G
64277	56C	64352	38B	64425	36D	64495	64C
64278	35A	64353	40D	64427	40E	64496	62C
64279	35A	64354	38A	64428	38E	64497	63B
64280	36E	64355	40B	64429	36C	64498	65E
64281	40E	64357	39A	64430	40A	64499	68E
64283	36E	64359	38B	64433	38D	64500	64C
64284	40B	64361	38A	64434	39A	64501	63B
64285	36B	64362	36D	64435	39A	64502	64E
64287	36E	64363	39A	64437	39A	64504	64F
64288	39A	64364	38B	64438	38A	64505	62C
64290	36D	64365	40B	64439	38B	64506	64A
64292	38D	64368	39A	64440	39A	64507	65E
64293	40E	64371	40A	64441	41A	64509	64G
64294	39A	64372	40B	64442	36D	64510	64F
64295	36E	64373	41A	64443	41A	64511	66A
64296	36D	64375	38C	64444	38D	64512	64F
64297	40E	64376	36D	64445	41A	64513	62C
64298	39A	64377	36B	64446	40B	64514	65C
64300	38E	64379	40E	64447	41A	64515	64A
64302	36D	64381	40A	64450	39A	64516	62C
64304	39A	64382	39A			64517	64C
						64518	64A
						64519	64A

64520	65D	64578	65A	64636	64E	64694	30A
64521	62A	64579	65E	64637	64A	64695	31A
64522	62A	64580	65A	64638	65A	64696	31A
64523	64A	64581	65A	64639	65A	64697	31B
64524	64A	64582	64A	64640	31C	64698	31B
64525	62C	64583	64F	64641	31B	64699	31B
64526	68E	64584	65C	64642	31B	64700	54C
64527	64C	64585	63B	64643	31B	64701	52A
64528	64E	64586	64A	64644	32A	64702	40A
64529	64F	64587	62B	64645	30E	64703	52B
64530	62B	64588	64E	64646	31A	64704	52A
64531	65E	64589	64E	64647	30E	64705	52C
64532	64A	64590	64A	64648	31B	64706	50D
64533	64A	64591	64C	64649	30E	64707	54C
64534	65E	64592	64E	64650	30E	64708	30A
64535	64A	64593	64E	64651	30E	64709	53A
64536	64C	64594	64A	64652	30E	64710	54C
64537	64E	64595	64A	64653	30E	64711	52D
64538	64A	64596	62A	64654	31A	64712	40A
64539	64G	64597	64A	64655	31B	64713	54C
64540	65A	64598	62B	64656	30A	64714	40A
64541	65A	64599	64A	64657	30A	64715	38A
64542	63B	64600	62A	64658	31A	64716	38A
64543	64A	64601	64A	64659	30E	64717	39A
64544	63B	64602	62A	64660	30E	64718	39A
64545	62B	64603	64A	64661	31B	64719	35C
64546	62A	64604	62C	64662	30A	64720	56B
64547	64A	64605	64A	64663	30A	64721	36A
64548	65E	64606	64A	64664	30A	64722	40A
64549	62A	64607	64A	64665	30A	64723	35C
64550	62A	64608	64A	64666	30E	64724	32B
64551	64E	64609	65C	64667	30E	64725	50C
64552	64A	64610	65H	64668	31B	64726	32B
64553	64F	64611	65A	64669	31B	64727	68E
64554	64C	64612	64C	64670	30A	64728	40A
64555	64A	64613	64A	64671	31B	64729	31A
64556	62B	64614	64A	64672	31B	64730	50C
64557	64A	64615	62B	64673	31A	64731	32A
64558	65A	64616	62A	64674	32A	64732	56B
64559	65C	64617	62C	64675	30A	64733	68E
64560	62C	64618	62A	64676	30A	64734	40A
64561	64C	64619	62B	64677	30A	64735	38A
64562	64A	64620	62B	64678	31B	64736	35C
64563	65C	64621	65C	64679	31B	64737	36A
64564	62A	64622	65A	64680	30A	64738	41A
64565	62A	64623	65A	64681	30A	64739	38A
64566	64A	64624	64A	64682	30A	64740	39A
64567	62C	64625	64A	64683	31B	64741	38A
64568	62C	64626	65C	64684	31B	64742	39A
64569	63B	64627	62B	64685	30C	64743	39A
64570	64E	64628	65A	64686	30A	64744	41A
64571	64E	64629	62A	64687	31B	64745	39A
64572	64A	64630	62C	64688	31A	64746	41A
64573	65C	64631	62B	64689	30A	64747	38A
64574	64C	64632	65A	64690	31B	64748	39A
64575	62B	64633	65A	64691	31B	64749	56B
64576	64A	64634	64F	64692	31B	64750	30A
64577	64A	64635	62A	64693	30A	64751	31A

64752	32B	64810	36A	64868	52D	64926	54C
64753	41A	64811	56B	64869	52A	64927	51F
64754	56B	64812	52C	64870	50B	64928	50F
64755	40A	64813	52D	64871	52A	64929	52A
64756	51F	64814	52C	64872	56B	64930	68E
64757	56B	64815	52C	64873	30A	64931	54C
64758	50B	64816	52C	64874	30A	64932	68E
64759	36E	64817	54A	64875	68E	64933	50B
64760	56B	64818	50D	64876	36A	64934	50B
64761	32A	64819	53A	64877	68E	64935	50B
64762	38A	64820	56B	64878	41A	64936	54C
64763	38A	64821	50D	64879	56B	64937	40A
64764	30F	64822	62B	64880	68E	64938	50F
64765	30A	64823	38A	64881	40A	64939	53A
64766	41A	64824	41A	64882	32B	64940	53A
64767	30A	64825	56B	64883	33A	64941	52D
64768	30A	64826	32B	64884	68E	64942	50D
64769	30A	64827	38A	64885	36A	64943	50B
64770	30F	64828	36A	64886	50B	64944	50D
64771	30F	64829	32B	64887	40A	64945	52B
64772	30A	64830	36E	64888	68E	64946	64A
64773	30F	64831	56B	64889	32A	64947	50F
64774	30A	64832	38A	64890	31A	64948	68E
64775	30A	64833	56B	64891	33A	64949	53A
64776	30F	64834	32B	64892	68E	64950	62B
64777	30F	64835	50B	64893	36E	64951	33A
64778	51F	64836	56B	64894	32B	64952	36A
64779	30A	64837	56B	64895	68E	64953	30F
64780	30A	64838	36A	64896	33A	64954	35C
64781	30A	64839	56B	64897	52D	64955	38A
64782	30A	64840	56B	64898	36E	64956	36A
64783	30A	64841	32B	64899	68E	64957	32B
64784	30A	64842	52C	64900	32A	64958	31A
64785	32B	64843	52D	64901	33A	64959	40A
64786	62B	64844	52D	64902	36D	64960	40A
64787	30F	64845	50D	64903	56G	64961	36E
64788	30F	64846	54C	64904	50C	64962	41A
64789	35C	64847	50D	64905	32B	64963	64A
64790	62B	64848	51F	64906	36E	64964	68E
64791	50B	64849	52C	64907	56G	64965	35C
64792	62B	64850	50B	64908	36E	64966	36A
64793	32B	64851	54C	64909	36A	64967	36A
64794	64A	64852	52A	64910	53A	64968	32A
64795	61B	64853	52B	64911	56C	64969	56B
64796	56B	64854	54C	64912	68E	64970	36E
64797	32A	64855	50D	64913	32A	64971	53A
64798	38A	64856	52B	64914	53A	64972	36A
64799	56B	64857	50D	64915	52B	64973	30A
64800	32B	64858	52C	64916	52D	64974	38A
64801	56G	64859	50D	64917	52D	64975	61B
64802	32G	64860	50C	64918	56B	64976	38A
64803	31A	64861	50D	64919	54A	64977	40A
64804	40A	64862	51F	64920	50B	64978	51F
64805	30A	64863	50B	64921	54C	64979	56B
64806	56B	64864	53A	64922	50B	64980	38A
64807	30A	64865	52A	64923	52B	64981	33A
64808	41A	64866	50D	64924	52D	64982	51F
64809	41A	64867	50F	64925	52D	64983	38A

64984	40A	65196	8E	65287	65E	65442	31A
64985	35C	65198	8D	65288	64A	65443	30A
64986	64A	65199	10A	65290	64F	65444	30A
64987	36A	65200	17E	65293	68E	65445	30E
64988	38A	65202	9G	65295	65C	65446	30A
		65208	17F	65296	65A	65447	32B
		65209	17F	65297	61C	65448	30E
		65210	65E	65300	65J	65449	30A
		65211	64F	65303	61A	65450	30A
		65213	61A	65304	61C	65451	31A
		65214	65E	65305	64A	65452	30A
		65216 *	66A	65306	64E	65453	30F
		65217 *	65E	65307	62C	65454	30A
		65218	62A	65309	62B	65455	30A
		65221	65A	65310	64A	65456	30E
		65222 *	64E	65311	64E	65457	31A
65033	52C	65224 *	64A	65312	68E	65458	30F
65039	54B	65225	64F	65313	65J	65459	32B
65061	52B	65227	65I	65315	65A	65460	32C
65064	51A	65228	65A	65316	64G	65461	31A
65070	52C	65229	64F	65317	64G	65462	32C
65091	52D	65230	64F	65318	64F	65463	30A
65099	52D	65232	66A	65319	62B	65464	30A
65103	52C	65233 *	64F	65320	62C	65465	30E
65110	52B	65234	64F	65321	68E	65466	30E
65117	52C	65235 *	64B	65323	62C	65467	30A
65131	10A	65237	65J	65325	65E	65468	30E
65132	17E	65239	62C	65327	64A	65469	32A
65133	27E	65241	64E	65329	64A	65470	30E
65134	9G	65242	61B	65330	62B	65471	32A
65135	17E	65243 *	64B	65331	64G	65472	32A
65138	10A	65244	64E	65333	62B	65473	30E
65140	10A	65246	64E	65334	64A	65474	31B
65142	8E	65247	61A	65335	65H	65475	31A
65144	17F	65249	65E	65338	64A	65476	30A
65145	8E	65251	64A	65339	65I	65477	31A
65146	10A	65252	62A	65341	64F	65478	32C
65147	8E	65253 *	62C	65342	64F	65479	34D
65156	10A	65257	64E	65343	65E	65500	31A
65157	17F	65258	64A	65344	64F	65501	31B
65158	9G	65259	64F	65345	62A	65502	31A
65159	10A	65260	65E	65346	64F	65503	31B
65160	17E	65261	64F	65361	30A	65504	31A
65166	8E	65265	64F	65388	32A	65505	31A
65167	17F	65266	65E	65389	32B	65506	30A
65169	9G	65267	61C	65390	31B	65507	32C
65170	10A	65268 *	64F	65391	31E	65508	30C
65175	10A	65270	65A	65405	31E	65509	32G
65177	27E	65273	65A	65420	31E	65511	30A
65178	17E	65275	64E	65424	30E	65512	32B
65184	8D	65276	64F	65432	30E	65513	32B
65186	17F	65277	64F	65433	32B	65514	30A
65187	17F	65280	64E	65434	30F	65515	31B
65191	17F	65281	62C	65438	31A	65518	31C
65192	27E	65282	64F	65440	30A	65519	32A
65194	17E	65285	65E	65441	30E	65520	31A
						65521	31C

65522	30E	65589	31A	65751	51B	65809	52E
65523	30A	65645	54C	65752	51B	65810	52F
65525	30A	65648	50B	65753	51B	65811	52F
65526	31C	65650	50B	65754	51B	65812	52E
65527	31C	65654	50B	65755	51B	65813	52E
65528	30C	65655	53A	65756	51B	65814	52E
65529	31C	65656	52B	65757	51B	65815	52F
65530	31C	65657	54C	65758	51B	65816	51C
65531	30E	65662	54A	65759	51B	65817	54A
65532	31A	65663	50G	65760	51B	65818	51C
65533	31C	65666	54B	65761	51B	65819	52F
65534	31A	65670	54B	65762	51B	65820	51C
65535	30C	65673	50D	65763	51B	65821	52E
65536	30C	65675	52C	65764	51E	65822	52F
65538	31B	65677	53A	65765	51B	65823	54C
65539	30E	65680	54B	65766	51B	65824	52F
65540	30A	65683	50B	65767	51B	65825	52E
65541	31A	65685	50A	65768	51B	65826	52E
65542	32A	65687	52C	65769	51B	65827	50F
65544	31C	65691	50A	65770	51B	65828	52F
65545	30C	65693	53A	65771	51E	65829	52F
65546	30A	65695	53A	65772	51B	65830	51G
65548	31A	65696	52F	65773	51B	65831	52E
65549	31C	65697	54C	65774	51B	65832	54A
65551	32G	65698	50C	65775	51D	65833	54A
65553	32A	65699	54B	65776	51D	65834	52F
65554	31B	65700	54C	65777	51B	65835	54A
65555	30A	65702	54C	65778	51B	65836	54A
65556	31B	65706	52F	65779	51D	65837	52E
65557	32A	65712	54C	65780	52E	65838	52F
65558	32C	65713	54B	65781	52F	65839	52E
65559	32C	65714	50A	65782	51C	65840	54A
65560	32B	65717	54B	65783	52F	65841	54A
65561	31A	65720	51D	65784	52E	65842	52E
65562	31C	65726	53A	65785	54C	65843	54A
65563	30A	65727	52F	65786	52F	65844	50F
65564	30E	65728	54C	65787	51G	65845	50A
65565	31A	65730	51B	65788	51E	65846	51C
65566	32A	65731	51F	65789	52F	65847	54A
65567	32G	65732	51B	65790	51G	65848	50F
65568	31C	65733	51F	65791	52E	65849	50F
65570	32A	65734	51B	65792	52F	65850	54A
65571	31B	65735	51F	65793	50A	65851	52F
65572	31B	65736	51B	65794	52F	65852	52E
65573	32A	65737	51D	65795	52E	65853	51G
65575	31A	65738	51B	65796	52F	65854	54A
65576	31B	65739	51E	65797	52F	65855	51G
65577	31B	65740	51B	65798	54A	65856	54A
65578	32B	65741	51B	65799	52E	65857	50A
65580	31A	65742	51B	65800	52F	65858	52E
65581	32F	65743	51B	65801	52F	65859	51G
65582	31C	65744	51B	65802	52E	65860	51A
65583	31B	65745	51B	65803	51C	65861	50C
65584	31D	65746	51B	65804	52F	65862	52F
65586	32F	65747	51C	65805	51G	65863	52F
65587	31A	65748	51C	65806	52E	65864	52B
65588	32G	65749	51B	65807	52E	65865	51C
		65750	51B	65808	52F	65866	51C

65867	52F	65930	62C	67311	53D	67450	39A
65868	51E	65931	62A	67315	50F	67460	65A
65869	52B	65932	62A	67319	50F	67474	65A
65870	51D	65933	62C	67320	54A	67482	65C
65871	54A	65934	64A	67323	52F	67484	62B
65872	54A			67324	54A	67485	65A
65873	54C			67325	50F	67486	62B
65874	50A			67326	52C	67487	65C
65875	50C			67329	54A	67488	64E
65876	52B			67338	54A	67489	64G
65877	52F			67340	52F	67490	62B
65878	54A			67341	52F	67491	62B
65879	52B			67342	54A	67492	64A
65880	52F			67343	54A	67494	64E
65881	50C			67352	35C	67496	61C
65882	52B			67357	35A	67497	61A
65883	50A			67362	35B	67500	65C
65884	51E			67363	33B	67501	61C
65885	50C			67365	35A	67502	62B
65886	52B			67366	32D	67600	65A
65887	50A	67192	30E	67367	35C	67601	65I
65888	50C	67193	30A	67374	31C	67602	65A
65889	52F	67195	30A	67376	35A	67603	65A
65890	50A	67200	30A	67379	35A	67604	65H
65891	50C	67202	30A	67380	35A	67605	64A
65892	54A	67203	30A	67386	31C	67606	64G
65893	54A	67212	30A	67391	35B	67607	64A
65894	50A	67214	32A	67394	35A	67608	64A
65900	64E	67218	30A	67397	35C	67609	64A
65901	62A	67221	30A	67398	35A	67610	64B
65902	62A	67227	30E	67413	6D	67611	65C
65903	62A	67228	30E	67416	34E	67612	65C
65904	62A	67229	32C	67417	39A	67613	65H
65905	62A	67230	30A	67418	34E	67614	65H
65906	64A	67231	32C	67419	39A	67615	64B
65907	62A	67246	54A	67420	34E	67616	65H
65908	62A	67248	54A	67421	39A	67617	64A
65909	64E	67250	50C	67423	36D	67618	65E
65910	62A	67253	52F	67424	41A	67619	65H
65911	62A	67254	54A	67427	56B	67620	64B
65912	64A	67258	54A	67428	6E	67621	65C
65913	62A	67259	54A	67433	56B	67622	65H
65914	64A	67261	53B	67434	36D	67623	65C
65915	64A	67262	50B	67437	39A	67624	64A
65916	64A	67263	52F	67438	56B	67625	65H
65917	64E	67265	54A	67439	41A	67626	65C
65918	64A	67270	54A	67440	39A	67627	65E
65919	64A	67273	50C	67441	39A	67628	65H
65920	64A	67274	50B	67442	6E	67629	64A
65921	62A	67277	52F	67443	39A	67630	64A
65922	64A	67278	54A	67444	39A	67631	65H
65923	62C	67280	53D	67445	39A	67632	65H
65924	62C	67281	52F	67446	39A	67633	65C
65925	62A	67282	53B	67447	39A	67634	52C
65926	62C	67297	54A	67448	39A	67635	52B
65927	64A	67305	51A	67449	6E	67636	52C
65928	62C						
65929	64A						

67637	52B	67703	32B	67760	38A	68015	51A
67638	53B	67704	32C	67761	34D	68016	54A
67639	52A	67705	32B	67762	34E	68017	54A
67640	52B	67706	32D	67763	51D	68018	40B
67641	52B	67707	32A	67764	51D	68019	54D
67642	52B	67708	32B	67765	51D	68020	36A
67643	65C	67709	32B	67766	51D	68021	51C
67644	65A	67710	32C	67767	34E	68022	36A
67645	52B	67711	32B	67768	34A	68023	51B
67646	52B	67712	30C	67769	34E	68024	54A
67647	52B	67713	30C	67770	32C	68025	51A
67648	65C	67714	32A	67771	38E	68026	40B
67649	64A	67715	32B	67772	34A	68027	51A
67650	63B	67716	32B	67773	34A	68028	40B
67651	52B	67717	32A	67774	34A	68029	50A
67652	52B	67718	30A	67775	32B	68030	17D
67653	52C	67719	32B	67776	35B	68031	50A
67654	52B	67720	30A	67777	51A	68032	50A
67655	65C	67721	30C	67778	34E	68033	40B
67656	52D	67722	30C	67779	34A	68034	6F
67657	52A	67723	30C	67780	34A	68035	52C
67658	52C	67724	30A	67781	34E	68036	52C
67659	64A	67725	30A	67782	34E	68037	51A
67660	65E	67726	30A	67783	34E	68038	52C
67661	65C	67727	30A	67784	34A	68039	51A
67662	65C	67728	32E	67785	34D	68040	50A
67663	53B	67729	30A	67786	38A	68041	54A
67664	65A	67730	30A	67787	34E	68042	50A
67665	65E	67731	30A	67788	38A	68043	51A
67666	64A	67732	30A	67789	38E	68044	50A
67667	65A	67733	30A	67790	34D	68045	51A
67668	64A	67734	30A	67791	34D	68046	50A
67669	62C	67735	30A	67792	34E	68047	51A
67670	64A	67736	32E	67793	34A	68048	54A
67671	65A	67737	30A	67794	34E	68049	51B
67672	62C	67738	30A	67795	34E	68050	51A
67673	52A	67739	32B	67796	34E	68051	51C
67674	65E	67740	34E	67797	34A	68052	51A
67675	63B	67741	34D	67798	38A	68053	51C
67676	65C	67742	51A	67799	38A	68054	51C
67677	53B	67743	34E	67800	35B	68055	51C
67678	65C	67744	34D			68056	51C
67679	65C	67745	34D			68057	51C
67680	65A	67746	34D			68058	54A
67681	65C	67747	34E			68059	52C
67682	52C	67748	34E			68060	51B
67683	52D	67749	34A			68061	50A
67684	53B	67750	51A			68062	51B
67685	53B	67751	38A			68063	6F
67686	53B	67752	34E			68064	39A
67687	52A	67753	34E			68065	6F
67688	52A	67754	51D	68006	17D	68066	6F
67689	52A	67755	51D	68007	51A	68067	40B
67690	52A	67756	34E	68008	51A	68068	40B
67691	53B	67757	34A	68009	40B	68069	40B
67701	30C	67758	34E	68010	52C	68070	40B
67702	32D	67759	51D	68011	51B	68071	40B
				68012	39A	68072	40B
				68013	17D		
				68014	52B		

68073	40B	68269	51F	68361	53C	68480	65A
68074	40B	68272	52A	68362	50C	68481	64B
68075	40B	68273	52C	68363	53B	68490	31C
68076	40B	68275	50C	68364	51C	68491	35A
68077	40B	68278	54C	68391	51F	68494	31D
68078	40B	68279	51A	68392	50D	68495	31C
68079	39A	68283	52A	68397	52F	68497	31E
68080	40B	68290	51D	68399	52F	68498	31C
68095	64A	68295	51C	68402	52F	68499	31C
68097	64A	68296	53A	68405	52F	68500	30A
68100	62B	68305	51E	68406	50C	68501	40F
68101	62C	68306	51C	68408	52F	68502	31C
68102	64A	68308	51A	68409	51D	68507	36A
68104	64E	68309	52A	68410	51A	68508	36E
68106	65E	68312	51D	68414	51D	68510	30A
68108	62B	68314	52A	68423	51G	68513	30A
68110	65E	68316	54C	68424	52F	68518	32B
68113	64E	68320	51A	68425	51A	68519	36E
68114	62B	68321	62A	68426	52F	68520	36A
68115	64A	68322	62A	68427	52F	68522	30E
68116	65E	68324	64E	68431	52F	68524	64E
68117	65E	68325	64A	68435	50A	68526	30A
68118	67C	68326	65F	68438	51E	68527	36E
68119	64A	68327	65A	68442	65E	68528	40A
68123	62B	68328	64B	68443	65E	68529	30A
68124	65E	68329	65E	68444	65E	68530	31A
68126	30A	68330	65A	68445	65E	68532	30A
68138	67C	68331	62A	68447	65A	68535	62B
68142	51E	68332	62A	68448	64A	68536	32G
68149	51F	68333	65D	68449	64A	68537	40A
68150	50C	68334	62A	68450	64A	68538	30A
68164	84G	68335	62A	68451	62A	68541	40A
68182	50C	68336	65E	68452	62B	68542	31D
68190	61A	68338	64A	68453	62A	68543	40F
68191	61A	68339	64B	68454	64A	68545	31C
68192	61A	68340	64A	68456	62A	68546	30A
68230	53A	68342	64A	68457	64B	68549	30A
68233	51C	68343	65E	68458	62A	68550	38A
68235	51A	68344	65E	68459	62A	68551	62B
68242	51F	68345	62C	68460	64B	68552	30E
68244	51C	68346	62C	68461	65E	68553	6E
68245	51D	68347	65A	68463	64A	68554	31A
68246	50A	68348	64A	68464	64A	68555	32A
68250	50A	68349	65A	68465	62B	68556	31C
68251	53A	68350	62C	68466	62B	68557	40F
68253	55E	68352	64A	68467	64E	68558	36A
68254	51F	68353	62A	68468	65A	68560	40F
6826C	51D	68354	64E	68470	62B	68561	36E
68262	54B	68355	51C	68471	64E	68563	30A
68263	52B	68356	50C	68472	64A	68565	32C
68264	52B	68357	50C	68474	64A	68566	31D
68265	54B	68359	51C	68475	65A	68567	31A
68267	52A	68360	53C	68477	64A	68568	30A
				68478	64B	68569	40A
				68479	65A		

68570	40F	68649	30A	68708	52B	68823	36A
68571	30A	68650	30A	68709	65A	68824	34B
68573	30A	68651	32F	68710	61A	68828	35A
68574	30A	68652	30A	68711	51C	68829	38A
68575	30A	68653	30A	68712	51D	68831	34A
68576	30A	68654	34D	68713	52B	68832	34A
68577	30A	68655	30A	68714	6E	68834	34B
68578	30A	68656	32D	68715	51C	68835	36A
68579	30C	68657	30A	68716	52B	68837	56B
68581	40F	68658	30A	68717	61A	68839	38C
68583	17F	68659	30A	68718	53A	68840	36A
68585	6E	68660	30A	68719	61A	68842	36A
68587	36A	68661	34D	68720	52A	68846	34B
68588	30A	68662	30E	68721	51D	68847	36B
68591	30A	68663	30A	68722	50A	68848	56B
68593	32B	68664	32C	68723	52A	68849	36A
68596	30A	68665	30A	68724	50A	68857	56B
68598	6E	68666	30E	68725	52D	68860	38A
68599	40A	68670	53A	68726	50A	68862	34A
68600	31A	68671	6E	68727	6E	68863	38A
68601	38A	68672	53A	68728	54C	68866	34B
68602	40F	68673	53C	68729	54B	68867	34C
68603	31B	68674	52A	68730	54C	68869	36A
68605	40A	68675	52A	68731	52A	68870	36B
68607	30A	68676	53C	68732	52A	68871	38A
68608	38D	68677	50A	68733	65A	68874	34A
68609	31A	68678	54A	68734	51C	68875	34B
68612	30A	68679	51A	68735	50A	68882	38A
68613	30A	68680	52A	68736	50D	68886	36A
68616	38D	68681	55E	68737	54C	68887	38A
68617	38D	68682	52D	68738	52B	68888	34A
68618	40A	68683	51C	68739	50A	68889	35C
68619	30A	68684	51D	68740	51D	68890	56B
68621	36A	68685	51F	68741	53A	68891	34B
68623	31D	68686	50A	68742	52B	68892	56G
68625	32G	68687	54B	68743	54B	68893	38A
68626	35A	68688	51D	68744	52A	68894	34B
68628	32D	68689	51D	68745	53C	68895	56G
68629	38A	68690	51D	68746	53C	68896	38B
68630	30A	68691	51F	68747	52B	68897	56G
68631	30A	68692	51F	68748	51A	68898	56G
68632	30A	68693	52A	68749	61A	68899	32A
68633	30A	68694	54C	68750	61A	68900	56B
68635	35A	68695	54C	68751	53A	68901	56B
68636	30A	68696	51E	68752	53C	68902	56B
68638	34D	68697	54C	68753	53A	68903	34B
68639	30A	68698	54A	68754	51A	68904	56B
68640	32A	68699	54C	68761	36A	68905	32A
68641	32A	68700	61C	68768	38A	68906	34B
68642	32A	68701	55E	68778	36A	68907	34B
68643	30F	68702	52B	68784	36A	68908	56G
68644	30A	68703	51C	68785	38A	68909	56B
68645	32A	68704	54A	68800	36E	68910	56B
68646	30A	68705	54C	68811	36A	68911	56C
68647	30A	68706	54B	68815	35A		
68648	30A	68707	51C	68817	36A		

68912	56G	68970	36C	69092	52A	69167	64A
68913	56C	68971	34B	69093	54B	69168	64A
68914	56B	68972	34B	69094	53A	69169	64B
68915	56B	68973	36C	69096	53A	69170	65A
68916	56B	68974	36A	69097	52A	69171	65A
68917	34B	68975	38A	69098	50B	69172	64A
68918	34B	68976	38B	69099	53A	69173	64A
68919	56B	68977	36C	69100	52A	69174	68E
68920	34B	68978	56C	69101	54A	69175	64A
68921	34B	68979	34B	69102	54B	69176	65D
68922	56G	68980	36A	69104	53A	69177	65D
68923	56G	68981	34B	69105	54B	69178	65A
68924	32A	68982	34B	69106	54B	69179	65A
68925	56C	68983	34B	69107	53A	69180	65A
68926	36A	68984	56C	69108	53A	69181	65A
68927	38A	68985	34B	69109	52A	69182	65A
68928	34B	68986	34B	69126	65A	69183	65A
68929	34B	68987	34B	69127	65A	69184	65D
68930	34B	68988	56C	69128	61B	69185	64A
68931	34B	68989	34B	69129	61B	69186	64A
68932	56G	68990	34B	69130	64A	69187	64C
68933	56G	68991	34B	69131	65A	69188	65A
68934	56G			69132	62A	69189	65A
68935	56B			69133	64A	69190	65C
68936	34B			69134	64A	69191	65A
68937	56C			69135	62C	69192	62C
68938	56B			69136	62C	69193	65C
68939	56B			69137	64E	69194	65C
68940	56G			69138	65A	69195	65C
68941	56B			69139	68E	69196	65E
68942	56G	69001	52B	69140	64A	69197	65A
68943	56G	69002	54A	69141	64A	69198	65C
68944	56G	69003	53C	69142	64F	69199	65C
68945	34B	69004	51A	69143	62A	69200	64E
68946	34A	69005	52A	69144	64A	69201	61B
68947	56B	69006	51D	69145	65E	69202	62C
68948	56B	69007	54A	69146	64A	69203	65D
68949	34B	69008	54B	69147	64A	69204	62C
68950	38A	69009	53C	69148	64A	69205	65D
68951	56B	69010	53C	69149	64A	69206	65E
68952	65A	69011	53C	69150	62A	69207	65E
68954	65A	69012	62A	69151	65C	69208	65D
68955	65A	69013	62A	69152	64A	69209	65C
68956	65A	69014	64A	69153	62A	69210	65C
68957	65A	69015	65C	69154	62C	69211	62A
68958	65A	69016	50E	69155	68E	69212	65C
68959	56G	69017	54C	69156	64F	69213	65C
68960	36C	69018	51F	69157	65C	69214	65A
68961	34B	69019	51D	69158	64F	69215	68E
68962	36C	69020	50A	69159	64F	69216	64F
68963	36C	69021	51A	69160	62C	69217	65C
68964	36C	69022	51A	69161	65C	69218	65A
68965	36C	69023	52C	69162	64E	69219	64A
68966	34F	69024	52C	69163	65A	69220	64B
68967	38A	69025	52C	69164	62C	69221	62C
68968	34B	69026	52C	69165	65C	69222	64A
68969	56G	69027	52B	69166	65C	69223	62A
		69028	52B			69224	62A

69257	34E	69362	6E	69535	34A	69591	34A
69258	8E	69370	17F	69536	34A	69592	34A
69259	41A	69434	56C	69537	34B	69593	34A
69261	40E	69443	56G	69538	34A	69594	34B
69262	17E	69450	56C	69539	34A	69595	65C
69263	38D	69452	56B	69540	34A	69596	65E
69265	27E	69453	56B	69541	34A	69600	30A
69266	41A	69462	56C	69542	34A	69601	30A
69267	6E	69472	56B	69543	34A	69602	30A
69268	36D	69474	56G	69544	34A	69603	30A
69269	38D	69477	34B	69545	34A	69604	30A
69271	41A	69484	56B	69546	34A	69605	30A
69274	6D	69490	34A	69547	34C	69606	30A
69276	17E	69491	34A	69548	34A	69607	30A
69281	6E	69492	34A	69549	34A	69608	30A
69283	36E	69493	34A	69550	34A	69609	30A
69284	40E	69494	34C	69551	34A	69610	30A
69286	41A	69495	34A	69552	34A	69611	30A
69290	6E	69496	34A	69553	65D	69612	34B
69292	41A	69497	34A	69554	34B	69613	30A
69293	6D	69498	34A	69555	34B	69614	30A
69294	41A	69499	34A	69556	34B	69615	34B
69295	41A	69500	65C	69557	34D	69616	31A
69296	41A	69501	34B	69558	34A	69617	31A
69297	36D	69502	34B	69559	34A	69618	34B
69298	27E	69504	34C	69560	34B	69619	31A
69299	17E	69505	34B	69561	34A	69620	31A
69300	36D	69506	34A	69563	65C	69621	32C
69302	41A	69507	65C	69564	65C	69622	30A
69305	36B	69508	65C	69565	65C	69623	30A
69307	39A	69509	65D	69566	34C	69624	30A
69308	36B	69510	64G	69567	34B	69625	30A
69309	38D	69511	65D	69568	34A	69626	30A
69312	41A	69512	34A	69569	34A	69627	30A
69314	36E	69513	34B	69570	34A	69628	30A
69315	36D	69515	34A	69571	34A	69629	34B
69319	34E	69516	34C	69572	34A	69630	30A
69320	36D	69517	34A	69573	34A	69631	34C
69322	36E	69518	65E	69574	34A	69632	34C
69326	17F	69519	34A	69575	34A	69633	30B
69327	41A	69520	34A	69576	34A	69634	30B
69329	6E	69521	34A	69577	34A	69635	34C
69332	6D	69522	34B	69578	34A	69636	30A
69335	6E	69523	34A	69579	34A	69637	34C
69341	34E	69524	34A	69580	34C	69638	34C
69342	6D	69525	34A	69581	34A	69639	34C
69343	17F	69526	34A	69582	34C	69640	34C
69344	27E	69527	34A	69583	34A	69641	30A
69346	6E	69528	34A	69584	34A	69642	30A
69347	17F	69529	34A	69585	34A	69643	30A
69349	6E	69530	34B	69586	34C	69644	34C
69354	36D	69531	34B	69587	34B	69645	30A
69355	36D	69532	34A	69588	34C	69646	30A
69360	39A	69533	34B	69589	34A	69647	30A
69361	17F	69534	34C	69590	34A	69648	34C

69649	34C	69705	30A	69823	39A	69885	50B
69650	34C	69706	32A	69824	40B	69886	53B
69651	31A	69707	32A	69825	38B	69887	51A
69652	30A	69708	32D	69826	40B	69888	53B
69653	30A	69709	34C	69827	35B	69889	51D
69654	34C	69710	30A	69828	39A	69890	50G
69655	30A	69711	30A	69829	40B	69891	51D
69656	30A	69712	30A	69830	51A	69892	51K
69657	30A	69713	30C	69831	51A	69893	51C
69658	30A	69714	30A	69832	51A	69894	51K
69659	30A	69715	30A	69833	51A	69910	50A
69660	30A	69716	30A	69834	51A	69912	50C
69661	30A	69717	30A	69835	53B	69913	50A
69662	30A	69718	30A	69836	53B	69915	50C
69663	30A	69719	30A	69837	53B	69916	50A
69664	30A	69720	30A	69838	51E	69917	54D
69665	30A	69721	30E	69839	51A	69918	51E
69666	30A	69722	30A	69840	51A	69920	54B
69667	30A	69723	30A	69841	51A	69921	51E
69668	30A	69724	30A	69842	51E	69926	36C
69669	30A	69725	30A	69850	54A	69928	40E
69670	30A	69726	30A	69851	51F	69929	40E
69671	30A	69727	30E	69852	51K	69930	36C
69672	30F	69728	30A	69853	54A	69931	50C
69673	30E	69729	30A	69854	51D	69932	36C
69674	30A	69730	30A	69855	51K	69933	50C
69675	30F	69731	30A	69856	51F	69934	36C
69676	30A	69732	30E	69857	54A	69935	36C
69677	30A	69733	30E	69858	53B	69936	36C
69678	30E	69772	53C	69859	51K		
69679	32C	69782	53C	69860	53B		
69680	30B	69786	53C	69861	50F		
69681	30B	69800	38A	69862	51D		
69682	30B	69801	39A	69863	54A		
69683	30B	69802	53B	69864	50G		
69684	30B	69803	38D	69865	50G		
69685	30B	69804	38A	69866	51K		
69686	30B	69805	39A	69867	50E		
69687	30B	69806	39A	69868	51F		
69688	30B	69807	38A	69869	51K		
69690	31A	69808	40F	69870	51F	70000 *	30A
69691	33B	69809	38B	69871	51A	70001 *	30A
69692	31A	69810	38A	69872	51F	70002 *	30A
69693	30B	69811	53B	69873	51C	70003 *	30A
69694	33B	69812	38A	69874	54A	70004 *	73A
69695	33B	69813	39A	69875	51F	70005 *	30A
69696	32D	69814	35B	69876	51D	70006 *	32A
69697	30A	69815	39A	69877	50F	70007 *	32A
69698	33B	69816	40A	69878	51D	70008 *	32A
69699	30A	69817	39A	69879	53B	70009 *	32A
69700	30A	69818	38B	69880	51K	70010 *	32A
69701	30A	69819	40A	69881	50B	70011 *	32A
69702	30A	69820	40A	69882	53B	70012 *	32A
69703	30A	69821	40B	69883	51C	70013 *	32A
69704	34C	69822	39A	69884	51K	70014 *	73A
						70015 *	86C
						70016 *	86C
						70017 *	86C
						70018 *	86C
						70019 *	86C

70020	* 86C	73006	63A	73064	66A	73122	67A
70021	* 86C	73007	63A	73065	19B	73123	67A
70022	* 86C	73008	63A	73066	55A	73124	67A
70023	* 86C	73009	63A	73067	16A	73125	84G
70024	* 86C	73010	55A	73068	17A	73126	84G
70025	* 86C	73011	19B	73069	55A	73127	84G
70026	* 86C	73012	82C	73070	6A	73128	84G
70027	* 86C	73013	84K	73071	34A	73129	84G
70028	* 86C	73014	86C	73072	6A	73130	84G
70029	* 86C	73015	17A	73073	15C	73131	84G
70030	* 32A	73016	19B	73074	19B	73132	84G
70031	* 9A	73017	82C	73075	66A	73133	84G
70032	* 9A	73018	82C	73076	66A	73134	84G
70033	* 9A	73019	82B	73077	65A	73135	6J
70034	* 32A	73020	82C	73078	65A	73136	6J
70035	* 32A	73021	84K	73079	67A	73137	6J
70036	* 30A	73022	82C	73080	73A	73138	15C
70037	* 30A	73023	84K	73081	73A	73139	6J
70038	* 30A	73024	86C	73082	73A	73140	6J
70039	* 30A	73025	86C	73083	73A	73141	15C
70040	* 30A	73026	86C	73084	73A	73142	15C
70041	* 30A	73027	82C	73085	73A	73143	15C
70042	* 30A	73028	82B	73086	73A	73144	15C
70043	* 9A	73029	82B	73087	71A	73145	65B
70044	* 9A	73030	17A	73088	73A	73146	65B
70045	6J	73031	17A	73089	73A	73147	65B
70046	6J	73032	82B	73090	10C	73148	65B
70047	6J	73033	84B	73091	10C	73149	65B
70048	6J	73034	84B	73092	10C	73150	65B
70049	6J	73035	84B	73093	10C	73151	
70050	* 66A	73036	84E	73094	10C	73152	
70051	* 66A	73037	84E	73095	10C	73153	
70052	* 66A	73038	84K	73096	10C	73154	
70053	* 66A	73039	82B	73097	10C	73155	34E
70054	* 66A	73040	6A	73098	10C	73156	34E
		73041	6A	73099	10C	73157	34E
		73042	6A	73100	67A	73158	34E
71000	* 5A	73043	10C	73101	67A	73159	34E
		73044	10C	73102	67A	73160	52A
		73045	55A	73103	67A	73161	52A
72000	* 66A	73046	15C	73104	67A	73162	50A
72001	* 66A	73047	71G	73105	65A	73163	50A
72002	* 66A	73048	19B	73106	65A	73164	50A
72003	* 66A	73049	71G	73107	65A	73165	50A
72004	* 66A	73050	71G	73108	65A	73166	50A
72005	* 68A	73051	71G	73109	65A	73167	50A
72006	* 68A	73052	71G	73110	70A	73168	50A
72007	* 68A	73053	55A	73111	70A	73169	50A
72008	* 68A	73054	17A	73112	70A	73170	
72009	* 68A	73055	66A	73113	70A	73171	
		73056	66A	73114	70A		
		73057	66A	73115	70A		
73000	16A	73058	66A	73116	71A	75000	82C
73001	82C	73059	66A	73117	70A	75001	81F
73002	16A	73060	66B	73118	70A	75002	82C
73003	15C	73061	66B	73119	70A	75003	82C
73004	15C	73062	66B	73120	63A	75004	86C
73005	63A	73063	66A	73121	67A	75005	89A

75006	89A	75062		76036	34E	76092	
75007	86C	75063		76037	34E	76093	
75008	86C	75064		76038	34E	76094	
75009	86C	75065	74C	76039	34E	76095	
75010	6G	75066	74C	76040	34E	76096	
75011	6G	75067	74C	76041	34E	76097	
75012	6G	75068	74C	76042	34E	76098	
75013	6G	75069	74C	76043	34E	76099	
75014	6G	75070	71A	76044	34E	76100	
75015	27C	75071	71G	76045	51F	76101	
75016	27C	75072	71G	76046	51F	76102	
75017	27C	75073	71G	76047	51H	76103	
75018	27C	75074	71A	76048	51H	76104	
75019	27C	75075	70D	76049	51F	76105	
75020	89A	75076	70D	76050	51F	76106	
75021	86C	75077	70D	76051	51H	76107	
75022	86C	75078	70D	76052	51H	76108	
75023	82C	75079	70D	76053	75B	76109	
75024	89A			76054	75B	76110	
75025	82C			76055	75B	76111	
75026	89A	76000	66B	76056	75B	76112	
75027	81F	76001	66B	76057	75B	76113	
75028	82C	76002	66B	76058	75B	76114	
75029	81F	76003	66B	76059	75B		
75030	1E	76004	66B	76060	75B		
75031	6A	76005	72B	76061	75B	77000	53B
75032	6A	76006	72B	76062	75B	77001	53B
75033	6A	76007	71A	76063	71A	77002	51F
75034	6A	76008	72B	76064	71A	77003	51F
75035	6A	76009	71A	76065	71A	77004	51A
75036	1E	76010	71A	76066	71A	77005	66C
75037	1E	76011	71A	76067	71A	77006	66C
75038	1E	76012	71A	76068	71A	77007	66C
75039	6A	76013	71A	76069	71A	77008	66A
75040	15D	76014	71A	76070	66B	77009	66A
75041	15D	76015	71A	76071	66B	77010	53B
75042	15D	76016	71A	76072	68B	77011	52C
75043	15D	76017	71A	76073	68B	77012	50G
75044	15D	76018	71A	76074	65A	77013	50G
75045	27A	76019	71A	76075	10D	77014	52C
75046	27A	76020	51H	76076	10D	77015	67B
75047	27A	76021	51F	76077	10D	77016	67B
75048	27A	76022	51H	76078	10D	77017	67B
75049	27A	76023	51H	76079	10D	77018	67B
75050	6G	76024	51F	76080	24D	77019	67B
75051	6A	76025	71A	76081	24D		
75052	1E	76026	71A	76082	24D		
75053	6A	76027	71A	76083	24D	78000	89C
75054	6A	76028	71A	76084	24D	78001	85A
75055	15D	76029	71A	76085	15C	78002	89C
75056	16A	76030	30A	76086		78003	89C
75057	15C	76031	30A	76087		78004	85A
75058	15C	76032	30A	76088		78005	89C
75059	15C	76033	30A	76089		78006	89C
75060		76034	30A	76090		78007	89C
75061		76035	34E	76091		78008	85A

78009	85A	80000	67A	80054	66A	80109	61A
78010	51J	80001	66A	80055	66A	80110	61A
78011	51J	80002	66A	80056	66A	80111	66A
78012	51J	80003	66A	80057	66A	80112	66A
78013	51J	80004	61A	80058	66A	80113	66A
78014	51J	80005	61A	80059	6A	80114	66A
78015	51J	80006	66A	80060	26A	80115	66A
78016	51H	80007	66A	80061	26A	80116	50G
78017	51H	80008	67A	80062	6A	80117	50G
78018	51H	80009	67A	80063	6C	80118	50G
78019	51H	80010	75A	80064	1C	80119	50G
78020	15B	80011	75A	80065	1C	80120	50G
78021	15B	80012	75F	80066	1C	80121	61C
78022	19B	80013	75F	80067	1C	80122	61C
78023	19B	80014	75F	80068	1C	80123	62B
78024	19B	80015	75F	80069	33B	80124	62B
78025	19B	80016	75F	80070	33B	80125	63B
78026	19C	80017	75F	80071	33B	80126	63A
78027	19C	80018	75F	80072	33B	80127	67A
78028	15C	80019	75F	80073	33B	80128	67A
78029	15C	80020	61A	80074	33B	80129	66A
78030	5A	80021	61A	80075	33B	80130	66A
78031	6D	80022	66A	80076	33B	80131	33A
78032	8D	80023	66A	80077	33B	80132	33A
78033	8D	80024	67A	80078	33B	80133	33A
78034	8D	80025	67A	80079	33B	80134	33A
78035	8D	80026	66A	80080	33B	80135	33A
78036	10B	80027	66A	80081	1E	80136	33A
78037	10B	80028	61A	80082	1E	80137	34E
78038	6D	80029	61A	80083	1E	80138	34E
78039	8D	80030	67A	80084	1E	80139	34E
78040	27D	80031	75A	80085	1E	80140	34E
78041	27A	80032	75A	80086	6C	80141	34E
78042	27A	80033	75A	80087	6H	80142	34E
78043	27A	80034	1C	80088	6H	80143	34E
78044	27A	80035	1C	80089	6H	80144	34E
78045	61A	80036	1C	80090	6H	80145	75A
78046	64G	80037	1C	80091	6H	80146	75A
78047	64G	80038	1C	80092	6H	80147	75A
78048	64A	80039	1E	80093	26A	80148	75A
78049	64A	80040	1E	80094	6H	80149	75A
78050	66B	80041	1E	80095	6H	80150	75A
78051	66B	80042	1E	80096	33A	80151	75A
78052	60A	80043	1E	80097	33A	80152	75A
78053	61C	80044	26A	80098	33A	80153	75A
78054	61C	80045	6A	80099	33A	80154	75A
78055	6D	80046	26A	80100	33A		
78056	6D	80047	6A	80101	33A		
78057	6K	80048	6A	80102	33A		
78058	6D	80049	6A	80103	33A		
78059	6D	80050	6A	80104	33A		
78060	27D	80051	6A	80105	33A	82000	84G
78061	27D	80052	6A	80106	61A	82001	88F
78062	27D	80053	6A	80107	61A	82002	88F
78063	27D			80108	61A	82003	88C
78064	27D					82004	83A
						82005	88F
						82006	83A
						82007	84G
						82008	85D

82009	83A	84020	74A	90046	38E	90104	38A
82010	72A	84021		90047	51A	90105	26A
82011	72A	84022		90048	51C	90106	35A
82012	71A	84023		90049	65A	90107	27B
82013	72A	84024		90050	38A	90108	36A
82014	71A	84025		90051	40E	90109	24B
82015	71A	84026		90052	38A	90110	26C
82016	71A	84027		90053	38A	90111	36C
82017	72A	84028		90054	54B	90112	56D
82018	72A	84029		90055	40E	90113	26A
82019	72A			90056	51A	90114	65D
82020	6E			90057	51A	90115	38A
82021	6E	90000	38A	90058	62A	90116	53C
82022	72A	90001	38A	90059	36C	90117	62A
82023	72A	90002	38A	90060	66A	90118	38A
82024	72A	90003	40B	90061	53C	90119	36A
82025	72A	90004	62A	90062	30A	90120	38A
82026	51H	90005	38A	90063	35C	90121	27D
82027	51H	90006	53A	90064	38A	90122	56E
82028	51A	90007	38D	90065	38E	90123	26D
82029	51A	90008	53A	90066	38E	90124	56D
82030	85A	90009	53A	90067	51C	90125	86C
82031	84G	90010	84G	90068	51B	90126	56F
82032	88F	90011	53C	90069	86A	90127	55C
82033	88F	90012	51C	90070	36C	90128	62A
82034	88F	90013	36C	90071	66C	90129	31B
82035	88C	90014	51B	90072	53A	90130	38A
82036	88C	90015	38A	90073	38A	90131	40B
82037	88C	90016	51B	90074	51B	90132	51B
82038	85A	90017	62C	90075	38A	90133	36C
82039	88C	90018	31B	90076	51B	90134	66A
82040	88C	90019	62A	90077	62B	90135	53E
82041	88C	90020	62A	90078	53A	90136	38A
82042	88C	90021	51A	90079	31B	90137	38E
82043	88C	90022	53A	90080	38E	90138	24B
82044	88C	90023	31B	90081	51B	90139	38A
		90024	38A	90082	50B	90140	26A
		90025	38A	90083	31B	90141	27B
84000	6C	90026	54B	90084	38A	90142	26A
84001	6D	90027	51B	90085	38D	90143	24B
84002	1E	90028	35A	90086	51E	90144	36A
84003	6C	90029	40B	90087	40E	90145	40B
84004	1E	90030	53A	90088	53A	90146	38A
84005	15D	90031	36C	90089	53A	90147	6B
84006	17B	90032	36C	90090	51B	90148	86C
84007	17B	90033	38E	90091	51B	90149	85B
84008	17B	90034	35A	90092	51C	90150	31B
84009	55D	90035	40B	90093	35A	90151	35A
84010	24B	90036	38A	90094	53C	90152	81C
84011	24B	90037	38A	90095	38E	90153	38A
84012	27A	90038	38A	90096	35A	90154	38A
84013	26E	90039	65D	90097	61B	90155	51E
84014	26E	90040	38E	90098	51B	90156	35A
84015	24F	90041	61B	90099	53A	90157	6B
84016	24F	90042	31B	90100	53A	90158	35A
84017	24F	90043	40E	90101	27B	90159	24B
84018	24F	90044	50D	90102	26C	90160	53A
84019	26E	90045	54B	90103	38A	90161	38A

90162	40E	90220	36B	90278	27B	90336	55C
90163	26A	90221	40B	90279	35A	90337	56A
90164	27B	90222	26A	90280	40B	90338	26A
90165	35A	90223	40B	90281	53E	90339	56A
90166	38A	90224	40B	90282	27B	90340	31B
90167	86G	90225	86A	90283	27B	90341	56A
90168	62A	90226	26D	90284	81F	90342	56A
90169	35A	90227	6B	90285	40B	90343	27B
90170	68A	90228	53E	90286	36B	90344	51C
90171	24B	90229	66A	90287	40E	90345	55G
90172	51E	90230	51B	90288	38A	90346	38E
90173	6C	90231	24B	90289	26A	90347	55G
90174	81C	90232	36C	90290	36B	90348	56D
90175	40B	90233	53C	90291	26A	90349	35A
90176	84G	90234	66A	90292	26B	90350	62A
90177	62C	90235	38A	90293	31B	90351	55C
90178	6B	90236	56E	90294	40B	90352	53C
90179	86A	90237	6B	90295	24C	90353	56A
90180	35A	90238	86C	90296	38A	90354	26B
90181	24B	90239	35A	90297	26C	90355	81C
90182	62A	90240	51E	90298	30A	90356	84G
90183	24B	90241	24B	90299	38E	90357	56A
90184	51E	90242	6B	90300	53E	90358	36B
90185	38A	90243	55G	90301	36A	90359	26D
90186	53E	90244	35A	90302	40E	90360	56E
90187	6B	90245	26A	90303	38A	90361	56A
90188	86C	90246	35A	90304	36B	90362	56A
90189	38A	90247	56A	90305	31B	90363	56A
90190	36B	90248	26A	90306	26B	90364	26D
90191	35A	90249	55G	90307	26B	90365	38E
90192	86G	90250	36B	90308	55C	90366	26A
90193	65D	90251	81F	90309	54B	90367	24C
90194	26D	90252	36B	90310	56E	90368	38A
90195	36B	90253	35A	90311	36B	90369	6C
90196	33A	90254	55C	90312	86C	90370	56A
90197	26A	90255	36A	90313	81C	90371	24B
90198	62B	90256	33A	90314	24B	90372	26B
90199	65F	90257	6B	90315	86G	90373	51B
90200	51A	90258	24C	90316	26A	90374	24A
90201	86C	90259	40E	90317	6B	90375	27B
90202	38A	90260	53E	90318	55C	90376	26A
90203	36A	90261	84G	90319	67C	90377	51E
90204	27B	90262	53E	90320	66A	90378	53C
90205	26D	90263	38A	90321	56D	90379	56A
90206	26C	90264	24B	90322	55C	90380	56A
90207	81C	90265	55G	90323	86C	90381	27B
90208	31B	90266	24C	90324	26B	90382	53A
90209	36B	90267	26C	90225	55G	90383	40B
90210	51A	90268	81C	90326	56D	90384	38A
90211	36B	90269	38A	90327	26A	90385	56A
90212	6C	90270	36B	90328	24C	90386	66C
90213	53E	90271	26C	90329	56E	90387	65D
90214	84K	90272	53A	90330	36B	90388	26A
90215	38A	90273	51B	90331	24C	90389	26A
90216	27B	90274	24B	90332	55G	90390	26A
90217	53C	90275	40E	90333	56A	90391	38D
90218	38E	90276	38D	90334	56A	90392	6C
90219	26D	90277	24C	90335	24C	90393	40B

90394	38A	90452	51B	90510	40B	90568	26D
90395	55C	90453	36A	90511	53C	90569	36A
90396	56A	90454	35A	90512	36C	90570	27D
90397	56F	90455	61B	90513	62A	90571	53C
90398	24C	90456	36C	90514	35A	90572	86C
90399	24A	90457	50D	90515	62B	90573	85B
90400	36B	90458	53A	90516	38E	90574	38E
90401	36B	90459	51B	90517	51B	90575	62C
90402	26C	90460	38A	90518	50D	90576	26A
90403	38E	90461	51B	90519	38A	90577	40E
90404	56A	90462	51B	90520	38E	90578	56D
90405	51E	90463	62B	90521	36B	90579	86C
90406	56F	90464	68A	90522	31B	90580	36B
90407	55C	90465	51B	90523	26A	90581	56A
90408	26D	90466	84C	90524	86C	90582	36B
90409	51B	90467	50B	90525	26A	90583	40B
90410	36B	90468	66C	90526	36B	90584	27D
90411	40E	90469	36A	90527	27B	90585	84C
90412	56E	90470	53C	90528	35A	90586	53C
90413	24C	90471	40B	90529	81C	90587	36B
90414	56A	90472	62A	90530	26A	90588	55C
90415	56A	90473	38A	90531	53E	90589	26A
90416	27B	90474	38E	90532	6B	90590	36B
90417	56A	90475	51B	90533	26A	90591	55C
90418	38D	90476	38A	90534	62A	90592	24B
90419	26D	90477	31B	90535	27B	90593	56D
90420	24B	90478	53C	90536	66A	90594	40E
90421	36B	90479	53A	90537	36A	90595	24C
90422	36C	90480	31B	90538	36A	90596	65D
90423	6B	90481	51B	90539	62A	90597	36C
90424	51B	90482	53C	90540	56A	90598	36C
90425	36C	90483	84D	90541	24C	90599	27D
90426	51B	90484	31B	90542	62C	90600	62C
90427	53C	90485	85B	90543	56D	90601	36C
90428	35A	90486	38E	90544	86A	90602	36A
90429	53C	90487	51B	90545	40E	90603	51B
90430	53A	90488	51B	90546	26B	90604	56A
90431	40E	90489	65A	90547	62C	90605	51B
90432	38A	90490	36C	90548	26A	90606	6B
90433	38E	90491	36A	90549	65D	90607	56A
90434	51B	90492	40E	90550	36A	90608	36A
90435	51B	90493	65D	90551	30A	90609	53A
90436	65D	90494	35A	90552	26A	90610	56A
90437	38A	90495	36B	90553	62C	90611	54B
90438	35A	90496	38A	90554	40E	90612	36B
90439	35A	90497	53C	90555	26D	90613	35A
90440	65D	90498	30A	90556	24C	90614	62A
90441	62A	90499	38A	90557	24B	90615	56A
90442	33A	90500	51B	90558	26A	90616	66A
90443	40B	90501	51B	90559	35A	90617	56A
90444	62B	90502	40E	90560	62C	90618	38A
90445	54B	90503	51B	90561	26A	90619	55G
90446	51B	90504	38E	90562	55C	90620	56A
90447	35C	90505	67C	90563	82B	90621	55G
90448	38E	90506	36B	90564	26B	90622	56D
90449	40E	90507	38E	90565	86C	90623	53C
90450	53A	90508	30A	90566	6B	90624	55G
90451	51B	90509	38E	90567	36A	90625	51B

90626	26D	90684	55C	90759	65F	92040	35A
90627	53A	90685	86A	90760	66B	92041	35A
90628	66B	90686	84K	90761	66B	92042	35A
90629	38A	90687	27B	90762	66B	92043	38B
90630	81C	90688	53C	90763	68A	92044	31B
90631	56A	90689	24C	90764	66B	92045	6F
90632	26B	90690	62A	90765	65F	92046	6F
90633	56A	90691	85B	90766	66B	92047	6F
90634	38A	90692	56A	90767	66A	92048	18A
90635	56A	90693	86C	90768	64D	92049	18A
90636	36A	90694	55G	90769	65F	92050	RTS
90637	56A	90695	53A	90770	66B	92051	18A
90638	38E	90696	36A	90771	66B	92052	18A
90639	56A	90697	38E	90772	66B	92053	18A
90640	66A	90698	55C	90773	65F	92054	18A
90641	26C	90699	55C	90774	65F	92055	18A
90642	56D	90700	36B			92056	18A
90643	27B	90701	84G			92057	18A
90644	56A	90702	6B	92000	86A	92058	18A
90645	55C	90703	38A	92001	86A	92059	18A
90646	36C	90704	53A	92002	86A	92060	54B
90647	36C	90705	62A	92003	86A	92061	54B
90648	38A	90706	26A	92004	86A	92062	54B
90649	55C	90707	56D	92005	86A	92063	54B
90650	55C	90708	26A	92006	86A	92064	54B
90651	56A	90709	35A	92007	86A	92065	54B
90652	56A	90710	56A	92008	15A	92066	54B
90653	33A	90711	55C	92009	15A	92067	38B
90654	56A	90712	27B	92010	38B	92068	38B
90655	56D	90713	26B	92011	35A	92069	38B
90656	56A	90714	36C	92012	35A	92070	38B
90657	35A	90715	26A	92013	38B	92071	38B
90658	24C	90716	84C	92014	38B	92072	38B
90659	35A	90717	38A	92015	15A	92073	38B
90660	30A	90718	26D	92016	15A	92074	38B
90661	53C	90719	56A	92017	15A	92075	38B
90662	38A	90720	24C	92018	15A	92076	38B
90663	50B	90721	56D	92019	15A	92077	18A
90664	55C	90722	56A	92020	15A	92078	18A
90665	35A	90723	56D	92021	15A	92079	21C
90666	55C	90724	27B	92022	15A	92080	18A
90667	6B	90725	26C	92023	15A	92081	18A
90668	36B	90726	55C	92024	15A	92082	15A
90669	26A	90727	62C	92025	15A	92083	15A
90670	53A	90728	55C	92026	15A	92084	15A
90671	27D	90729	26C	92027	15A	92085	15A
90672	38E	90730	35A	92028	18A	92086	18A
90673	56A	90731	56D	92029	15A	92087	38B
90674	40B	90732 *	36A	92030	35A	92088	38B
90675	27B	90750	66B	92031	35A	92089	38B
90676	86A	90751	66A	92032	35A	92090	38B
90677	53C	90752	66B	92033	35A	92091	38B
90678	56D	90753	64D	92034	35A	92092	38B
90679	56A	90754	66B	92035	35A	92093	38B
90680	55G	90755	65F	92036	35A	92094	38B
90681	24C	90756	66B	92037	35A	92095	38B
90682	56A	90757	65F	92038	35A	92096	38B
90683	35A	90758	66B	92039	35A	92097	54B

92098	54B
92099	54B
92100	18A
92101	18A
92102	18A
92103	18A
92104	18A
92105	15B
92106	15B
92107	15A
92108	14A
92109	21A
92110	14A
92111	14A
92112	14A
92113	18B
92114	18B
92115	18B
92116	18B
92117	18B
92118	18B
92119	18B
92120	18B
92121	21A
92122	15A
92123	15A
92124	15A

92125	15A
92126	15A
92127	15A
92128	18A
92129	21A
92130	21A
92131	
92132	
92133	
92134	
92135	
92136	
92137	
92138	
92139	
92140	
92141	
92142	
92143	
92144	
92145	
92146	
92147	
92148	
92149	
92150	
92151	

92152
92153
92154
92155
92156
92157
92158
92159
92160
92161
92162
92163
92164
92165
92166
92167
92168
92169
92170
92171
92172
92173
92174
92175
92176
92177
92178

92179
92180
92181
92182
92183
92184
92185
92186
92187
92188
92189
92190
92191
92192
92193
92194
92195
92196
92197
92198
92199
92200
92201
92202

ALLOCATION OF SERVICE LOCOMOTIVES

Service No.	Region.	B.R. No.	Type.	Allocation.
1* ...	E.	68845	J52	Doncaster Works.
2* ...	E.	68816	J52	Doncaster Works.
3* ...	E.	68181	Y3	Ranskill Wagon Works.
4* ...	E.	68132	Y1	Ranskill Wagon Works.
5* ...	E.	68165	Y3	Doncaster
6* ...	E.	68133	Y1	Peterborough Engineer's Yard.
7* ...	E.	68166	Y3	Boston Sleeper Depot.
8* ...	E.	68183	Y3	
21* ...	E.	68162	Y3	Cambridge Engineer's Dept.
31* ...	E.	68382	J66	Stratford Works.
32* ...	E.	68370	J66	Stratford Works.
33* ...	E.	68129	Y4	Stratford Works.
36* ...	E.	68378	J66	Stratford Works.
38* ...	E.	68168	Y3	Lowestoft Engineer's Dept.
39* ...	E.	68131	Y1	Lowestoft Engineer's Dept.
40* ...	E.	68173	Y3	Lowestoft Engineer's Dept.
41* ...	E.	68177	Y3	Lowestoft Engineer's Dept.
42* ...	E.	68178	Y3	Cambridge Engineer's Dept.
51* ...	N.E.	68136	Y1	Faverdale Works, Darlington.
52* ...	N.E.	11104	0–4–0 Diesel	West Hartlepool P.W. Depot.
53* ...	N.E.	68152	Y1	York (Engineer's Yard).
54* ...	N.E.	68153	Y1	Darlington P.W. Depot.
56* ...	N.E.		0–4–0 Diesel	Hull Engineer's Dept.
57* ...	N.E.	68160	Y3	Faverdale Works, Darlington.
C.D.3 ...	M.		L.N.W. 0–6–0 ST	Wolverton Carriage Works.
C.D.6 ...	M.		L.N.W. 0–6–0 ST	Wolverton Carriage Works.
C.D.7 ...	M.		L.N.W. 0–6–0 ST	Wolverton Carriage Works.
C.D.8† ...	M.		L.N.W. 0–6–0 ST	Wolverton Carriage Works
51304 ...	M.	51304	L.Y.R. 0–6–0 ST	Horwich Works.
51305 ...	M.	51305	L.Y.R. 0–6–0 ST	Horwich Works.
51324 ...	M.	51324	L.Y.R. 0–6–0 ST	Horwich Works.
51638 ...	M.	51368	L.Y.R. 0–6–0 ST	Horwich Works.
51394 ...	M.	51394	L.Y.R. 0–6–0 ST	Horwich Works.
E.D.1 ...	M.		0–4–0 Diesel	Beeston Creosote Works.
E.D.2 ...	M.		0–4–0 Diesel	Ditton Creosote Works.
E.D.3 ...	M.		0–4–0 Diesel	Lenton P.W. Depot.
E.D.4 ...	M.		0–4–0 Diesel	Northampton
E.D.5 ...	M.		0–4–0 Diesel	Beeston Creosote Works.
E.D.6 ...	M.		0–4–0 Diesel	Castleton P.W. Depot.
E.D.7 ...	M.		0–4–0 Diesel	Fazakerley.
DS74 ...	S.		Bo-Bo Electric	Durnsford Rd. Power Station
DS75 ...	S.		Bo Electric	Waterloo & City Line.
DS77 ...	S.		C14	Redbridge Sleeper Depot.
DS377 ...	S.		A1X	Brighton Works.
DS600 ...	S.		0–4–0 Diesel	Eastleigh Carriage Works.
DS680 ...	S.		A1	Lancing Carriage Works.
DS681 ...	S.		A1X	Lancing Carriage Works.
DS1173 ...	S.		0–6–0 Diesel	Engineer's Dept.
DS3152 ...	S.	30272	G6	Meldon Quarry.
23 ...	W		0–4–0 Petrol	Didcot Stores.
24 ...	W.		0–4–0 Petrol	Taunton Engineer's Dept.
26 ...	W.		0–4–0 Petrol	Didcot Stores.
27 ...	W.		0–4–0 Petrol	Reading Signal Works.

* Numbered in E. & N.E. Region Departmental stock.   † Named *Earlestown*.

JOIN NOW!

Ian Allan Locospotters Club

This famous club is waiting to welcome you as a new member. Its aim is to bring together those interested in railways and to make them recognisable to one another by their badges and to promote a code of good "spottership," so that existing privileges by which we can all enjoy our hobby of locospotting are not endangered by irresponsible behaviour. Groups all over the country arrange local activities in which you can take part, as well as large-scale programmes which are organised by headquarters from time to time.

Send off now, enclosing 2½d. stamped addressed envelope for enrolment form

and remember that

ON ENROLMENT EVERY LOCOSPOTTER NOW RECEIVES WITHOUT FURTHER CHARGE

- AN IAN ALLAN LOCOSPOTTERS CLUB PENCIL
- AN IAN ALLAN LOCOSPOTTERS CLUB REFERENCE BOOK
- THE CLUB BADGE
- MEMBERSHIP CARD

and the membership fee is 1/3d. inclusive.

The address to write to is :

CRAVEN HOUSE · HAMPTON COURT · SURREY

First published 1957
Reprinted 2016

ISBN 978 0 7110 3845 5

Published by Ian Allan Publishing

an imprint of Ian Allan Publishing Ltd, Hersham, Surrey KT12 4RG.
Printed in Wales by Gomer Press.

This is a facsimilie reprint of an original edition first published in 1957,
and as such, all advertisements are no longer valid.

Visit the Ian Allan Publishing website at www.ianallanpublishing.com

Front cover:
In early 1957 Great Western Railway No 3440 *City of Truro* was returned to
service. Shedded at Didcot, it was generally confined to working scheduled
services over the Didcot, Newbury & Southampton line. However, it is pictured
at Ruabon on a Festiniog Railway Society special on 30 March 1957.
Colour-Rail (312507)

Rear cover:
Ex-LNER Class B12/3 No 61535 awaits departure from Liverpool Street with a
parcels train bound for Ipswich. *Brian Morrison*